Within Reach of Everyone:
A History of the
University of Toronto
School of Hygiene
and the
Connaught Laboratories,

Volume I, 1927 to 1955

Paul Adolphus Bator, M.A., Ph.D. (Toronto)
with
Andrew James Rhodes, M.D., F.R.C.P. (Edin.),
F.R.C.P.(C), F.F.C.M., F.R.S.C.

Published by
The Canadian Public Health Association

For Maureen Anne, Sean Michael,
Thomas Matthew and Timothy Ignatius

First Printing
1990

Price
$35.00 (Casebound)
$25.00 (Paperback)

1565 Carling Avenue, Suite 400, Ottawa, Ontario K1Z 8R1

Printed in Canada
by M.O.M. Printing, 300 Parkdale Avenue, Ottawa, Ontario K1Y 1G2

ISBN 0-919245-40-4 (Casebound)
ISBN 0-919245-39-0 (Paperback)

Canadian Cataloguing in Publication Data

Bator, Paul Adolphus, 1948-
Within Reach of Everyone

Partial contents: v. 1. 1927 to 1955.
Includes bibliographical references.
ISBN 0-919245-40-4 (bound) —
ISBN 0-919245-39-0 (pbk.)

1. University of Toronto. School of Hygiene—History. 2. Connaught Laboratories—History. I. Rhodes, Andrew James, 1911- . II. Canadian Public Health Association. III. Title.

RA440.7.C32T6 1990 362.1′071′1713541 C90-090036-9

COVER PHOTOS

FRONT: Plaque from Hygiene Building (Connaught Archives)

BACK: Original School of Hygiene Building in 1927 (University of Toronto Archives)

TABLE OF CONTENTS

Acknowledgements		vii
Introduction		ix
Chapter One	Roots of the School of Hygiene, University of Toronto	1
Chapter Two	The FitzGerald Era, 1927-1940	31
Chapter Three	"Vital to the War Effort": The University of Toronto School of Hygiene, Robert D. Defries and the Second World War	71
Chapter Four	"A Unique Partnership": The University of Toronto School of Hygiene, The Faculty of Medicine and the Connaught Medical Research Laboratories, 1945-1955	107
Chapter Five	The School's Department of Hospital Administration, 1947-1955	141
Chapter Six	Nutrition, Parasitology and Virology, 1945-1955	161
Conclusion		179
Abbreviations		186
Notes		187
Appendix A	Graduates of the School of Hygiene	205
Appendix B	Graduate Degrees Awarded in the School of Hygiene, 1927-1955	212
Appendix C	Staff of the School of Hygiene, the Connaught Laboratories, and the Connaught Medical Research Laboratories, 1928-1955	217
Index		229
Note on Authors		243

The publication of this book was made possible by grants from the Connaught Laboratories Limited and the Division of Community Health, University of Toronto Faculty of Medicine.

CREDITS FOR PHOTOGRAPHS AND ILLUSTRATIONS

Canadian Journal of Public Health, Pages 66, 67, 68, 75, 101 and 102.

City of Toronto Archives, Pages 12 and 82.

Connaught Archives, Pages 19, 20, 47, 69, 70, 84, 140, 171 and 178.

IMS, Faculty of Medicine,
University of Toronto, with special thanks to Alan Bakes, Pages 39 (Brown), 43, 54, 80, 83 and 97.

Professor Ron McQueen,
Department of Health Administration, Division of Community Health,
Faculty of Medicine, University of Toronto, Pages 142, 144, 150, 153, 154 and 159.

University of St. Michael's College Archives, Pages 52 and 56.

University of Toronto Archives, Pages 5, 6, 14, 16, 17, 33, 34, 35, 36, 39 (MacLean), 41, 44, 50, 58, 60, 78, 92, 112, 113, 114, 115, 123, 129, 136, 151, 160, 164, 180, 181 and Appendix A.

Mrs. Audrey Williams, Page 11.

Dr. R.J. Wilson, Page 174.

ACKNOWLEDGEMENTS

The goal of the University of Toronto School of Hygiene Project is the publication of the history of the School from its inauguration to its dismantling in 1975. This book, covering the period from 1927 to 1955, is the first volume of that story. Its completion is a testament to the efforts and support of a number of individuals, companies and foundations who must be recognized.

The initial impetus came from the University of Toronto Community Health Alumni Association. The financial support over the years of the Alumni Association is gratefully acknowledged. The backing of Dr. Gordon Martin for the completion of volume one during his term as President of the Association must be noted with gratitude.

Dr. Eugene Vayda, Associate Dean, Division of Community Health, University of Toronto Faculty of Medicine from 1981 to 1988, provided assistance and encouragement. Ms. Jan Barnsley, then a research associate in the Division, helped the authors in resolving a number of problems over the years from 1984 to 1986.

Along with Dr. Rhodes, three members of the faculty of the School of Hygiene contributed valuable oral histories: Dr. John Hastings, Dr. F. Burns Roth and Dr. George Beaton.

The Hannah Institute for the History of Medicine made available a grant for one year to pay the half-time salary of the project historian. Thanks must be offered to Dr. G.R. Paterson, then the Executive Director of The Hannah Institute, for this financing which made it possible to launch the first volume of the history of the School.

The Ontario Heritage Foundation awarded a research grant in 1986 that facilitated the completion of the research on the period prior to 1956. Miss Elizabeth Price's help in arranging this funding is appreciated.

The Rockefeller Archive Center in North Tarrytown, New York provided a grant which enabled the project historian to use their collections in August, 1986. The help of Mr. Joseph Ernst, Director Emeritus of the Rockefeller Archive Center, is appreciated. Thanks must also be extended to the very able staff of the Center, especially Mr. Thomas Rosenbaum, who made the visit of the project historian very rewarding.

The contributions of the following are appreciated: Connaught Laboratories Limited, Canada Liquid Air Limited, E.B. Lilly Limited and the Department of Public Health, Borough of East York.

For two years, Principal John Browne of Innis College provided the use of an office for Bator and Rhodes, and they are thankful to him for this accommodation.

The University of Toronto Archives is the key source for the history of the School of Hygiene. The staff of the Archives, especially the Archivist, Kent Haworth, and his associate, Harold Averill, facilitated the research of the project historian who is very grateful for their interest and support. In addition, the project historian must express his gratitude to President George Connell for permission to examine the relevant correspondence of the Office of the President of the University of Toronto, to former Dean Frederick Lowy for access to the records of the University of Toronto Faculty of Medicine, and to Associate Dean Eugene Vayda for permission to consult the records of the School of Hygiene and the Division of Community Health.

The advice and the assistance of the late Dr. Robert J. Wilson, a former Director of the Connaught Laboratories and a member of the faculty of the School of Hygiene, was greatly appreciated in bringing to light the human dimensions of the members of the School. In addition, thanks must also be given to Mrs. Leanne Johnson, the librarian of the Connaught Laboratories Limited who made available records in that institution's Archives.

Dr. John Hastings, Associate Dean, Division of Community Health, University of Toronto Faculty of Medicine during his term of office of 1988-1989 who, as mentioned above, contributed to the research for the history of the School, and Karin D. Pierre, a research associate in the Division, must be thanked also for their efforts to secure the publication of this volume.

Officials of the Canadian Public Health Association expedited the transformation of the manuscript into a book. The authors are appreciative of the contributions of Mr. Gerald Dafoe, Executive Director of the CPHA and the diligent editorial work of Ms. Karen Devine, Assistant Editor of the *Canadian Journal of Public Health.*

My gratitude must be expressed to Mary Ellen Perkins for her help with the layout of the book in its final stages.

I am thankful to Mrs. Harriett Rhodes (née Banting) for her typing of numerous items as well as her comments over the years.

Personally, I want to acknowledge the love and support of my wife, Maureen Anne Bator (née Matthews). Maureen's help was vital to the completion of the book.

Although he is already noted on the title page, Dr. Andrew J. Rhodes' contributions to this volume warrant special mention. For over two years, Dr. Rhodes volunteered many hours to the project. His insights into the School of Hygiene and its role enabled the project historian to come to a better understanding of the significance of the School in the history of medical education and research, and the development of health care in Ontario and Canada. I thank Dr. Rhodes for the opportunity to work with such a distinguished medical scientist and a gentleman.

Paul Adolphus Bator, Ph.D.
"Lakeview, Toronto Township"

October 15, 1989

INTRODUCTION

The University of Toronto School of Hygiene was a landmark in the history of health services and medical research in Ontario and Canada during the first half of the twentieth century. Dr. John FitzGerald, assisted by Dr. Robert Defries, established the School which functioned as an independent division of the University of Toronto from 1927 to 1975. In the middle of the 1920s, FitzGerald had laid the foundation for federal and provincial health programs across Canada. The basis of his approach was a triad of research, teaching and public service. The first stage in the realization of FitzGerald's plan was the establishment of the Connaught Laboratories in 1914. The second was the restructuring and increase in the staffing of the Department of Hygiene within the Faculty of Medicine. After the First World War the third stage was the founding of the School of Hygiene as one of the Rockefeller Schools of Public Health, the third in North America. The School of Hygiene Building, constructed at 150 College Street in Toronto with financing from the Rockefeller Foundation, housed all of the programs developed by FitzGerald to improve general health conditions. This book is a history of the School of Hygiene and its building from 1927 to 1955. It is the story of the successes of a remarkable group of men and women. Together they saved hundreds of thousands of human lives in Canada and around the world.

The principal goal of this book is the preservation of the history of the University of Toronto School of Hygiene. Unfortunately, it has disappeared largely since 1975. There are very few references to the School in the catalogues of the University of Toronto Library. Very little has been written generally by historians on public health education programs in Canada. Until recently, the only historical works were produced by individuals who discussed their own involvement in the field of public health education, teaching and medical research in immunology. Dr. Robert Defries' writings are the best example of that autobiographical approach. The following study places on the public record a much larger picture of Defries' work with the School of Hygiene. Because almost all the scientific staff of the School of Hygiene held joint appointments in the Connaught Laboratories from 1927 until 1955 (a fact that enabled the School to survive during the 1930s and 1940s), one must examine the history of both of these institutions in order to appreciate the scope of activities undertaken by the faculty of the School. In fact, the School was the academic arm of the Connaught Laboratories for almost thirty years. The close relationships between the School and the Laboratories ended in 1956 with the appointment of a separate director for each organization. Previously, Dr. FitzGerald and then Dr. Defries had headed both institutions. As a result of this change which reflected a variety of academic, political, scientific, social and economic changes in Canadian society, the year 1955 constituted an end to one era of the School. Therefore, it is a logical point at which to conclude the first volume of the School's history. A second volume, it is hoped, will study the School of Hygiene from 1956 to its dismantling in 1975 when the departments of the School were merged into different divisions of the Faculty of Medicine.

The writings of Dr. Robert Defries form the basis of this history of the School of Hygiene. From the 1920s, Defries recorded in articles, annual reports, announcements and editorials as the editor of what became the *Canadian Journal of Public Health*, the evolution of the public health profession in Canada. Because the School of Hygiene was the primary public health education centre in the country for decades, Defries' works present an invaluable source of data on the different courses and research offered by the staff of the School that trained most of the health officers who established the municipal, federal and provincial public health services in Canada.

Shortly after his retirement in 1955, Defries produced "Postgraduate Teaching in Public Health in the University of Toronto 1913-1955" which appeared in his *Canadian Journal of Public Health* for July, 1957. That article of over five thousand words, until the appearance of this volume, constituted the only work to concentrate on the history of the School of Hygiene, its staff and departments.

Over ten years later, Defries completed *The First Forty Years: The Connaught Medical Research Laboratories University of Toronto 1914 to 1955* (Toronto: University of Toronto Press for the Connaught Medical Research Laboratories, 1968). This book provided an extensive but undocumented history primarily of the Connaught Laboratories. In over three hundred pages of text and photographs, there are fewer than ten pages devoted exclusively to the School of Hygiene. Significantly, there is no mention in that book of the School's departments of Parasitology or Hospital Administration and a minimal discussion of Earle McHenry's contribution to the development of public health nutrition and nutritional sciences.

Most of Defries' historical work on the School, it appears, was based on his memory. Clearly, what distinguishes our study from Defries' writing is the use of a number of archival sources largely closed or unavailable to the public.

The intention of this history of the School of Hygiene is not to duplicate Defries' publications. Rather it is the preservation, documentation, and organization of much of what Defries wrote concerning the University of Toronto School of Hygiene in one reference book. The story of the School can only be found in a variety of public and private records. One of the accomplishments of our research was to bring together from disparate sources a body of information about the School not available anywhere else.

There were three types of sources consulted in research on the history of the School:

1) the public and closed records of the School in the Archives of the University of Toronto and the Connaught Archives in the Balmer Neilly Library of Connaught Laboratories Limited in North York, Ontario;
2) the correspondence of the Directors and the faculty of the School with agencies and individuals outside the university now deposited in the Rockefeller Archive Center, the Archives of Ontario, the City of Toronto Archives and the National Archives of Canada;
3) the information available in generally published sources including the coverage of the School and its staff in newspapers, journals and magazines.

The six chapters in the book describe and document the story of the School of Hygiene from 1924 to 1955. Each chapter has a set of notes citing the documents consulted in the preparation of the text. The objective of the extensive references is to preserve the record of the School as an institution of higher learning and scientific research. These notes also substantiate the contribution of individual members of the faculty of the School of Hygiene. The conclusion is a summary and an assessment of the significance of the School of Hygiene as a model for health education programs, research and public service.

To facilitate the coverage of a multiplicity of subjects relating to the activities and faculty of the School of Hygiene, sub-headings divide each chapter, a reflection of the eclectic nature of the School's history.

The research and writing of volume one of the history of the University of Toronto School of Hygiene was the responsibility of Paul A. Bator, Ph.D. Dr. Andrew J. Rhodes, the Director of the School of Hygiene from 1956 to 1970, was a medical and scientific advisor who assisted in the drafting of the text. The approach of a team of an historian working with the help of a medical scientist has resulted in a more revealing study of the School of Hygiene's history.

Before closing, one must provide the background to the title "Within Reach of Everyone". In August, 1915, an article, "Lowering the Cost of Life Saving: How the University of Toronto is performing active public service", by Dr. Gordon Bates, appeared in *MacLean's* (as it was then spelt). Bates described the work of Dr. J.G. FitzGerald who founded the Antitoxin Laboratory of the University of Toronto to produce antitoxin for diphtheria. The basic problem that FitzGerald tackled was how to make the biological product available to as many children as possible in order to save their lives from diphtheria. Bates pointed out the human story behind the treatment of the disease:

> The important thing to note about the antitoxin question is that unfortunately, in the past, every child could not have it: the reason — it cost too much. Everyone realized that it cost a lot, especially the father and mother without money. The realization that to save their child's life meant many thousands of units of antitoxin and—alas—perhaps twenty-five dollars [then more than two weeks salary for the average working man in Toronto] which they did not have often meant the difference between life and death. . . . A story is told, a true story of a physician coming to a home in which two children had diphtheria. There was money enough to pay for antitoxin for one child but not for two. The parents decided which child should have the antitoxin—the other died.

FitzGerald's objective in establishing the Antitoxin Laboratory was, in the words of Bates, to "put the life-saving antitoxin *within reach of everyone* — even the poorest." That goal guided the Connaught Laboratories and then the University of Toronto School of Hygiene which soon applied it to an expanding range of health services beyond immunization, thus laying the foundation for the modern Canadian health care system.

CHAPTER ONE

ROOTS OF THE SCHOOL OF HYGIENE UNIVERSITY OF TORONTO

We are confronted by the lamentable fact that the knowledge essential for our people to be in possession of, as regards disease-producing germs and the ways and means by which they gain access to the body, has been kept for the most part in past years within the precincts of universities and laboratories. This, to be of practical value, must be democratized. It must be translated into a language that will be understood by the man on the street and by the housewife in the humblest home.[1]

Dr. Charles J. Hastings
Toronto's Medical Officer of Health
December 9, 1918

In the second decade of the twentieth century, the large number of children dying from diphtheria in Canada, despite the existence of a method of treating the disease with antitoxin, angered and baffled many doctors. During the fall of 1913, an associate professor of hygiene in the University of Toronto decided to do something about this loss of life. With money borrowed from his wife's inheritance,[2] John Gerald FitzGerald started the production of diphtheria antitoxin in horses in a stable off College Street in Toronto. This activity led eventually to the establishment of the internationally famous Connaught Laboratories.[3]

FitzGerald's work on diphtheria antitoxin was just the beginning of a long struggle against one of the major killers of the young. There was to be no sudden and spectacular victory over diphtheria. Rather it was a gradual campaign spanning two decades before the disease was brought under control in Ontario. Over those years, FitzGerald learned how much more there was to do than just conduct research in the laboratory and manufacture an antitoxin in the struggle to prevent diphtheria. Someone had to get the serum into the ordinary Canadian child. That realization was behind FitzGerald's founding of the University of Toronto School of Hygiene. The School was dedicated to the postgraduate education of physicians who were to direct public health services in municipal, provincial and federal health departments. The bridging of the gap between medical research in the laboratory and the saving of human lives that FitzGerald and others had sought was to stimulate the School of Hygiene staff and students for almost fifty years.

THE BATTLE AGAINST CONTAGIOUS DISEASES

The forces behind the establishment of the University of Toronto School of Hygiene in the 1920s were the result of a variety of scientific changes and social conditions during the last decades of the nineteenth century in Canada and elsewhere. Advances in Europe and the United States in sanitary engineering, the use of microscopes, and the application of the new medical sciences of bacteriology and immunology laid the groundwork for an unprecedented era of improvements in public health.[4] Within years these developments influenced medical education and the practice of medicine in Toronto. Most significantly, inspired by the success of the British system, the Ontario government initiated the appointment of local boards of health and health officers to control contagious diseases in 1882.[5]

By the 1910s, many of the contagious diseases which had taken so many lives for centuries could be controlled due to medical, scientific and technological advances. However, there remained innumerable problems that frustrated the efforts of health officials to introduce these breakthroughs in order to save the lives of average Canadians.

In Ontario, the campaign against typhoid fever illustrated the complexities facing FitzGerald and others. In the early twentieth century, typhoid fever was a common feature of life in the province. From 1880 to 1931, it claimed over 21,000 lives.[6] One of the ancient scourges of humans, the disease flourished in cities before the installation of water and sewage treatment. The main sources of typhoid fever were the faeces and urine of typhoid victims or typhoid carriers who continued to excrete the bacillus after the illness. Water, dairy products, vegetables and other foods, contaminated with the bacteria, easily spread the disease. The symptoms included headaches, diarrhoea, vomiting and the development of rose spots on the abdomen. Typhoid bacteria entering through the gastrointestinal tract overtook the body with the patient falling into a coma and often dying.[7]

The history of typhoid fever in Toronto illustrated the necessity of building a sewage system and plants to filter and chlorinate the water supply as well as the compulsory pasteurization of milk. The municipal actions cut down significantly the rates of typhoid fever within Toronto although cases of the disease were still brought into the city from rural areas.[8] During the First World War, health officers in the Canadian army introduced mass immunization against typhoid and paratyphoid to control outbreaks among soldiers.[9] Despite these improvements, typhoid fever, much to the chagrin of health authorities, continued to be a threat into the 1930s.[10]

Diphtheria was another major killer, especially of the young, in Ontario. A contagious disease, diphtheria produces a thick membrane over the victim's throat as well as high fever and exhaustion which is debilitating. In the last century many children with the infection slowly died of suffocation from the membrane or bled to death after the cutting or tearing of the membrane in their throat.[11] Even though an antitoxin for diphtheria, "the first biological drug to be produced by scientific medicine",[12] had existed since the 1890s, the disease killed hundreds of children in the province each year until the 1930s. From 1880 to 1929, over 36,000 youngsters died from diphtheria.[13] One of the early Master of Arts' theses completed in the School of Hygiene noted in 1928, that in 1925 "in Ontario diphtheria ranked second among the causes of deaths in children between the ages of 2 and 14 years."[14] More than a decade after FitzGerald's initiation of the production of diphtheria antitoxin, diphtheria continued to kill children. One of the principal tasks of the School of Hygiene was to develop the health professionals and the types of organization required to take advantage of medical and scientific discoveries.

ORIGINS OF CANADIAN PUBLIC HEALTH MOVEMENT

While the School of Hygiene did not begin instruction until the 1920s, many of the people who brought about its existence were leaders in the public health reform movement. The goal of that crusade was to better the health of average Canadians by providing them with basic health services to control contagious diseases. The leadership of Canadian public health reform came largely from a small group of scientists and medical practitioners in Toronto in the last decades of the nineteenth century. Most of these reformers were medical graduates who had completed postgraduate work overseas or in the United States where they learned of major discoveries in bacteriology and immunology.[15]

News of the microbiological discoveries of Louis Pasteur in Paris, Robert Koch in Berlin and Joseph Lister in Glasgow, Edinburgh and later in London spread quickly to Toronto. Some local scientists and physicians recognized very early the value of the study of bacteria in the laboratory. In January, 1883, a professor of biology in the University of Toronto delivered a summary of the "Germ Theory of Disease" before the Royal Canadian Institute. Robert Ramsay Wright in his address advocated the use of laboratory examinations to identify bacterial contamination of water in order to prevent the outbreak of diseases.[16] Almost thirty years later, after hundreds of deaths from typhoid fever, the Toronto Department of Public Health implemented fully Wright's advice.[17]

The principal reason for the delay in taking advantage of the scientific knowledge to control communicable disease in Canada was the slow development of general health services. The formation of the Ontario Provincial Board of Health (O.P.B.H.) in 1882 was the beginning of the modern system of health care. Its founding and the first decades of operation were largely the result of the efforts of one man, Peter H. Bryce.[18]

Peter Bryce was the first secretary of the Ontario Provincial Board of Health. He is a largely forgotten but genuine pioneer of Canadian health care. By 1884, he was one of the early, if not the first, full-time health officer in Canada.[19] Almost single-handedly he organized the O.P.B.H. Later in 1904, Bryce moved to Ottawa where he established the federal Medical Inspection of Immigrants service. He ended his career in the federal Department of Health after the First World War.[20]

Bryce's educational background was a key to his involvement in public health. After receiving his undergraduate, graduate and finally a medical degree from the University of Toronto, he went in 1880 to study in Great Britain and Europe just as Pasteur, Koch and Lister were making some of their major discoveries. Armed with this knowledge, he returned to apply what he had learned through the Ontario Provincial Board of Health.[21]

The major contribution of Bryce was his plan for full-time health officers with an adequate salary paid for by the local government in every town or city throughout Ontario.[22] Originally called Medical Health Officers, the title was changed to Medical Officer of Health or M.O.H. to conform with the British model.[23] Interestingly, many viewed Bryce's proposal as too radical[24] which may explain the fact that his plan became a full reality only after more than fifty years of struggle.

In Toronto, the City Council appointed reluctantly the first M.O.H., Dr. William Canniff, only after a threat of further legislation from the province.[25] Canniff resigned eventually after numerous clashes with the city fathers over his work, which some viewed as too costly and an interference with private property rights.[26] With opposition like that in a major urban centre, no wonder rural areas were against the appointment of local health officers.

RE-ESTABLISHMENT OF TORONTO'S FACULTY OF MEDICINE

As was to be the case so often in the twentieth century, many of the discoveries that improved the health of the general population came from experts outside the traditional medical profession. They were the products of the research and technological innovations of biologists, chemists and engineers. In the 1880s, these breakthroughs began to bring under control certain infectious diseases such as diphtheria and typhoid fever which had killed so many for centuries. Educational reformers advocated the introduction of these new sciences to the instruction of physicians in universities. The "spirit of science" forced an alteration in the old system of medical education.

In Toronto, reformers campaigned for the transfer of the responsibility for the education of physicians from medical practitioners to the professoriate. Their efforts led to the re-establishment in 1887 of the Faculty of Medicine in the University of Toronto that had been abolished in 1853. The university, those reformers argued, was the best place to instruct upcoming doctors in the basic sciences of bacteriology, biology and physiology.[27]

RAMSAY WRIGHT 1852-1933

A leader of the movement in the 1880s to re-establish a Faculty of Medicine, Robert Ramsay Wright helped to transform the study of medicine in the University of Toronto. Together with a professor at Harvard University, Wright was credited with the introduction of the laboratory method and the use of microscopes in undergraduate medical education.[28] A biologist by training, he contributed to the growth of a number of disciplines now included in modern departments of Zoology[29] and Microbiology.

In the reconstituted medical faculty, Ramsay Wright was professor of general biology and physiology.[30] Later he held the Chair of Biology in the Faculty of Medicine until his retirement in 1912.[31] Because of his influence, the University built biological laboratories in 1889[32] and later in 1904, laboratories for medicine.[33] These facilities fostered the growth of research in medical science.[34]

Wright also made a direct contribution to the teaching of public health in the University of Toronto. In 1902, he was one of the drafters of the Senate Statute for the establishment of the "Diploma of Public Health" as it was then called.[35] Moreover, Wright supervised a number of students who later helped to shape the growth of the teaching of public health within the university and public health services outside the confines of the university.[36]

JOHN JOSEPH MACKENZIE 1865-1922

A student of Ramsay Wright, J.J. Mackenzie was a practitioner, teacher and researcher in the field of bacteriology. Following his undergraduate degree from Toronto, he continued his studies in medicine and biology in Germany where he worked for the Koch Institute in Berlin. Upon his return to Toronto, Mackenzie assumed the responsibilities of provincial bacteriologist, teaching medical students and completing, himself, a degree in medicine. From 1900 until his death in 1922, Mackenzie was a professor of bacteriology and pathology in the Faculty of Medicine.[37]

Between 1890 and 1900, John Mackenzie was the first bacteriologist in the Ontario Provincial Board of Health, then a division of the Department of Agriculture.[38] Mackenzie

Robert Ramsay Wright

Dr. J.J. Mackenzie

established one of the early laboratories for public health work in North America.[39] He did pioneering research on rabies in 1895. His inauguration of bacteriological examinations of water supplies and human specimens for evidence of typhoid fever and tuberculosis was among the early systematic laboratory programs in North America.[40] The laboratory also imported from L'Institut Pasteur in Paris diphtheria antitoxin which it distributed for a few months.[41] Looking back in 1919, Mackenzie cited the growth of public health laboratories as "the most striking medical development . . . in the field of preventive medicine."[42]

Mackenzie's tenure as Provincial Bacteriologist was the beginning of an intimate relationship between the laboratory of the Ontario Provincial Board of Health and the professors of bacteriology, hygiene and preventive medicine in the University of Toronto.[43] The cross appointment of provincial health officials to part-time teaching posts in their specialty in the Faculty of Medicine became an established practice throughout the history of the School of Hygiene. Furthermore, the laboratory was located in University buildings for almost twenty years. After using office space above stores in downtown Toronto, the Provincial Laboratory occupied a room in the Biological Building of the University of Toronto from 1893[44] until about 1904 when it moved into the Medical Building and remained until 1911.[45] The sharing of staff and facilities provided the province with the expertise and the university with the teachers it needed at a minimal cost.[46]

PUBLIC HEALTH COURSES IN THE FACULTY OF MEDICINE

After 1900, the changing social conditions in Ontario as the province became more urbanized were reflected in the emergence of courses in public health in the University of Toronto Faculty of Medicine. There were three streams of instruction in the expanding field of public health: sanitary science or hygiene, bacteriology and preventive medicine. These subjects demonstrated the eclectic nature of public health which proved initially to be a strength, but later became a liability in teaching medical undergraduates in an era of increasing specialization.

John FitzGerald, the founder of the Connaught Laboratories and the School of Hygiene, was conscious of the value of the teaching of the history of "hygiene, public health and preventive medicine." He can be considered one of the first historians of public health education in Canada. It was his investigations of the origins of public health instruction that influenced the developments in Toronto. Although it must be noted that there was a chair of hygiene in the University of Dublin in 1867, he traced the beginning of courses in preventive medicine to the first chair of hygiene in Munich in 1865 and the first institutes of hygiene in Budapest in 1874, in Vienna in 1874 and in Munich in 1879.[47] FitzGerald also credited the passage of the Public Health Act of 1875 in Great Britain for providing the model for organized public health work.[48]

In Toronto, hygiene was part of the curriculum in private medical schools. Even before the re-establishment of the Faculty of Medicine in the University of Toronto, hygiene was taught first in 1871 in the Faculty of Medicine of Trinity University, which amalgamated with the University of Toronto in 1903, and four years later in the Toronto School of Medicine that formed the basis of the reconstituted Faculty of Medicine in the University. The early instructors in hygiene were associated with the Ontario Provincial Board of Health. Dr.

William Coverton, who lectured in sanitary science in Trinity University from 1878 to 1891, was the chairman of the Board in 1888. Dr. William Oldright, the first chairman of the Ontario Provincial Board of Health, taught sanitary science first in the Toronto School of Medicine and then the Faculty of Medicine in the University of Toronto for a combined total of thirty-five years until his retirement in 1910.[49]

The early courses in sanitary science and hygiene stressed sanitation. There was no reference to bacteriology. Professor Oldright established a museum of hygiene in 1896 that moved into the new Medical Building in 1903. It contained models, drawings and lantern slides displaying proper ventilation and clothing, heating, plumbing, drainage sewers, sewage and water treatment, and meteorological instruments.[50] The exhibits illustrated the "mains and drains" approach which constituted the first phase of the public health movement.[51]

Unfortunately, the original emphasis on sanitation in public health courses created problems later on for medical educators. Later in reflecting on the historical evolution of public health, John FitzGerald blamed the "environmental notion" for the retarded progress in the teaching of preventive medicine. The teaching of hygiene, he explained, was based initially on meteorology, physics and chemistry and then grew to include the new sciences of bacteriology, immunology and nutrition. However, these new sciences developed into independent fields in medical schools. "In the meantime, what of hygiene?", FitzGerald asked. "Literally, it was what remained after the desertion of microbiology and physiology." After the first decades of the twentieth century, when the new basic sciences of medicine had opened an era of advances against contagious diseases, FitzGerald lamented the fact that medical students "have been lulled to rest while listening to lengthy disquisitions on air, soil and water."[52]

That there was a need to teach medical undergraduates how to use the knowledge generated by the new sciences to stop the spread of infectious diseases was the reason behind the growth of preventive medicine in faculties of medicine. In 1903, the establishment of a Chair of Preventive Medicine in the Faculty of Medicine of the University of Toronto announced the advent of the serious study of a systematic approach to the control of communicable diseases. Dr. Charles Sheard, head of the Toronto Department of Public Health from 1893 to 1910,[53] was appointed a part-time professor of preventive medicine.[54] His experience made him aware of the practical problems facing health departments in the day-to-day task of checking the spread of outbreaks of diseases such as diphtheria and scarlet fever.[55] Sheard was also familiar with the exasperating experience of trying to convince civic politicians to spend large sums of tax money on the building of water and sewage treatment plants in order to rid the city of typhoid fever and other illnesses.[56] Significantly, Sheard resigned from office in the face of allegations of dereliction of duty following a typhoid fever epidemic.[57] Apparently, the mastery of politics as well as medical science was necessary for the creation of a system of preventive medicine within any municipality.

JOHN A. AMYOT 1867-1940

The teaching of public health entered a new era with the appointment on a part-time basis of Dr. John Amyot to the Chair of Hygiene and Sanitary Science in the Faculty of Medicine. Like his predecessor in the provincial laboratory, Amyot combined his work for the Ontario

Provincial Board of Health with teaching in the University of Toronto. Between 1900 and 1910, he was an associate professor of pathology. Amyot was professor of hygiene from 1910 until 1919 when he moved to Ottawa to assume the office of deputy-minister of the new federal Department of Health. He retired in 1933.[58]

When Amyot became Provincial Bacteriologist, the state of affairs in the laboratory was still primitive:

> When I took over the laboratory in 1900 I was alone. I cleaned the glassware, fed the animals, made up the media and standard solutions, did the examinations, the results of which (1,250 that year) I reported in longhand. When we moved into the Medical Building we had both bacteriological and chemical assistants and a cleaner. We lacked a stenographer, but signalled to the Parliament Buildings with a white towel when we wanted one. This plan did not work well.[59]

The housing of the laboratory in the Medical Building on the campus of the University of Toronto from 1903 to 1911 allowed Amyot to promote the specialty of public health to a number of medical students. Popular as a lecturer, he was a persuasive advocate known for his theatrical performances before classes. One of his junior associates wrote in a retrospective account that Amyot's laboratory "soon developed into a favorite rendezvous for the more scientific young doctors, who dropped in to discuss 'interesting' medical cases and gradually the place became a sort of open forum for aggressive young investigators." A little research in the area of immunology was carried out in the laboratory.[60]

During these years, Amyot pioneered the development of sewage and water treatment in Ontario to control the spread of infectious diseases like typhoid fever. In 1902, he initiated field work in sewage disposal in Berlin, now called Kitchener, Ontario.[61] Two years later, Amyot was instrumental in the establishment of an experimental plant for sewage and water treatment in Stanley Park in Toronto, which opened in 1908.[62] Although a civil servant who was supposed to stay out of the public eye, John Amyot was an outspoken advocate of treatment plants[63] as well as the pasteurization of milk.[64] His outspoken positions soon got him in trouble with his political masters and he decided to tone down his stance.[65] Yet Amyot's promotion of sewage and water treatment, and pasteurization resulted eventually in a dramatic fall in the incidence of typhoid fever and other infections.[66]

CANADIAN PUBLIC HEALTH ASSOCIATION

Most of the doctors behind the foundation of the School of Hygiene were active in the establishment of a national organization to improve general health conditions. In October of 1910, a meeting of health officials led to the formation of the Canadian Public Health Association (C.P.H.A.). That gathering adopted a Toronto publication as its official organ and named it The Public Health Journal (P.H.J.).[67]

Dr. George Dana Porter, on the staff of the School of Hygiene in 1927 to 1928, was a founding member of the C.P.H.A.[68] A graduate of the University of Toronto Faculty of Medicine in 1894, about a decade later Porter helped to organize the Canadian Anti-Tuberculosis Association, one of the early voluntary public health bodies in this country.[69] He served as the first treasurer of the C.P.H.A. from 1910 to 1914. In 1917, when economic difficulties threatened the P.H.J., Porter and FitzGerald along with a few others rescued financially the publication.[70]

In the early 1920s, the C.P.H.A. formed a lobby to pressure federal and provincial governments into improving public health services. Within the Association, the formation of sections devoted to child welfare, laboratory work and vital statistics revealed the beginnings of specialization.[71] This move signalled the increasing professionalization of public health work. It was being transformed from primarily a voluntary and part-time activity for physicians and lay persons into a professional and full-time employment for experts. By the end of the 1920s, the leaders in Canadian public health were almost entirely on the faculty of the School of Hygiene in Toronto. Significantly in 1928, Dr. Robert D. Defries, Associate Director of the School, took over the position of the editor of C.P.H.A.'s renamed monthly, the *Canadian Public Health Journal*.[72]

CHARLES HASTINGS 1858-1931

From 1910 to 1920, the growth of public health activities in Toronto gave impetus to the national public health movement. In the fall of 1910, Dr. Charles J. Hastings assumed the position of Medical Health Officer in Toronto, a post he held until 1929.[73] Charles Hastings was the consummate reformer. Knowledgeable about bacteriology, he used the latest laboratory procedures in the struggle against disease. He hired Dr. John Amyot's assistant, George Nasmith, a chemist with a Ph.D., to take charge of the municipal laboratory.[74] Nasmith was awarded the Diploma in Public Health from the University of Toronto in 1918 for his services with the Canadian Army in France during the First World War and is the only non-physician to hold the D.P.H.[75] Politically shrewd, Hastings won a succession of battles with the city fathers. The municipality's water was chlorinated.[76] Special clinics for babies, and neighbourhood visitations to their homes by public health nurses as well as the expansion of medical inspection of school children provided general health services.[77] Despite bitter opposition and legal complexities, Hastings brought about the compulsory pasteurization of milk.[78] All of these activities saved the lives of thousands, especially the very young.[79] Hastings established a model system of public health administration whose facilities became an important part of the undergraduate and postgraduate training of physicians in preventive medicine in the University of Toronto.

ESTABLISHMENT OF THE D.P.H.

When the Ontario Provincial Board of Health reorganized its operations in 1912 with the appointment of full-time district health officers,[80] the Chief Medical Officer of Health, Dr. J.W.S. McCullough, turned to Dr. John Amyot in the University of Toronto for help. Assisted by a stronger Public Health Act,[81] McCullough was determined to organize across the province a system of permanent and qualified health officers. This goal took decades to achieve. The first step in that direction was the appointment of ten district health officers to monitor public health in a large area including many municipalities. To prepare the first district health officers for their work, they attended a special course in Amyot's department in the Faculty of Medicine.[82]

McCullough's request for a course in the University was probably the reason for the inauguration of the course for the Diploma in Public Health in the University of Toronto. As early as 1901, the Senate of the University had received a proposal to establish a Diploma.[83]

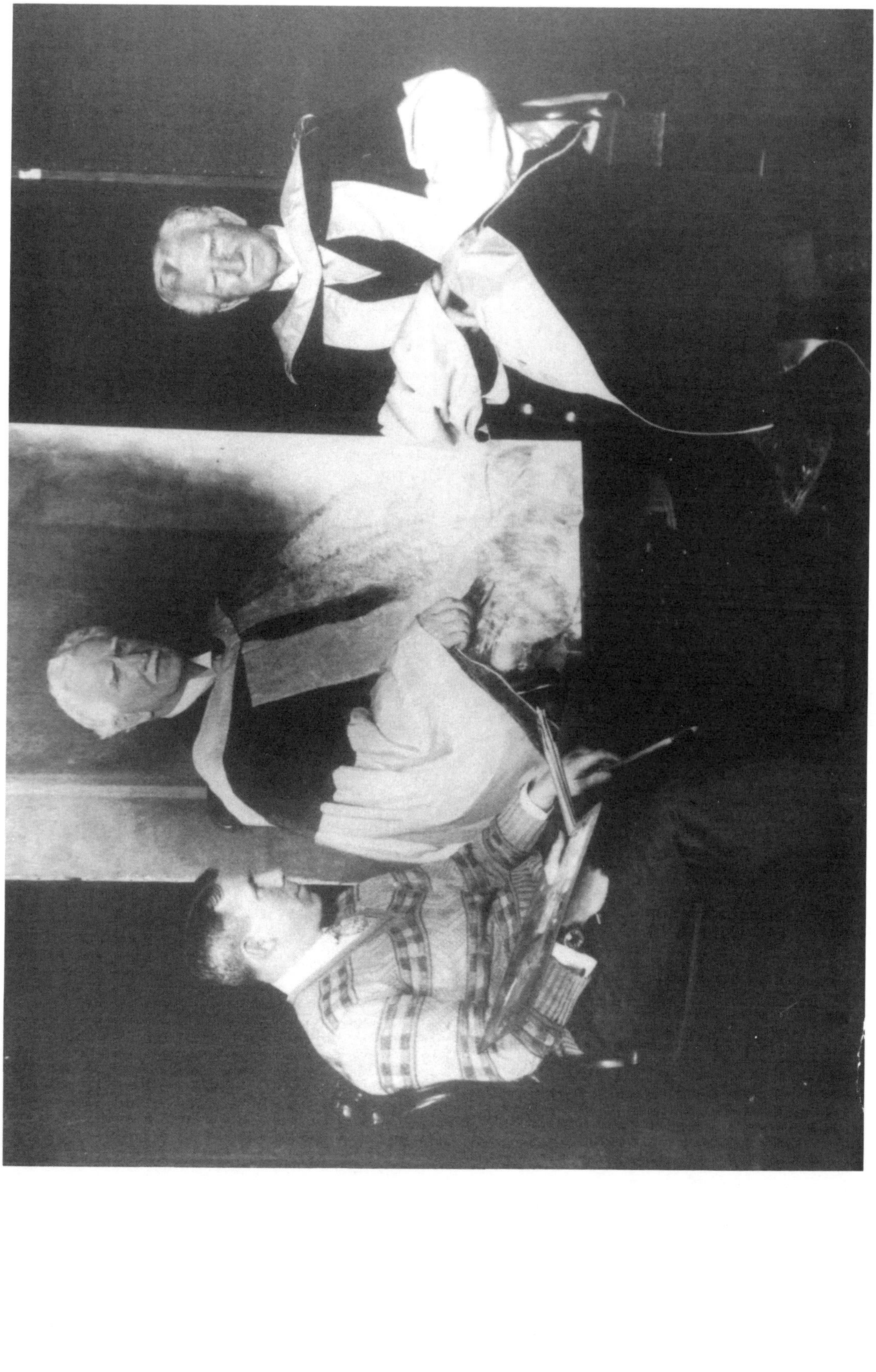

Dr. Charles J. Hastings being painted by the portrait artist Eugene Forbes.

Dr. George Nasmith
1877-1965

Three years later, the Senate passed a statute on May 20, 1904 to establish a "Diploma of Public Health" (D.P.H.), as it was originally known. The statute provided for the granting of the D.P.H. to physicians only.[84] The first mention of the Diploma in the calendar of the Faculty of Medicine was in 1904.[85] The first graduate to receive the D.P.H. was Dr. Hibbert W. Hill.[86] He qualified for the Diploma in 1911 without taking any courses. The requirements of the original D.P.H. allowed for that procedure by enabling anyone who had worked as a health officer to take an examination for the Diploma.[87]

Much later, in 1928, Amyot spoke about his part in the origins of the "Diploma of Public Health" course in the University of Toronto as well as the reasons for its location in that city:

> The first curriculum for public health was drawn up by Professor Ramsay Read, and I was taken in as a consultant. I gave the first lecture, Dr. Defries being one of my victims. This department [now] has increased and it is unique . . . . It is unique . . . in the training of its men . . . . They have entry into the clinics, Central Office, Central Laboratory, milk testing plants, and into all the services, and means are taken to put the men in there to see the actual thing being carried on . . .[88]

The Dr. Defries mentioned by Amyot was Dr. Robert Defries, the first candidate to take courses for the D.P.H. in the session of 1912 to 1913.[89]

That first course taken by Defries was structured very loosely. The model for the curriculum was the course for the Diploma in Public Health in the United Kingdom which changed with the addition of a more North American orientation in the subsequent years. The courses stressed sanitation, sanitary engineering, geology, meteorology, surveying, ventilation, bacteriology, parasitology, and the study of fevers. A variety of professors provided Defries with instruction. For example, Professor E.M. Walker of the Department of Biology instructed Defries in human parasitology in relation to public health.[90] Practical field work also formed a part of Defries' course. He studied public health engineering in the School of Applied Science and Engineering.[91] There was also a term of work in the provincial laboratories, where Defries worked later as a bacteriologist.[92] Unable to take examinations until the following year due to the absence of Amyot, Defries passed examinations for the D.P.H. in 1914,[93] to become the first individual to complete the course work for the diploma.

In the fall of 1913, FitzGerald and Defries worked together for the first time. This was the beginning of a partnership lasting the next twenty-seven years. At the request of Amyot, FitzGerald had returned from the University of California to assume the position of associate professor of hygiene. Defries who had just finished the first course for the D.P.H. became a demonstrator.[94] In the session of 1913 to 1914, FitzGerald and Defries taught the course for the "Diploma of Public Health". The second class to complete the D.P.H. included Dr. John McCullough, Chief Officer of Health in Ontario, Dr. A. Grant Fleming, a professor of preventive medicine at Montreal's McGill University in the 1920s, and Dr. Fred Adams, later Medical Officer of Health in Windsor.[95] FitzGerald and Defries had begun the task of teaching the generation of physicians who established modern public health services in Canada.

JOHN GERALD FITZGERALD 1882-1940

At the age of twenty, John Gerald FitzGerald was the youngest member of the Class of 1903 in Medicine in the University of Toronto.[96] A red-head of Irish lineage,[97] he was born in

Dr. John Gerald FitzGerald

Drayton, Ontario, north of what is now Kitchener, where his father ran a drugstore.[98] A small circle of close friends called him Gerry.[99] Appalled by the suffering he encountered in practice, following graduation, FitzGerald returned to university for postgraduate studies to upgrade his skills in a specialty. An intense, restless and ambitious individual, FitzGerald regarded medicine as a way to improve the human condition.

After a brief employment as a ship's physician on the trans-Atlantic run from New York to Southampton, FitzGerald completed a year of internship in psychiatry at the Buffalo State Hospital. Another three years were devoted to similar work in Baltimore with a year as an assistant in neurology at Johns Hopkins University. In 1907, FitzGerald returned to Toronto to become Clinical Director of the Hospital for the Insane and a demonstrator in psychiatry at the University of Toronto. Shortly thereafter, he went to study at Harvard Medical School from 1908 to 1909. When he came back to Toronto, his interest had shifted to bacteriology, a subject on which he lectured in his alma mater from 1909 to 1911. In 1910, he married Edna Leonard of London, Ontario; they had two children, a son and a daughter. Determined perhaps to upgrade his skills in bacteriology, FitzGerald studied at L'Institut Pasteur in Brussels and Paris from April to August of 1911. He was also a research student at the University of Freiburg in Germany. His European experience provided him with competence in French and German and a background in the latest advances in bacteriology, which resulted in his appointment as an associate professor of bacteriology in 1911 at the University of California at Berkeley.[100]

ROBERT DAVIES DEFRIES 1889-1975

The Defries family's roots in Toronto extended back to late 1820s. R.D. Defries' great-grandfather, Robert, came to York in 1829 from England. He was the Postmaster of the House of Assembly from 1835 to 1871 and also built a brewery in the east end of Toronto. His son, Dr. Defries' grandfather, married Elizabeth Davies, whose family operated in 1885 five of the thirteen breweries in Toronto.[101] A street, named Defries after the family of Dr. Defries, exists to this day in the city near the west bank of the Don River, north of Queen Street East and south of Dundas Street, running from River Street.[102]

Dr. Defries' father, William Thomas, managed the Dominion Brewery until his death at the age of twenty-eight. Dr. Defries' mother, a deeply religious lady, was determined that both of her sons stay out of the brewery business. She wanted them to go to university. They did. Both boys graduated in medicine from the University of Toronto.[103] A graduate of the Class of 1911 in medicine in the University of Toronto, Defries went on to earn a M.D. in 1912 and a D.P.H. in 1914.[104] The undergraduate yearbook, *Torontonensis*, referred to him as "Curly" because of his hair and added "To have Bob for a friend is to have one who will never spare himself if he can be of help to others."[105] These words foretold much about Defries' career. Deeply religious, in later years Defries was a very active supporter of what became the Bloor Street United Church.[106] An early interest in public health was linked to Defries' plan of entering the medical mission field. In 1917, it was FitzGerald who convinced Defries to give up his desire to be a missionary in order to help with the development of the Connaught Laboratories.[107]

Dr. Robert Davies Defries

The Class of 1911 in Medicine. Dr. Defries in 3rd row, 3rd seat from right.

THE FOUNDING OF CONNAUGHT LABORATORIES

When John FitzGerald came back to Toronto in 1913, he had a definite plan that led to the establishment of the Connaught Laboratories. For a number of years he had studied and visited health laboratories and institutes like L'Institut Pasteur in Paris, France.[108] He was aware of what could be accomplished using biological products from these facilities. In a laboratory provided by Amyot, FitzGerald prepared the Pasteur anti-rabies vaccine in the Provincial Laboratories at 5 Queen's Park Crescent in Toronto.[109]

Encouraged by his success, he decided to begin production of diphtheria antitoxin in order to make it available cheaply in Canada and to eliminate the necessity of importing the serum from America. With the help of William Fenton, he produced the antitoxin in horses kept behind Fenton's house on Barton Avenue in Toronto while he awaited the approval of the Board of Governors of the University of Toronto. The Board approved his proposal. On May 1, 1914, the Antitoxin Laboratory of the Department of Hygiene in the Faculty of Medicine opened officially.[110] It was the forerunner of what became in 1918 the Connaught Antitoxin Laboratories[111] and then in 1923, the Connaught Laboratories.[112]

FitzGerald did more than just produce the diphtheria antitoxin. He set up a system to deliver the product into the community. In what appears to be a very far-sighted and advanced diagnostic procedure, FitzGerald organized a series of "culture stations and antitoxin depots" across Toronto. Realizing the importance of early detection of diphtheria as the key to treatment, FitzGerald with the co-operation of the Toronto Department of Public Health established a network of over fifty druggists throughout the city to collect specimens from suspected victims of diphtheria and to maintain an adequate supply of antitoxin.[113] Physicians were notified about the availability of diphtheria antitoxin and other products.[114] Yet, despite all these efforts, scientific, professional and economic obstacles slowed down progress in the battle against diphtheria.

Very early on, FitzGerald in his crusade to make diphtheria antitoxin available to everyone, unearthed a grim fact of life. Many families with sick children could not afford the antitoxin at any price. Diphtheria, FitzGerald wrote in 1916,

> is a disease the ravages of which are felt mostly amongst the classes of our people who have least money with which to purchase medical supplies. A child in such a family is taken ill with diphtheria; the father goes to a nearby drugstore to buy the diphtheria antitoxin which the doctor has ordered; he requires a dose of five thousand units; he is asked to pay from three to five dollars for this. He is unable to do so and he either buys a smaller dose of, say, one thousand units at a dollar, or he waits until the next day with the hope that the child will then be better and he will not need to buy antitoxin at all. Next day the child is worse and eventually dies, even though given antitoxin. The delay has been fatal. The child should have been given as large a dose as possible at the very earliest moment after the disease was diagnosed.[115]

Clearly, lack of money was one of the major reasons for the persistence of diphtheria in Ontario.

To deal with economics, FitzGerald enlisted the help of Dr. McCullough in the Ontario Provincial Board of Health. Over the next two decades, FitzGerald and McCullough introduced a number of modern health services. Few were as significant as the provision of

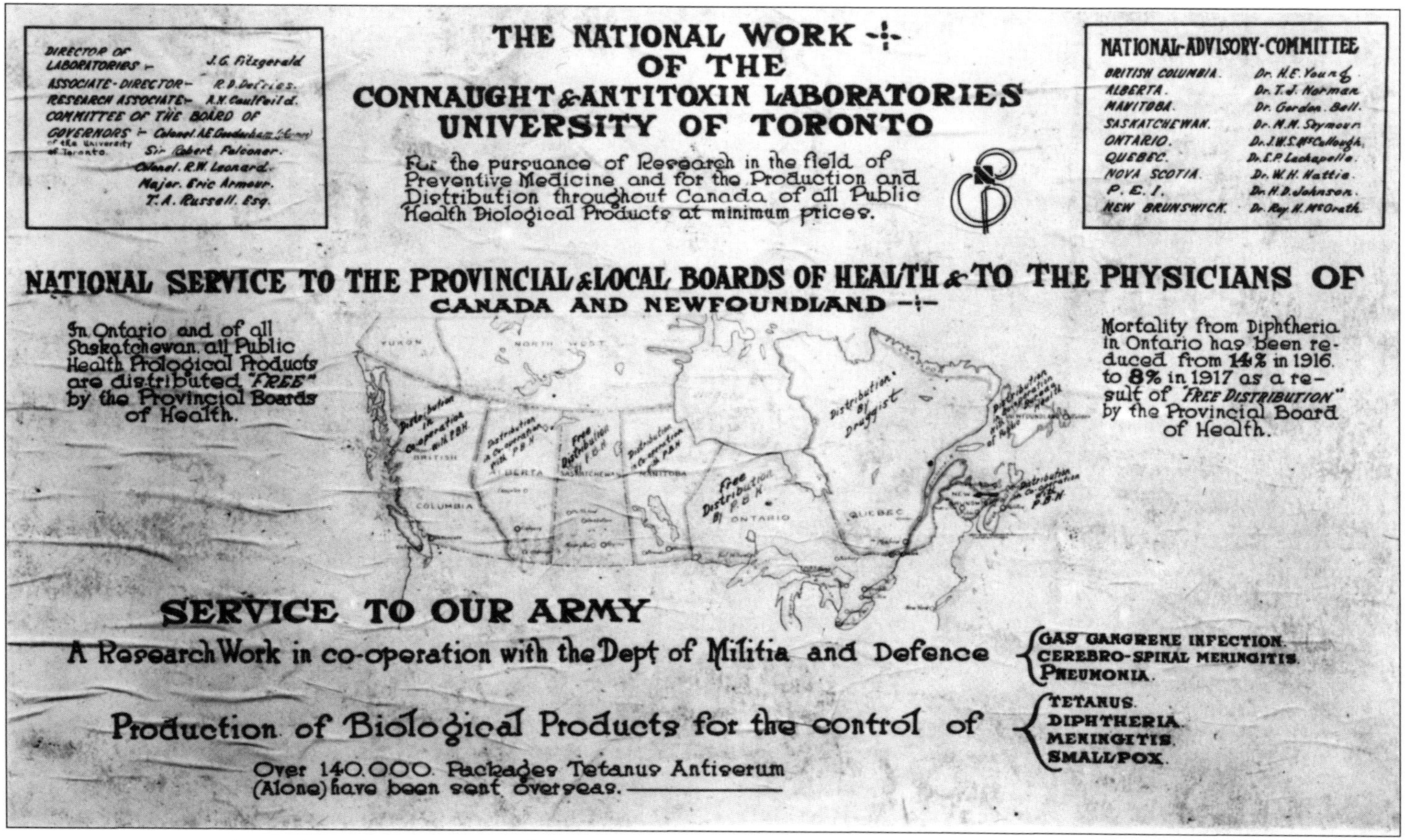

An early advertisement of the Connaught Laboratories stressing its national role.

An early advertisement of the Connaught Laboratories emphasizing an international market for its products.

free biological products to the general population. At first, in 1914, McCullough gained approval for the distribution of diphtheria antitoxin at a minimal cost to users.[116] Two years later, Ontario adopted a system of free distribution. That policy was a major step in the control of infectious diseases that had ravaged poor families who could not afford medical treatment.

THE CONNAUGHT LABORATORIES AND THE WAR

Ironically, the initiation of the manufacture and distribution of diphtheria antitoxin by FitzGerald's laboratory which saved human lives came about in the midst of the "Great War" of 1914 to 1918. Just four months after the establishment of the Antitoxin Laboratory by the University of Toronto, war had broken out in Europe. The demands generated by the First World War soon turned FitzGerald's small factory into a wartime industry and thereafter a national institution.[117]

It was the need by the armed forces for tetanus antitoxin to protect wounded troops that brought about a major expansion of the Antitoxin Laboratory in Toronto. With a grant from the Department of Militia and Defence, Defries in early 1915 took charge of the production of the antitoxin. By the war's end, the Canadian Army received over 250,000 doses from the Laboratory.[118] The University of Toronto Antitoxin Laboratory also provided smallpox vaccine for soldiers and civilians, having taken over the old Ontario Vaccine Farm established in 1885, in Palmerston, Ontario.[119] The era from 1914 to 1918 witnessed the first large-scale immunization program in Canada to protect troops from smallpox and tetanus.

When the demand for tetanus antitoxin overwhelmed the facilities of the Antitoxin Laboratories, a member of the Board of Governors of the University of Toronto who worked with the Canadian Red Cross stepped in to help. In 1915, Colonel Albert E. Gooderham, knighted in 1934, donated a farm of fifty-eight acres twelve miles north of Toronto for the use of the Laboratories. Later he provided additional funds to construct a laboratory facility. Gooderham decided to name the property after the Governor General at the time of his gift, the Duke of Connaught.[120] The name Connaught is used to this day.

The opening of the Connaught Antitoxin Laboratories and University Farm took place on October 25, 1917. Present at these ceremonies was Dr. Simon Flexner, Director of the Rockefeller Institute of Medical Research in New York City. In the evening at Convocation Hall in the University of Toronto, Flexner delivered an address on the contribution of medical research to the war effort.[121] His presence may well have led to the Rockefeller Foundation's decision to fund the establishment of the School of Hygiene which opened almost a decade later.

MILITARY SERVICE OF AMYOT AND FITZGERALD

The personal experiences of Amyot and FitzGerald, who left the department of hygiene at the University of Toronto to join the army during the First World War, had an important influence on the development of Canadian public health services.[122] The two men helped to organize in the Canadian Army a system to treat and control contagious diseases which was a reality in the military long before its application to the civilian population in Canada. According to Amyot, the preventive measures adopted by the Canadian Corps in France reversed the trend of more men dying from disease than from wounds.[123]

Enlisting in the Canadian Expeditionary Force in March, 1915, Amyot joined the Number 4 Canadian General Hospital at the rank of major. He sailed for England in the middle of May, 1915, where he transferred to the Second Canadian Division in the position of sanitary officer. On reaching France in September of that year, Amyot was the commander of the Sanitary Section First Canadian Division and later advisor in sanitation to the Canadian Corps in 1916 and then with the Second British Army in France. After leaving the western front, Amyot was the consultant in sanitation, Canadian Overseas Forces, from 1916 to 1918 at the rank of lieutenant-colonel.[124]

On the battlefield, Amyot introduced a number of practices to cut down on infectious diseases. The sterilization of drinking water and eating utensils cut down significantly gastrointestinal illness. The daily provision of dry towels and socks prevented trench foot. The formation of field baking facilities, laundries and disinfestation procedures for fleas and lice reduced trench fever.[125] All of these procedures helped to control the spread of typhoid, diphtheria and cholera outbreaks.[126] Amyot saw first-hand how these practical steps worked so well.

Amyot's junior colleague, FitzGerald, spent most of the war on the homefront. His military service in Ontario consisted of the provision of health services to troops before their departure overseas. In May, 1915, FitzGerald entered the Royal Army Medical Corps. Placed in charge of the laboratory unit in military district number 2 which centred on the Toronto region, FitzGerald rose to the rank of major. Not until March, 1918, did FitzGerald proceed to England. He reached the western front in France in June where he commanded a mobile laboratory. Later he was an advisor in pathology to the British Fifth Army.[127]

FitzGerald's military experience was important to his later work. It magnified his awareness of the prevalence of certain health dangers. For example, he developed an understanding of the extent of the pollution of drinking water in Southern Ontario. On the route of the march of units from Toronto to Camp Niagara, FitzGerald examined the water supplies used by troops. Even the wells constructed properly with cement tops showed evidence of contamination.[128]

The prevalence of polluted water convinced FitzGerald of the need for an inoculation program to protect the soldiers. FitzGerald oversaw the introduction of mass immunization of all new units in the Toronto region. "Inoculation and vaccination parades in this district", he and another officer reported in 1917, "were regarded as of the utmost importance from both the military and medical viewpoint".[129] There was a policy of mandatory vaccination against smallpox for all men. Because typhoid fever was "endemic all over Canada", typhoid inoculations were also given. After May, 1916, a mixed vaccine for typhoid and paratyphoid was adopted. The University of Toronto Antitoxin Laboratory provided all these biological products.

Mindful of the controversy surrounding compulsory inoculations, FitzGerald and a colleague described in detail the procedures to counter possible criticisms of the program:

> The techniques consisted in the use of a 10cc. sterilized syringe and separate needle for each man. Immediately below the collarbone an area about one inch in diameter was painted with tincture of iodine, and the injection made subcutaneously. The first and second doses contained 500 million of mixed dead bacteria, and the third 1,000 million. The injections were given at intervals of seven days, and vaccination was done on the day preceding the last

> injection, so that the entire process was completed in two weeks. Men were not required to do any heavy duty such as marching, for the next twenty-four hours. While there was a moderate reaction in the majority of cases, evidenced by slight headache, malaise, slight chills, etc., comparatively few cases showed any marked disability and there has in no case resulted any permanent ill-result. Very few cases went to hospital; the longest hospital period in any case for this cause did not exceed forty-eight hours.[130]

To minimize the potential anxiety of the soldiers, it was pointed out, special inoculation and vaccination parades became part of the routine:

> It was very desirable to have the entire unit paraded at the time, with band, if the unit possessed a band. Furthermore, the moral effect was excellent, if the band played during the time the inoculations and vaccinations were being done. Also it was found that when all officers, including the commissioned officers were inoculated or vaccinated with the men of the unit, the commissioned officers coming up first, the example was of value. The men saw that everyone was playing the game.[131]

The success of the effort was reflected in the low number of communicable diseases in the ranks.

FitzGerald's laboratory unit also checked regularly the water supplies of the troops, examined "throat cultures for B. diphtheriae", blood samples, smears, urine samples and gastric contents for signs of infections.[132]

The identification and treatment of venereal diseases was the other major breakthrough in which FitzGerald participated during the war.[133] In early 1918, he attended a special meeting on social diseases at the Toronto Academy of Medicine. He became the chairman of the "Advisory Committee on Venereal Diseases for Military District No. 2". Like others leading the campaign against V.D., FitzGerald saw the problem as a civilian not a military one because the army had a system in place to detect and treat the diseases.[134] Education of the medical profession, social agencies, governments and the lay public was the solution in the opinion of FitzGerald.[135] The involvement in the crusade against syphilis and gonorrhoea reinforced FitzGerald's commitment to the development of better public health education programs which was a theme that emerged later in his administration of the School of Hygiene.

Returning to civilian life after their wartime experiences, Amyot and FitzGerald, like so many other veterans, wanted to apply the lessons of wartime to peacetime. FitzGerald summed up that aspiration when he stated that the war had demonstrated how "the nation's entire resources may be unified and co-ordinated in the struggle against preventable disease."[136]

PUBLIC HEALTH BECOMES A FEDERAL RESPONSIBILITY

What peacetime could not bring about for public health, wartime did in terms of the federal government accepting a larger role in public health services. "At this time when we are suffering from the losses due to the war, and when the value of human life has become of greatest moment", Newton Rowell stated in the House of Commons at the second reading of a bill respecting the Department of Health, "it is fitting that the House and the country should turn attention to considering better measures for conserving the health of our people."[137]

Fears about the physical and mental inferiority of many Canadians prompted the call for federal action. In his speech, Rowell pointed to the "more than one-half" of the males between 20 and 34 years of age examined under the Military Service Act who were found "to be more or less physically unfit."[138] Another shocking statistic cited by Rowell was the infant mortality rate in 1916 in six of the largest Canadian cities per 1,000 births: Toronto was 109; Winnipeg, 126; Vancouver, 144; Quebec, 203; Montreal, 207; Ottawa, 224. These figures were alarming when compared with infant mortality rates per 1,000 births in 1916 for the following cities in the United Kingdom: London was 89; Bristol, 95; Edinburgh, 100; Glasgow, 111; Manchester, 111; Nottingham, 116; Liverpool, 118; Leeds, 129. "We are willing to spend money to bring immigrants to Canada", Rowell reported, "yet there are dying in some of the great cities of our country, during the first years of their lives, twenty-five percent of the babies born."[139]

The worldwide epidemic of influenza in 1918 near the war's end was another factor highlighting the national importance of public health measures. Despite the many medical advances, especially in the control of contagious diseases, made as a result of the war, the "Spanish flu" dramatized the potency of some infectious diseases. In October, the epidemic hit Toronto with devastating results and the city came to a standstill. Thousands were affected and hundreds died,[140] although the Connaught Antitoxin Laboratories under the leadership of Defries produced a vaccine for the outbreak.[141] Dr. Donald Fraser, later a member of the staff of Connaught Laboratories and the School of Hygiene, wrote that the influenza "has lasted for many months and has been the cause . . . of greater mortality than the war" with no "accepted solution." What was needed was more research into the origin of the pandemic of influenza.[142] This was still to come.

Within months of the passing of the influenza pandemic, the Canadian government established a Department of Health in the spring of 1919.[143] Significantly, in terms of the Toronto public health movement, Dr. John Amyot became the first deputy minister. Amyot's position in Ottawa opened up even more a national role for FitzGerald and later the School of Hygiene.[144]

The Department of Health embodied both old and new trends in public health. There were eventually twelve branches. The older units dating from the period before 1914 were the quarantine service, including leper stations, the marine hospital's service, food and drugs, immigration medical service and proprietory or patent medicine. The post-1918 sections were venereal disease control, child welfare, opium and narcotic drugs, publicity and statistics, housing, the laboratory of hygiene and public health engineering. When the post-war zeal subsided, federal authorities abolished the publicity and statistics, housing, child welfare and venereal disease control branches.[145]

DOMINION COUNCIL OF HEALTH

That public health was a concurrent responsibility of both federal and provincial governments in Canada since 1869 posed a continuous problem in the organization of an effective national standard of public health services. "The decentralization of public health control, while advantageous in many respects", a history of the National Health Division of the Department of Pensions and National Health reported in 1935, "had the one great disadvantage of isolation. Each of the provinces worked independently, none knew what the other was doing.

There was overlapping, wasted effort, perpetuation of obsolete methods, and progress was indefinitely delayed."[146] To work towards the formation of a Canadian system of public health services, the Dominion Council of Health was formed, largely it appears, as a result of Toronto's public health lobby.

The Dominion Council of Health consisted of the chief medical officer of health from every province, the deputy minister of the federal health department and five others usually representing labour, women, farmers and medical educators. The Council met twice a year in the spring and the fall. Its first meeting was held from October 7 to October 9, 1920 in Ottawa.[147] The agenda of the D.C.H. reflected the scope of the public health issues addressed in the 1920s and 1930s:

> interprovincial relations in regard to patients suffering from tuberculosis and other diseases who may have recently removed from one province to another; standardization of venereal disease treatment; workmen's compensation; maternal and child welfare; hospital standardization; industrial hygiene; medical examination of immigrants; quarantine; vital statistics; pasteurization of milk; purification of water; pollution of streams; sanitation of railway, steamboat, and other conveyances; publicity and public health propaganda; protection of health of Indians and Eskimos; drug addiction.[148]

What was noteworthy about these subjects was the expansion of the concerns of public health officials beyond communicable diseases into areas such as pediatrics, obstetrics, hospital care and industrial health.

From the very beginning of the Council, FitzGerald played a leadership role. The minutes of the D.C.H. revealed his contributions. Although not officially a part of the group, he attended the founding meeting in October, 1919.[149] The following year, FitzGerald addressed the spring gathering about the creation of a national organization "to deal with the problems peculiar to Child Welfare". He also moved a resolution recommending the employment by health departments of "properly trained Public Health Nurses."[150] In 1923, FitzGerald was appointed as a scientific advisor formally to the Council, after attending its first five meetings. Amyot explained the reasons for FitzGerald's appointment; "it was thought well to have someone who would be carrying on all the time with scientific matters, particularly in the teaching of those subjects to medical students and other students attending Universities, so that we have the educational side and the scientific side represented by one of the members of his group."[151] By the time the School of Hygiene opened, FitzGerald's national role on the Dominion Council of Health was established clearly.

Increasingly after 1927, the membership of the Dominion Council of Health came from the graduates of the School's D.P.H. course. More importantly, the Council reflected the concerns of the faculty of the University of Toronto School of Hygiene.

ONTARIO DEPARTMENT OF HEALTH

Perhaps the most noteworthy advances in public health services took place at the provincial level. In Ontario, Dr. J.W.S. McCullough, an early graduate of the D.P.H. program of the University of Toronto, expanded the activities and staff of the Ontario Provincial Board of Health. McCullough worked closely with FitzGerald who later persuaded McCullough to teach in the new School of Hygiene. The increasing importance of the work of the O.P.B.H. was reflected in the elevation of its status to the Ontario Department of Health with a deputy minister by 1925.[152] By the mid 1920s, the O.D.H. provided a variety of services carried out by divisions of sanitary engineering, preventable diseases, maternal and child hygiene, laboratories which included a number of branches across the province, industrial hygiene, dental services, vital statistics and public health education.[153]

An example of how wartime conditions influenced the emergence of new public health activities in Ontario was the beginnings of industrial hygiene. The demands for industrial products made by the First World War raised a consciousness about the dangerous side effects of certain types of manufacturing. In 1919, J.J.R. MacLeod, a professor of physiology in the University of Toronto undertook a study entitled "Survey of General Conditions of Industrial Hygiene in Toronto with Results of an Investigation into Lost Time due to Sickness." That same year, the department of hygiene and preventive medicine instituted courses on industrial hygiene for undergraduate and graduate medical students. In 1920, the O.P.B.H. formed the division of industrial hygiene.[154]

McCullough's expansion of services provided by the Ontario Department of Health as well as the growth of federal and provincial health departments across Canada in the 1920s created a need for courses to provide physicians and nurses with postgraduate education in public health. One example of such a program was provided by the Institute of Public Health at the University of Western Ontario in London, Ontario. Established in 1912, the Institute granted from 1920 to 1927, the Diploma of Public Health to seven physicians as well as the Certificate of Public Health Nurse to a number of nurses.[155] In a different context and on a much larger scale, the University of Toronto School of Hygiene became the primary centre for the education of these new professionals.

PUBLIC HEALTH NURSING EDUCATION

Inaugurated by Dr. Charles Hastings, Toronto's M.O.H. after 1910, the Toronto plan of public health nursing demonstrated the value of using nurses to provide basic health care for working class infants, children and mothers.[156] These nurses were the type of health workers that FitzGerald and others who were planning the organization of public health services in Ontario wanted to put into the field. Following the First World War, the establishment of a course for public health nursing at the university level became a priority for Toronto's health educators. That program constituted an important part of the School of Hygiene's teaching from the beginning.

Following a pattern of many other health professionals, the education of public health nurses originated in an on-the-job program. The Toronto Department of Public Health developed its own "in house" training system. Eunice Dyke, head of the department's nursing division, was a strong advocate of the need for special courses at a university which became mandatory for all public health nurses in the city.[157]

Reflecting the growing appreciation of the economic and social basis for sickness, public health nursing education originated in University of Toronto's Department of Social Services founded in 1915, the forerunner of the School of Social Work. There were two courses, "The Field of Social Work" and "Medical Social Service" which combined lectures, seminars and field work to familiarize nurses with the laws and government organizations available in the community.[158]

The growth of health services during the war and the widespread reliance on nurses and nursing assistants during the influenza epidemic of 1918 convinced many of the need to organize a formal educational program for public health nurses. The Canadian Red Cross initiated the process by financing courses in a variety of Canadian universities. In the University of Toronto, the Red Cross funded the Department of Public Health Nursing in 1920. The University appointed Kathleen Russell to the position of director. The department, located at 1 Queen's Park Crescent East, also used the facilities of the Department of Social Services at 8 Queen's Park Crescent East. The first class of fifty students enrolled in the session 1920 to 1921.[159] It was a postgraduate program opened to graduates of nursing schools. Problems with continued financing and limited accommodation led to its incorporation temporarily into the School of Hygiene which shared a common commitment to the improvement of general health conditions.[160]

PUBLIC HEALTH PROBLEMS IN THE 1920s

In the aftermath of the war, there was a public backlash against mass immunization as carried out in the army. When smallpox broke out in Toronto in the fall of 1919,[161] strong opposition surfaced to compulsory vaccination of school children. In an ugly legal confrontation between the Medical Officer of Health, Dr. Charles Hastings, and City Council over his authority to order inoculation of youngsters in the schools, Hastings lost the battle.[162] Many of the popular fears about the method of immunization against smallpox which caused often hurtful and disfiguring side effects were justified.[163] Unfortunately, some health officials did little to allay the terror surrounding the procedures. So convinced was FitzGerald of the safety of vaccination against smallpox that he had himself inoculated before medical students in the University of Toronto and then had the whole class immunized.[164] As late as the fall of 1927, a few months after the opening of the School of Hygiene, students in Victoria College of the University of Toronto, were placed under quarantine due to smallpox.[165]

FitzGerald and his associates still faced an uphill battle on many fronts to control communicable diseases. Even the initial success of FitzGerald's use of diphtheria antitoxin in lowering the frequency rate of diphtheria suffered a setback. From 1918 to 1921, diphtheria mortality in Ontario increased. The Chief Medical Officer of Health in the province, Dr. J.W.S. McCullough, blamed the rise on the existence of a different strain of diphtheria, the influence of quack doctors and the high fees charged by physicians to administer the "free" antitoxin.[166]

Much of the hope for rapid improvements in public health generated by the First World War disappeared in the realities of postwar Canada. The continuation of part-time health officers in most municipalities remained a major stumbling block to the delivery of effective public health services.[167] For example, in the fast growing suburbs of Toronto in 1924, there were no full-time health officers but thirty part-timers.[168] Just before the opening of the School of Hygiene, Ontario's Deputy Minister of Health, Dr. W.J. Bell, expressed his frustration with the lack of progress in the previous decade:

> Sometimes we feel that we are not getting ahead as rapidly as we might and that progress is so slow as to be almost imperceptible. The job is so big and our efforts so small in comparison, that at times we get a bit discouraged.[169]

Yet there were signs of some measurable advances in the events leading to the formation of the School of Hygiene.

REVISION OF D.P.H. COURSE

Following the war's end, the curriculum of the Diploma in Public Health of the University of Toronto underwent a significant overhaul.[170] Before 1919, the D.P.H. was an apprenticeship program. After that date, the course requirements were formalized to extend over a winter session of eight months and a summer session of three months. The winter session involved laboratory courses and lectures in bacteriology, sanitary chemistry and parasitology. Students attended clinics for communicable diseases, mental illness, venereal disease and tuberculosis. There were also well-baby clinics and antenatal clinics. According to the Calendar, there were lectures and practical work in general hygiene, immunology, applied physiology, sanitary engineering, public health organization and legislation, vital statistics, preventive medicine and epidemiology, nutrition and dietetics, and industrial hygiene. The course took advantage of the facilities of the Ontario Provincial Board of Health, the Toronto Department of Public Health, and the special clinics in the Toronto General Hospital and the Hospital for Sick Children. The summer session was devoted to field work in a public health department including a study of the networks of dealing with communicable diseases, inspection of schools and other public buildings, factories, dairies; inspection of water supplies and sewage disposal plants; food and meat inspection and other forms of municipal sanitation; and medical inspection of school children.[171] The D.P.H. course had evolved considerably from its beginnings in 1912 and 1913.

FITZGERALD CHANGES UNDERGRADUATE MEDICAL EDUCATION

A new era of teaching and research had arrived in the University of Toronto Faculty of Medicine, the era of preventive medicine. With the financial resources of the Connaught Laboratories, FitzGerald was able to promote undergraduate and postgraduate instruction in public health. FitzGerald had succeeded Amyot in the fall of 1919.[172] The name of the Department was changed to the Department of Hygiene and Preventive Medicine.[173] Dr. J. Grant Cunningham began the instruction in Industrial Hygiene in 1919.[174] Although not in the Faculty, a Department of Public Health Nursing gave impetus to the whole field of practical work in public health.[175] Money from the Connaught Laboratories funded the formation of a Student Health Service in the university.[176] In 1924, FitzGerald pushed through a regulation requiring all medical undergraduates to take a field course in preventive medicine.[177]

The publication of *An Introduction to the Practice of Preventive Medicine* in 1922 by an American Company in St. Louis, Missouri, indicated FitzGerald's increasing stature in the field. In fact, the book, like so many of FitzGerald's ventures, was a co-operative effort. Professor Peter Gillespie, an instructor of applied mechanics in the University of Toronto, contributed important chapters on sanitary engineering as did Dr. H.M. Lancaster, the Director of the Division of Laboratories in the Ontario Provincial Board of Health; Dr. J. Grant Cunningham, the Director of the newly created Division of Industrial Hygiene; and Professor Andrew Hunter, a biochemist in the Faculty of Medicine of the University of Toronto. The volume contained twenty-five chapters with appendices in over eight hundred pages.[178] It stressed the etiology, treatment and prevention of communicable diseases such as diphtheria, scarlet fever, measles, German measles, mumps, whooping cough, tuberculosis, poliomyelitis, typhoid fever, typhus, smallpox, rabies, chickenpox, syphilis, gonorrhea and tetanus.

But FitzGerald's work was more than just a textbook on public health. In his first chapter, while acknowledging the advances in health services, he called for the adoption of a system of free state-supported health supervision. "This system should include provision for antenatal supervision, home visitation, and infant welfare centres to safeguard the health of infants and little children; medical, nursing and dental supervision in schools and colleges, and finally, clinics for periodic medical examination of adults."[179] FitzGerald's proposal was hardly radical. It was not a universal health insurance. Rather, he wanted a scheme similar to the one in Toronto:

> In cooperation with the Department of Health of the City, there are clinics and centers, the medical work of which is done by physicians who are also engaged in private practice. Examples of this are to be seen in the Associated Tuberculosis Clinic of Toronto; in the Venereal Disease Clinics, the Psychopathic Clinics, and also, in part of the "Well-Baby" Centers, and the Antenatal Clinics.[180]

FitzGerald's aim was not to upset the private medical system but to expand the scope of preventive medicine. Nonetheless, it demonstrated the evolution in the perspective of FitzGerald beyond public health measures to a consideration of the whole field of health care.

THE ROCKEFELLER FOUNDATION IN TORONTO

By the early 1920s when Dr. Frederick Banting and his associates discovered insulin, Toronto was already a recognized centre for medical research and public health administration, a fact that caught the eyes of officials in an American foundation. After the First World War, the Rockefeller Foundation had donated a million dollars to improve the clinical departments of the Faculty of Medicine in Toronto as part of its North American program.[181] The innovative services of Dr. Charles Hastings in his Toronto Department of Public Health as well as the Provincial Board of Health and local hospitals were acclaimed. In 1922, a visiting French health official, Dr. Leon Bernard, praised the situation in Toronto as "the best system existing anywhere in the world of close and productive co-operation among public health departments in all their phases, including that of social service, the department of the university, and the city hospitals."[182] So impressed with the situation in Toronto was the International Health Board of the Rockefeller Foundation that it sent regularly its fellows from different countries to get practical experience in the city.[183] President George E. Vincent of the Rockefeller Foundation expressed his organization's high regard for Toronto's system:

> The people who come here to visit the combination you have here go away saying, "This on the whole is unique." Here you have a university medical school working in close co-operation with a university school of public health and working in close co-operation with an extremely efficient and finely organized city department of public health. . . . You have the whole working with a broad-minded, forward-looking Provincial Department of Public Health. You have one of the finest systems of public health to be found anywhere in the world. . . . We send to Toronto almost all of the nurses and

> Fellows that we bring from other countries, because they get more here in a smaller compass and shorter time than anywhere else.[184]

Not surprisingly, when the Rockefeller Foundation was looking for a showcase of public health, its representatives went to Toronto to see FitzGerald.

With the expansion of the responsibilities of the Connaught Laboratories in the production of insulin[185] and other products as well as the growth of instruction in undergraduate and postgraduate courses in preventive medicine, the most pressing demand of all FitzGerald's teaching, research and manufacturing operations was to house most of them in one building. When representatives from the Rockefeller Foundation visited Toronto in 1923 to inquire about what he needed, the answer was very simple—a building.[186]

ROCKEFELLER FOUNDATION'S GRANT TO SCHOOL OF HYGIENE

The decision to locate a School of Hygiene in Toronto was part of the larger international policy of the Rockefeller Foundation to ameliorate health conditions. The University of Toronto School of Hygiene was to be the third School of Public Health in North America supported by the Foundation. The first one opened in 1916 at Johns Hopkins University in Baltimore, Maryland.[187] Five years later, the Harvard School of Public Health that began before the First World War received similar funding.[188]

In 1924, the International Health Division of the Rockefeller Foundation announced a gift of $400,000 to construct a building for the University of Toronto School of Hygiene and a further donation of $250,000 to be an endowment for the operation of a Department of Epidemiology and Biometrics and a Department of Physiological Hygiene in the School.[189] More funding came in the 1930s and 1940s. The University of Toronto School of Hygiene had joined the ranks of an elite establishment with a common goal, the Rockefeller Schools of Public Health. Built on this rich tradition of public health reform and medical research, the School of Hygiene established very soon its own reputation.

CHAPTER TWO

THE FITZGERALD ERA, 1927-1940

In the early years of the life of a School responsible for the development of scientific and professional personnel for public health work in a country where progress is very rapid, as is the case in this Dominion, an attempt must be made to establish and maintain high standards of training and preparation. Two groups or categories of students have to be provided for, those who are to be prepared to contribute substantially to increasing knowledge of preventive medicine in the years to come, and those responsible for the conduct of routine public health, in all its aspects, both at the present time and in the future.[1]

Dr. John G. FitzGerald in 1934

Thursday, June 9, 1927 was the date of the official opening of the University of Toronto School of Hygiene Building.[2] The actual ceremonies took place in Convocation Hall. True to custom, the Chairman of the Board of Governors, Canon H.J. Cody, thanked the International Health Board of the Rockefeller Foundation for the gift of the new building and the endowment for the School of Hygiene. Then the President of the University, Sir Robert Falconer, introduced the principal speaker at the gathering, Sir George Newman, Chief Medical Officer of the Ministry of Health of England and Wales. Newman's address was a combination of a brief history of advances in medicine and a commentary on contemporary medical problems and education. Thereafter Falconer invited the audience for a short walk to inspect the new building. With British traditions and American money, the School of Hygiene embarked on its first decade.[3]

Full credit for the construction of the School of Hygiene Building belonged to John FitzGerald. Canon Cody highlighted that fact in a speech to the Canadian Club of Toronto:

> It is Dr. Fitzgerald's [sic] idea and it is unique as far as I am aware and gave the lead to other universities. It is a curious combination. It combines a certain measure of medical education. It combines a large measure of research and then it adds to those two features of teaching and research the third function of providing a public medical service, for it is a manufacturing establishment and it manufactures there all kinds of serums and vaccines which are distributed through the Dominion and far beyond its boundaries. This combination is absolutely unique.

To the applause of the assembled business community, Cody explained how FitzGerald had solicited the funds for the building from the Rockefeller Foundation and then added that the structure had been completed within the allocated budget.[4]

With the School of Hygiene Building in operation, John FitzGerald's master plan to improve general health conditions in Canada had become a reality. The establishment of the Connaught Laboratories and later the expansion of the teaching and research in the Department of Hygiene and Preventive Medicine demonstrated both the value and the viability of postgraduate and graduate work in public health within the university. The construction of the School of Hygiene Building to accommodate undergraduate, postgraduate and graduate teaching[5] and research as well as the production of biological products was the fulfillment of FitzGerald's triad, specifically:

> the promotion and extension of knowledge in the field of Preventive Medicine through research, investigation and teaching; the creation of adequate and complete facilities for such work and finally the conduct of a public service undertaking the preparation and distribution of public health biological products which shall be self-sustaining and at the same time provide a measure of support for abstract research in the field.[6]

The linking of the School of Hygiene to the Connaught Laboratories was a brilliant strategy on the part of FitzGerald, particularly at a time when there was very little money forthcoming for such endeavours from provincial and federal governments in the 1920s and even less in the 1930s.

The School of Hygiene Building exemplified the inseparable relationship between the School of Hygiene and the Connaught Laboratories as well as the interdisciplinary character of the School itself in the 1920s and 1930s. The building was both the headquarters on the campus of the Connaught Laboratories — its University Division — and the classrooms and laboratories of the School.[7]

Designed by the Toronto firm of architects, Mathers and Haldenby, the building's exterior was in the Georgian style finished in red brick with stone trimmings. Located on a site adjacent to the Electrical Building near the corner of Queen's Park Crescent West and College Street, it faced west with one front on College Street. E.W. Haldenby in 1926 described the structure in the following way:

> The building in plan is a long rectangle with two wings at each end extending to the east, forming a paved court-yard enclosed by a wall and containing a garage. The plan shows central corridors with offices and laboratories on both sides. These corridors generally run through at the ends to a window, which provides plenty of light and ventilation. The building contains a sub-basement, a basement and four floors. The fourth floor is considerably smaller than the other floors, and in it are the Elevator Pent Houses and the Animal Houses. The Animal Houses open directly to the Animal Runs on the roof. The main entrance is on the west front on the ground level. There is a students' entrance on the north side of the building, and an entrance to the Connaught Laboratories in the basement on the College Street side.

One "special feature" was the inclusion of a large area of glass "essential for laboratory work." Haldenby described the interior in the following way:

> the walls and ceilings with the exception of the corridors and the lecture room on the ground floor, are plastered. The latter will be finished in grey brick to a height of eight feet, and plastered above that level. The main entrance will be used on the main staircase up to the second floor. The stair balustrades will be constructed of ornamental iron work. On the second floor a large library is to be built, with panelled walls and stone fireplace. The Director's room is on the third floor above the Library, and it also is panelled and has a fireplace. All floors of the building are served by a freight elevator, and a passenger elevator will run from the sub-basement to the third floor.
>
> The floors will be finished with asphalt, except in the Library, Lecture Rooms and Offices, where hardwood is to be used.

The use of "vast amounts of piping and conduits for gas, hot and cold water, compressed air, refrigeration, ventilation, steam heating and electric power" was another outstanding

Beginning the construction of the Hygiene Building in fall 1925.

Hygiene Building in summer 1926.

Original north end of the Hygiene Building in 1926 before expansion.

Original north end of Hygiene Building on December 12, 1931.

characteristic of the building. Although heated from the Central Heating Plant, a miniature heating plant was constructed to provide steam for the production of insulin.[8] Sir William Mulock, Chancellor of the University of Toronto, laid the cornerstone on January 21, 1926.[9] The building was finished essentially by August of 1926.[10] Its floor space was almost 28,000 square feet.[11]

Months after its opening, the Toronto magazine, *MacLean's* (as it was then spelt), featured the Hygiene Building in the leading article with the catchy title, "A Peacetime Munitions Plant: Where science fashions its weapons for the war against the armies of Disease." The author characterized FitzGerald as a "tall, lean, bespectacled Canadian" with an idea "so unusual as to approach the revolutionary."[12] He described the operations of the Connaught Laboratories in the Building in the following way:

> The enterprise started with three people, now [1928] it employs around 125. Besides the splendid facilities at the University Farm, the laboratory occupies more than fifty rooms in the School of Hygiene building. The entire basement and sub-basement are devoted to its activities, with the two top floors, several rooms on the intermediate floors, and special quarters for test animals on the roof. Incubators, and refrigerators, testing laboratories, departments for the manufacture of insulin, vaccines, serums and antitoxins are there, each fully equipped with the latest devices for expediting the accurate preparation of its products. There are executive offices on the ground floor, a large and smartly organized packing and shipping department in the basement, kitchens, a cafeteria, and a room devoted to salvage. The bulk of the employees are women, who, robed in clinical white, sterilize, test, measure and pack all day long. Its production laboratories are presided over by chemists and biochemists who are particularly trained for the highly specialized duties which they perform.
>
> It is a perfectly functioning munitions factory for public health.[13]

Also included in *MacLean's* survey of the Hygiene Building in January, 1928 was a graphic account of the preparation of antitoxins. The first stage of production was the inoculation of horses and then the removal of their blood which underwent chemical treatment with sodium nitrate. This raw material, "a yellowish-white mixture", was refined at 150 College Street in a process "consisting of filtration through tubes of porous clay, precipitation with ammonium sulphate, filtration through glass funnels, lined with a specially prepared filter paper, and final solution in bags of parchment paper which are suspended in water for a period of days, which dissolves the antitoxin, for the final tests, dilution and measurement into vials, capillary tubes and syringes."[14]

Similarly, the *MacLean's* article detailed the manufacturing of insulin from the pancreas of "freshly slaughtered animals . . . ground fine in an oversized meatchopper":

> The chopped meat is soaked in acidified alcohol, and the liquid filtered off by centrifugal motion through a fine cloth screen. Further filtration is through parchment paper and glass funnels, and the result is a fine gray powder very similar in appearance to the various pulverized cleansing agents marketed by soap manufacturers. Purification and solution of this powder result in a clear, blue-white, sterile water solution, which is the insulin of medical practice.[15]

Insulin was the most famous of the sixteen biological products distributed from the Hygiene Building in 1928 which was then the "Largest Insulin 'Factory' in the World."[16]

DEPARTMENTS OF SCHOOL TO 1940

At the beginning, the School of Hygiene consisted, in fact, of three departments: Hygiene and Preventive Medicine, Epidemiology and Biometrics, and Physiological Hygiene. Another department, Public Health Nursing, housed within the Hygiene Building, was an independent division that left the School in 1933.[17] The first sub-department, Chemistry in Relation to Hygiene, came into existence in 1931.[18] In addition to undergraduate and postgraduate teaching, the faculty, all part-timers, taught a small but growing number of graduate students.

The Department of Hygiene and Preventive Medicine, also a department in the Faculty of Medicine, was the largest with a staff of one professor, J.G. FitzGerald, two associate professors, R.D. Defries and D.T. Fraser, one assistant professor, P.J. Moloney, a lecturer in hygiene, G.D. Porter, three demonstrators in hygiene, F.S. Burke, Miss F. Fraser, and P.A.T. Sneath, and four class assistants, D.C.B. Duff, Miss C.J. Fraser, Miss E.M. Taylor and Miss H. Plummer.[19]

Hygiene and Preventive Medicine was the largest department in the School of Hygiene in the 1930s. It was the launching pad for a number of lifelong careers in the School. Frieda Fraser, an original member, taught a variety of courses, rising eventually to the rank of full professor.[20] Similarly, Dr. Milton Brown, appointed a demonstrator in 1931, eventually took over as head of the department.[21] Another example was Dr. Frank Wishart. Following his graduation as a physician and then his completion of a M.A. degree in the University of Toronto, Wishart lectured on immunology in the School.[22] He took over the direction of the immunization clinic in the Building.[23] Three other noteworthy individuals were Dr. Claude Dolman, Dr. Robert Wilson and Dr. Ronald Hare. Dolman, who had come from England to the Connaught Laboratories in 1931,[24] joined the department in the fall of 1933.[25] Two years later, he helped to start the Western Division of the Connaught Laboratories in British Columbia.[26] R.J. Wilson was an assistant to Dolman who was appointed a Fellow in the department in 1938.[27] Ronald Hare, like Dolman, also from England, arrived in 1936. He participated in FitzGerald's attempt to reform the undergraduate medical teaching of preventive medicine, a subject recounted years later in his memoirs.[28]

From 1924 to the early 1930s, the Department of Epidemiology and Biometrics was made up largely of three individuals, Dr. Defries, the head,[29] Dr. Neil McKinnon who was also in charge of the Farm Division of the Connaught Laboratories,[30] and Dr. Mary Ross who was an original member. Two part-timers from the Ontario Department of Health, Dr. J.W.S. McCullough, who taught public health administration and Dr. Albert Berry, who was a demonstrator in public health engineering, provided practical experiences on how to operate within the provincial system.[31]

Ross had studied for five months in 1926 in the Johns Hopkins School of Hygiene and Public Health to prepare for her responsibilities.[32] Later she received a M.A.[33] and a Ph.D.[34] for work done in the School of Hygiene. Her dissertations for both degrees analyzed the drop in the mortality and morbidity rates of certain communicable diseases in Ontario.

In the 1930s, Defries, McKinnon and Ross assisted in a revamping of vital statistics in Canada, especially the classification of the causes of stillbirths and morbidity.[35] These efforts resulted in the preparation and adoption of a new death registration certificate by the Dominion Bureau of Statistics.[36] The instruction of students in the D.P.H. course stressed the imaginative use of statistics in the planning and direction of health services.[37]

Dr. Milton H. Brown
1898-1985

Dr. Donald L. MacLean
1901-1969

Initially, the Department of Physiological Hygiene consisted of an assistant professor, C.H. Best, three research assistants, Miss J. Ridout, Mrs. R.C. Partridge and E.W. McHenry, and a demonstrator in industrial hygiene, J.G. Cunningham.[38]

The staff, teaching and research of the Department of Physiological Hygiene illustrated the interdisciplinary character of the School of Hygiene. It also was very much a part of the Department of Physiology in the Faculty of Medicine. The best indication of that fact was the role of Dr. Charles Best, one of the discoverers of insulin, as the head of the Department from 1927 until the death of Sir Frederick Banting in 1941.[39] Best received no salary for his position.[40] His international reputation for research enhanced the stature of the small school department.[41] In addition, pioneer research in the new field of nutrition originated during the 1930s in the department under Dr. Earle W. McHenry who instructed medical undergraduates.[42] Dr. J. Grant Cunningham continued to expand an understanding of the field of industrial health with his part-time teaching.[43] Another figure of the department was Dr. Donald L. MacLean. A medical graduate of the University of Toronto, he was appointed in 1929 to both the Connaught Laboratories and the Department of Physiological Hygiene. In 1935, he earned a Diploma in Public Health from the School and thereafter was promoted to the rank of associate professor when the Second World War changed the direction of his career.[44] Much of the research and teaching in Physiological Hygiene was carried on throughout the 1930s by a trio of research associates, Jessie Ridout, Ruth Partridge and Ethel Gavin.[45]

The emergence of new fields and faculty in the 1930s was very much the result of the graduate work done in the School of Hygiene. There were seventeen graduate dissertations completed in that decade.[46] Many of those who wrote these theses went to teach in the School. For example, Wishart under the supervision of Dr. James Craigie earned a M.A. for his study of the serology of vaccinia-variola virus.[47] The inauguration of graduate research in nutrition produced a Ph.D. dissertation by Ethel Gavin in 1939 on B vitamins and fat metabolism.[48] Dr. Gavin worked with McHenry in launching the field of nutrition in the School.[49] During this period, there were twelve Ph.D. degrees completed under the supervision of the faculty of the School of Hygiene.[50]

FELLOWSHIPS

More than a building and faculty members, FitzGerald realized, were necessary to establish the School of Hygiene as the staff college of Canadian health officers in the late 1920s and the 1930s. Students required financial help. Before 1948, there was little provincial or federal assistance in Canada for postgraduate studies in public health. Fortunately, the Rockefeller Foundation, through its International Health Board, even before the opening of the School, provided fellowships to physicians in provincial health departments to return to university for the D.P.H. After 1927, many of the students entering the School of Hygiene's course for the D.P.H. received these Rockefeller Fellowships and others a homegrown version.[51]

With the financial resources generated by the Connaught Laboratories, FitzGerald announced in 1928 the establishment of a fellowship program to offer even more candidates an opportunity to take up postgraduate work in the School. At a meeting of the Dominion Council of Health in June, 1928, FitzGerald explained how these fellowships were to be divided among the provincial health departments:

SCHOOL OF HYGIENE
UNIVERSITY OF TORONTO
HOLDERS OF FELLOWSHIPS IN PUBLIC HEALTH
granted by
THE CONNAUGHT LABORATORIES
1928 - 1942
FELTON '28
F. JACKSON '28
R. JENKINS '29
F.S. LEEDER '29
E.W. MADER-MACDONALD '29
G.F. AMYOT '30
J.G. CHOQUETTE '30
H.W. JOHNSTON '30
J.A. BASSINOTTE '31
I.M. CLEGHORN '31
J.J. FRASER '31
C.F.W. HAMES '31
B. LA HAYE '31
A.M. MENZIES '31
M.G. THOMPSON '31
T.D. KENDRICK '32
E. LALANDE '32
J.A. PATENAUDE '32
A. ROY '33
E.S. BOLTON '34
R.P. DOW '34
J.S. KITCHING '34
A.E. ALLIN '35
E.D.R. BISSETT '35
H.B. BUSTIN '35
J.S. CULL '35
A.R.J. BOYD '36
A. GAGNON '36
A.D. LAPP '36
J. PAQUIN '36
J.S. SIROIS '36
A. LANGIS '37
F. LECLERC '37
W. MOSLEY '37
P. POLIQUIN '37
W.J. WOOD '37
P. BEAUDET '38
P. PION '38
P. AUGER '39
H.G. BAKER '39
W.N. TURPEL '39
P. CLAVEAU '40
M.B. DONALDSON '40
A.C. McGUGAN '40
D.V. CURREY '41
D.S. FLEMING '41
O. LECLERC '41
G.S. BALDRY '42
R. NADEAU '42

> As you perhaps are aware, the candidate (Dr. R. Felton), nominated by Dr. H.E. Young, Provincial Health Officer of British Columbia, held the first Connaught Laboratories' fellowship during 1927-28. The representatives of the other western provinces, Alberta, Saskatchewan, and Manitoba, might arrange to choose one candidate, and the representatives of the remaining provinces, Ontario, Quebec, New Brunswick, Nova Scotia, and Prince Edward Island, the other candidate. The fellowship will become tenable in September, 1928. Fellows chosen will receive $1,500, which will permit them to complete the course leading to the Diploma in Public Health in the University of Toronto. It is hoped that the provision of these fellowships will lead to an increase in the number of trained public health workers available for service in Canada.[52]

FitzGerald's partner, Defries, in attendance at the gathering in June, 1928, elaborated on the objectives of the fellowships plan:

> The idea that Dr. FitzGerald has is that the provincial men would be the best qualified to name the candidate, and the candidate comes without any idea that a position is awaiting him in the particular province from which he comes. At the present time, there are requests for epidemiologists in one of the Western [provinces], and one in the Central [provinces], and one in the East. Provision is also made so that the course can be taken one-half of the work in four months, October to January, and the remaining part of the course, February to the end of May . . .[53]

The sensitivity displayed by the administration of the School to the needs of the individual provincial health departments across the country strengthened the influence of the School of Hygiene's program on the development of public health services.

EXPANSION OF HYGIENE BUILDING

Almost as soon as it opened, the School of Hygiene Building required an enlargement to accommodate the growth of the School and the University Division of the Connaught Laboratories. In bringing about the expansion of the original building, FitzGerald relied on the financial resources of the Connaught Laboratories and the generosity of the Rockefeller Foundation.

The needs of the insulin plant for more space prompted the first extension in the School of Hygiene Building and more efficient stills for the removal of alcohol from extracts of pancreas resulted in the construction of a southeast wing in 1931. "This latter addition will consist of three floors", FitzGerald reported in 1931, "38 by 33 feet in dimension. The frontage of 33 feet extends easterly on College Street. Urgently needed space will be thus made available for the rapidly expanding insulin and liver extract production." The cost of extending the sub-basement, basement and ground floors was $45,000.[54] It was paid for entirely by the Connaught Laboratories.[55] In 1937, the addition of a second and third floor to the extension completed the southeast wing.[56] This portion of the School of Hygiene Building was the centre for the production of insulin from 1927 until the closing of the plant in 1969, although some equipment machinery remained until 1981.[57]

FitzGerald's major goal in the late fall of 1930 was the construction of a northerly extension to the original building. In early November, 1930, without any authorization, he telegraphed, then wrote confidentially to Dr. F.F. Russell of the Rockefeller Foundation

D.P.H. Class of 1930 — **Back row:** E.W. Flahiff, J.G. FitzGerald (Director of the School), G.F. Amyot, J.C. Choquette. **Second row:** W.M. Robb, J.L. Little, H.W. Johnston, L.P. Savoie, R. Deschênes. **Front row:** J.E. Sylvestre, L.P. Thiboulot, J.R. Larose, G.B. Moffat.

Northern extension to Hygiene Building in fall 1932.

seeking his assistance.[58] Russell came to Toronto at the beginning of December to hammer out the details. He expressed a willingness to offer additional funds from the Rockefeller Foundation, conditional on the employment of money from the surplus fund of the Connaught Laboratories to extend the building[59] and an increase in the longstanding annual grant from the Province of Ontario to the Connaught Laboratories.[60] In a memorandum to the Chairman of the Board of Governors of the University of Toronto, FitzGerald cited the jump in the undergraduate enrollment of students from medicine, household science, public health nursing and university extension. In addition, more physicians were entering the course for the Diploma in Public Health. FitzGerald also needed space for a new Sub-department of Chemistry in Relation to Hygiene. Moreover, annual visitors from countries around the world who stayed for days and often weeks to study and to observe—in 1930 there were nineteen visitors—necessitated more facilities to allow the School to perform its role as a major international graduate centre for the instruction of health officers and research in public health.[61] On April 1, 1931, FitzGerald reported to Russell that his proposals had been accepted by all parties.[62] The Connaught Laboratories provided the financing of $350,000 to build the north wing. To cover this outlay from the Laboratories' research funds which represented some of the accumulated surplus of its operations over many years, the Province of Ontario agreed to return these funds to the Connaught in annual payments over a number of decades. On its part, the Rockefeller Foundation agreed to increase the endowment of the School of Hygiene by $600,000,[63] increasing the total grants to the School of Hygiene in Toronto to $1,250,000. In making the grant, the Foundation attached the provision that "Fifty Years after the date of the gift, not only the income but the principal as well may be expended in whole or in part by those then responsible for its use, either for the specific purpose for which the gift was originally made or for any other specific purpose which in their judgment will best promote the original purpose of the gift."[64]

The northern addition relieved the problem encountered in the original building with the housing of animals and the machine shop. FitzGerald explained his reasons for the changes in 1932:

> The new animal quarters will also be located in this north wing. They have been so planned that complete separation of small groups of animals will be possible. Furthermore, as the result of experience, radical change has been made effected [sic] in the location of the animal quarters. They have been placed in the sub-basement where, owing to certain novel features in construction, excellent light will be available and, in addition, mechanical ventilation and temperature control will, it is believed, make it possible for animals to be maintained under relatively constant environmental conditions. The previous animal quarters on the top floor of the present hygiene building will be converted into quarters for those responsible for the development, manufacture and maintenance of scientific equipment and apparatus . . .[65]

The new facilities for animals included nineteen rooms with space for sterilization of feed, and dog runs.[66]

The northern extension of the School of Hygiene Building added to the central block of the original structure and also provided a third wing, a northeast wing made up of six stories at a cost of $450,000.[67] Completed in December of 1932,[68] the northern addition increased substantially the space available.[69] With the price of the original structure plus the expenses of the construction of the complete southeast wing and northern addition, the total cost of the School of Hygiene Building was almost $950,000.[70]

DEVELOPMENT OF FACULTY IN 1930s

In sharp contrast to the downturn in the rest of the economy during the depression of the 1930s, the School of Hygiene Building was the centre of a growth industry. In June of 1930, the staff of the Connaught Laboratories, housed in two divisions which included almost all of the faculty of the School of Hygiene, numbered one hundred and twenty-one,[71] up from eighty-one in 1926.[72] In 1936, the staff had grown to two hundred and forty-five, including scientists, technicians and support personnel, staying at that level until the war years of the 1940s. Of that number, one hundred and forty-six worked in the School of Hygiene Building.[73]

In the 1930s, an important characteristic of the individuals working in the School of Hygiene Building was the familial spirit. To many, it was more than just a job. John FitzGerald wanted to instill in his senior staff a way of life. He promoted that feeling in a number of ways. While there was a subsidized cafeteria in the basement, FitzGerald had a special "officers' mess" on the third floor for the scientists; this was later moved to the fourth floor. FitzGerald sat always in a chair reserved for him at a table only for the top eight scientists in the hierarchy of the institution.[74] Tea was also served in the late afternoon to the scientists who were able to share ideas at these gatherings, a tradition carried on by FitzGerald's successor.[75] The familial spirit of the building promoted by FitzGerald was definitely paternalistic. According to one member of the FitzGerald team, he detested noise and loud laughter or singing.[76]

Recreational activities played a significant role in the building. FitzGerald expected his staff to play deck tennis on a court located on the roof of the School of Hygiene Building. Doubles, not singles, were the order of the day, with a definite objective of promoting co-operation and a team effort.[77] A trophy, appropriately named "The FitzGerald Cup" was awarded to the winners of an annual tournament from 1930 to 1937. It was first won by the team of Dr. Charles Best and Dr. P.A.T. Sneath. FitzGerald won it three times with Dr. D.A. Scott in 1931, Dr. L.N. Silverthorne in 1933, and Dr. D.L. MacLean in 1935.[78] The daily routine of three-quarters of an hour of actual exercise following lunch playing deck tennis caught the attention of a visitor from the Rockefeller Foundation who noted in his diary that they "all keep very fit by so doing — only instance I have ever seen of an hygienist trying to live an hygiene [sic] existence."[79]

On a more serious level, John FitzGerald's conception of scientific research impressed and influenced his staff and visitors. In the fall of 1927, just after the opening of the School of Hygiene Building, Gaston Ramon, a French scientist from L'Institut Pasteur in Paris, who was the first to prepare diphtheria toxoid,[80] lauded FitzGerald's view of the "research man":

> The "research man" should doubtless in the first place observe those biological phenomena, which he encounters or succeeds in eliciting thanks to his power of initiation. He must by reasoned and carefully planned experimentation try to ascertain the laws which govern these phenomena, while endeavouring also to deduce theoretical principles, and all the possible practical applications thereof. When this work is done he

Dr. D.W. Cameron playing deck tennis with Dr. J.G. FitzGerald.

> should set forth his researches and results in precise and clear publications in order to make them known. But the research man does not stop there, as I have until now believed and as there is a great tendency to believe in France generally. To remain "in splendid isolation" as we say. He must in meetings, such as you have arranged for me, discuss problems with those who are working in other places and in other conditions in the same field; he must examine and discuss in conversation with his colleagues the questions which interest them mutually. These meetings, these discussions, these exchanges of ideas are one of the essential conditions for spreading the truth and for scientific progress, towards which all the efforts of the "research man" must tend.[81]

Significantly, more than seventy years later, FitzGerald's model for a research scientist continues to warrant consideration.

FitzGerald was, in fact, the architect of an efficient team. "His organizing ability, and fine judgment, in choosing promising and capable men for his associates and helpers", a colleague who knew him wrote in the 1950s, "were two of his outstanding qualities."[82] A variety of strong personalities were attracted to the Connaught Laboratories and the School of Hygiene. That fact revealed the leadership, as Dr. Claude Dolman later wrote of his experiences in the 1930s, exercised by the "keen-minded visionary" FitzGerald, as well as "the earnest and devout" Dr. R.D. Defries, "unobtrusively and efficiently watching over numerous projects", and "the irrepressible" Dr. Donald Fraser, who invested "the plainest issue with touches of quixotic gallantry."[83]

If FitzGerald was the architect, Defries, his partner, was the manager and Fraser was the academic spirit of the School. Together they assembled a remarkable band of men and women. The "Toronto Group", as one health officer named them,[84] developed a tradition of teaching, research and public service that distinguished the Connaught Laboratories and the School of Hygiene. It was also a team that stressed an interdisciplinary approach to public health.

Individuals on the team assembled by FitzGerald, Defries and Fraser combined the roles of stimulating teacher and trail-blazing scientist. The recruitment of staff for the Connaught Laboratories was made with an eye to the needs of the School of Hygiene for faculty. A Report to the International Health Board of the Rockefeller Foundation noted this policy:

> The growth of the Connaught Laboratories necessitated from time to time additional appointments to the staff and in selecting these, choice was made of persons who could make a definite contribution to the postgraduate teaching in public health, providing instruction in subjects for the Diploma of Public Health course which could not be made through the Department of Hygiene and Preventive Medicine . . .[85]

With this type of recruitment, FitzGerald, Defries and Fraser laid the groundwork for the future development of the School and the Canadian health system after the Second World War. They displayed an unusual degree of foresight in the selection of staff to positions within the Connaught Laboratories and the School. It was this generation of scientists and administrators who established the new teaching and research sub-departments of Virus Studies, Nutrition and Parasitology. Included in that group were the pioneers in development of provincial and federal health policies.[86]

DONALD THOMAS FRASER 1888-1954

Along with FitzGerald and Defries, Donald Thomas Fraser was one of the builders of the School of Hygiene. Don Fraser personified not only the School's tradition of research and teaching, but a "fusion of humanistic and scientific learning" in the university.[87]

Fraser was born into a university family. His father, Professor William T. Fraser, headed the Department of Spanish and Italian Studies in the University of Toronto.[88] Don Fraser spoke fluently French and German.[89] Later as an adult, he moved into the university-oriented community in Wychwood Park and the summer life of Go-Home Bay.[90] Don Fraser's sister, Frieda Fraser, also a physician and medical scientist, was, as her brother, one of the original members of the faculty of the School of Hygiene.[91]

Graduating in 1912 with a B.A. from the University of Toronto, Don Fraser completed a medical degree in 1915. Like so many of his fellow graduates, he went off to war in France where he won the Military Cross at the Somme.[92] Later, he travelled to China with a British detachment and experienced first-hand the horror of an outbreak of typhus. Sometime during the war, Fraser met FitzGerald who invited him to join the Antitoxin Laboratory,[93] which he did in December of 1918.[94] Two years later, he became a lecturer in the Department of Hygiene and Preventive Medicine.[95] He completed the course for the D.P.H. in 1921.[96] Increasingly, FitzGerald relied on Fraser to revise the text of his book on preventive medicine.[97] He helped plan the northerly extension to the School of Hygiene Building.[98] In the 1930s, he represented the Connaught Laboratories at the meeting of the health section of the League of Nations.[99]

More than a scientist, Fraser had the talent to convey simply the complex world of research to a lay audience. With George Porter, Fraser wrote in 1925 the *Ontario Public School Health Book* for children.[100] Fraser's ability to communicate was evident in an article on immunization that appeared in the Canadian Forum:

> The experiments of Pasteur had demonstrated that immunity to a pathogenic micro-organism could be conferred upon an animal by an inoculation of an attenuated or changed culture without causing more than a transient and harmless reaction upon the animal thus protected. In response to this stimulus the body cells of the injected animal have themselves produced or taken on the quality of increased resistance. This method of protection is spoken of as active immunization in contrast to passive immunization. By the latter is meant the transference of the serum of an actively immunized animal to another which thereby in turn becomes protected. A familiar illustration is the injection into a human being of a diphtheria antitoxin or tetanus antitoxin produced by a horse in response to methods of active immunization. The horse has done the work; the person receives the protective substance contained in the serum, passively.[101]

Fraser was an enthusiastic proponent of the use of vaccines and antitoxins. He was an ardent advocate of the gospel of prevention by immunization.[102]

In the 1920s, there was still a strong and vocal opposition in Canada and elsewhere to inoculations.[103] Some of the unfortunate accidents with diphtheria immunization in the 1920s provided these opponents of the procedure with proof for their position.[104] In 1928, twelve children in Bundaberg, Australia died from staphylococcus toxins that contaminated a diphtheria toxin-antitoxin mixture.[105] Yet, convinced of the worth and safety of the products

Dr. Donald Thomas Fraser

he was developing, Fraser used himself and his family as "guinea pigs". "I tried a tetanus toxoid on myself and my children", Fraser stated in 1929 to a reporter, "and it did not do any harm. I would not try anything on anybody that I wouldn't try on myself and my children."[106] His children were probably the first in North America to receive diphtheria and tetanus toxoid.[107] At least one of Fraser's self-experimentations had a lasting effect on him. After testing a chemical spray to prevent viral infections, Fraser lost his sense of smell. "He told me once", an American scientist recalled in an interview, "that the only objection he had to this loss was that he couldn't enjoy his sherry any more."[108] This habit of using himself and his family as "guinea pigs" stopped when he became quite ill after administering something to himself. His wife, Mary Fraser, who was up with him all night, persuaded Fraser to halt the practice.[109]

Fraser's scientific work involved him in much of the research undertaken in the School of Hygiene Building. In the early 1920s, he assisted in the research to improve the production of insulin by introducing the use of mice in the assay of insulin. Fraser was a member of the team that perfected diphtheria toxoid. It was in the development of diphtheria toxoid that Fraser made his major contribution:

> Diphtheria and its nemesis, toxoid gave him a splendid field for study. He dug into the mechanisms of transmission, the types of organisms involved and the response of the host to infection and the administration of toxoid. Using animal skin and diphtheria toxin he perfected a method of assaying very small amounts of antitoxin which was to prove of great value in the study of individual immunity in the appraisal of the Schick Test and in following [the]response to immunization. His studies in the duration of immunity and the importance of the recall dose in firming up a more durable immunity were of basic importance.[110]

Moreover, Fraser was a valuable source of encouragement and consultation for several of his colleagues. He aided P.A.T. Sneath in the development of tetanus toxoid which proved to be of immense importance in the Second World War. Dr. Nelles Silverthorne also benefitted from Fraser's guidance in his work on the control of whooping cough.[111] As one colleague put it, "Ask Fraser" was a common solution to any baffling problem facing researchers or students in the School of Hygiene Building.[112]

By 1933, Don Fraser was not only a full professor but also a leading influence in the Department of Hygiene and Preventive Medicine.[113] The titular head was FitzGerald. However, he was preoccupied with duties as Dean of the Faculty and his obligations to the International Health Board of the Rockefeller Foundation and the League of Nations as well as his national responsibilities as an advisor to the Dominion Council of Health.[114] Fraser was the *de facto* head of the department.

Of particular significance for the future of the School of Hygiene was Don Fraser's introduction of the science of microbiology into the curriculum of Hygiene and Preventive Medicine. Until 1937, microbiology was taught by the department of botany.[115] In the fall of 1937, Fraser, with the help of Frank Wishart,[116] taught the subject to students in the Faculty of Household Science, the Faculty of Arts and the College of Pharmacy. Graduate students were instructed in lectures and laboratory work in the techniques of isolation, cultivation and identification of bacteria as well as antigens, antibodies and serological reactions.[117]

PETER J. MOLONEY 1891-1989

The study of vaccines and antitoxins in the School of Hygiene and the Connaught Laboratories advanced significantly because of the work of Peter J. Moloney. FitzGerald, realizing the role of chemistry in the production of biological products, recruited Moloney, a chemist by training, to join the Connaught Laboratories in September, 1919.[118] Born in 1891, Moloney graduated in 1912 with a B.A., having majored in philosophy, from St. Michael's College, one of the University of Toronto's federated colleges. In graduate school, he turned to chemistry and earned a M.A. in 1915 at his alma mater.[119] This step was the beginning of Moloney's career in the field of immunochemistry.[120] He assisted in the purification of insulin, the subject of his Ph.D. thesis.[121] His pioneering research in the preparation of diphtheria toxoid overcame many of the initial complications in the development of this product.

The subsequent success of diphtheria toxoid after years of research has put into the background much of the controversy surrounding its early use. Discovered by Dr. Gaston Ramon of L'Institut Pasteur in Paris, the toxoid sparked a great deal of disagreement about its potential value and safety.[122] In 1925, Peter Moloney was the first scientist in North America to prepare that toxoid[123] and he was very conscious of the dangers:

Dr. Peter J. Moloney

> There was the simple but sobering fact that toxoid derived from toxin by the action of formaldehyde was indistinguishable from toxin save that it was non-toxic, and hence the alarming possibility of a fatal mistake was always present. And then there was the question of the mode of action of formaldehyde on toxin. Certain chemical reactions of formaldehyde are reversible. Was it possible that the toxin-formaldehyde-toxin reaction was of this type and that toxoid could be transformed into toxin? A great deal of thought and work were expended on this question. There was indeed suggestive evidence that reversibility might occur. For example, it was found that the intradermal reaction elicited by diphtheria toxoid in certain individuals could be neutralized in part by antitoxin (horse) mixed with the toxoid before injection. The findings seemed to conform to the very definition of diphtheria toxin and hence to suggest the obvious and very disturbing possibility that in some individuals toxoid could be converted to toxin. Then there was the observation curious at the time, that guinea pigs injected with completely detoxified toxin developed paralysis before death and showed at the time of death appreciable levels of diphtheria antitoxin. Here were guinea pigs which had become actively immune and which nevertheless died with symptoms of diphtheritic paralysis. Was it possible that antitoxin was not effective in preventing disease? One can now give reasonable explanations for these odd phenomena, but when first observed they were very puzzling and very disturbing.[124]

Moloney's important contribution was the development of an intradermal test, known in many countries as the Moloney test,[125] to identify children who responded adversely to the diphtheria toxoid. This discovery facilitated the introduction of the toxoid in Canada long before its use elsewhere.[126]

In 1930, with the expansion of the School of Hygiene Building and the additional funding from the Rockefeller Foundation, Moloney was appointed the head of the School's first sub-department, Chemistry in Relation to Hygiene. Moloney taught a laboratory course on the chemical principles of the examination of water and milk, water purification and sewage treatment.[127] Moloney was one of the early scientists who did not have a degree in medicine employed by the Connaught Laboratories and the School. His contributions revealed the growing importance of non-medical specialists in public health.

CRAIGIE AND VIROLOGY

Probably the leading recruit of FitzGerald was Dr. James Craigie (1899-1978) from Scotland. Craigie graduated from University College, Dundee, University of St. Andrew's, with a M.B., Ch.B. in 1923 and then completed a Ph.D. and a D.P.H. in the same institution. In 1927, he was appointed an assistant in bacteriology in Dundee. In 1931, he came to Toronto with an appointment in the Connaught Laboratories. Two years later, he joined the Department of Epidemiology and Biometrics in the School of Hygiene. In 1935, he was named the Secretary of the School, a post he held for a decade. In fact, according to his biography, Craigie, who died in 1978, did his "best work. . . before World War II in the University of Toronto School of Hygiene when he was working by himself or with one technician."[128]

A gifted researcher, Craigie was eccentric. His biographer described his personality:

> He was essentially a kindly man and troubles that arose stemmed from a difficulty in communication. In discussing a scientific problem he would start in the middle, assuming

> that his hearers knew the background and, in particular, his own earlier writings. Junior workers were too shy to admit that this left them all at sea. A number of people have confessed that they were often baffled by a frustrating habit he had; he would start to explain something, break off in the middle of a sentence and look up with a smile, assuming one would know how the exposition would end. As one commonly did not, one was none the wiser. Ensuing difficulties would be overcome only by those with some sense of humour. He was reluctant to delegate and too apt to devote himself to his own research . . .[129]

Craigie's originality, diligence, curiosity and fascination with gadgetry were expressed best within his own laboratory.

In Toronto during the 1930s, Craigie, with the help of his student and then junior colleague Dr. Frank Wishart, undertook research on vaccinia. Together they published "three classical papers" on the soluble precipitable substances of vaccinia.[130] Another area of research Craigie pursued in Toronto was his investigation of the antigenic properties of typhoid bacilli. He had begun studies on the serology of typhoid under Professor W.J. Tulloch at St. Andrew's University. His efforts focussed on typhoid bacteriophages. In 1936,

Dr. F.O. Wishart

he and K.F. Brandon detailed "a phage specific for strains of *B. typhosus* (now called *Salmonella typhi*) containing what he described as Vi-agglutinogen." Two years later, he and C.H. Chen uncovered "other typhoid phages divisible into four types according to a range of properties." Craigie and his colleagues found that "typhoid bacilli could be divided into a number of types." This discovery had "wide repercussions" which led to an understanding of the "differentiation of strains of various salmonellas and other organisms."[131]

During the late 1930s, Craigie established a course on virus studies in the School of Hygiene. It constituted one of the early courses on virology taught in all of North America. Students taking the D.P.H. program were given ten hours of instruction in a field that was just beginning. Lectures provided a general discussion of the characteristics and classification of viruses, the range of size, the virus and host cell, in vitro cultivation, resistance to physical and chemical agents and preservation. The course also included a review of the current views on the nature of viruses, serology and active and passive immunization.[132] By 1939, two fellows, Dr. N.A. Labzoffsky and Dr. A.S. Lazarus, assisted in the teaching of virus infections.[133]

Craigie's work in the Connaught Laboratories and the School of Hygiene laid the basis for the modern science of microbiology in Canada. During the 1930s and into the 1940s, Craigie was, in the words of his biographer "one of those who helped to raise [the science of virology] to its present position as a discipline in the forefront of biological knowledge."[134]

RELATIONS WITH ONTARIO DEPARTMENT OF HEALTH

Throughout the 1920s and the 1930s, the School of Hygiene and the Department of Health in Ontario were partners in the development of general health services. The Director of the School and the Chief Health Officer realized the inter-relatedness of each of their tasks. Most significantly, the Ontario Department of Health provided both the facilities and the part-time instructors from staff that enabled the School to offer effective postgraduate teaching in the Diploma of Public Health.

In 1927 when the School started, John FitzGerald and J.W.S. McCullough, the Chief Health Officer of Ontario, had co-operated for over a decade. Together they had planned the growth and staffing of the Ontario Department of Health and its predecessor, the Ontario Provincial Board of Health. These efforts had led to the formation of travelling clinics to treat tuberculosis, the establishment of a Division of Industrial Hygiene and the preliminary work on the creation of county health units.[135] FitzGerald was a consultant to the Provincial Board.[136] McCullough was one of the original part-time lecturers in public health administration in the Department of Epidemiology and Biometrics.[137]

McCullough's successor was Dr. John T. Phair, Chief Medical Officer of Health in Ontario from 1935 until 1945. A graduate of the University of Toronto in medicine in 1909, Phair received his Diploma in Public Health from his alma mater in 1927. He joined the Ontario Department of Health in 1925.[138] Phair began to teach part-time in the School of Hygiene in 1933 in the rank of a clinical associate.[139] As honorary secretary of the Canadian Public Health Association from 1921 until 1945, Phair was part of the small group, largely from the School, that kept alive a national organization for public health professionals in Canada.[140] Phair's experiences during the depression convinced him of the necessity for a system of full-time qualified health officers. He turned to the School of Hygiene to provide the postgraduate training of these officials and this became possible in the 1940s.[141]

JOHN GRANT CUNNINGHAM 1890-1965

An excellent exemplification of the close working relationship between the School and the Ontario Department of Health was the career of John Grant Cunningham, the founder of industrial hygiene in both institutions. A graduate of the class of 1915 in medicine from the University of Toronto, Cunningham, following war service, investigated industrial fatigue in the Toronto area for the National Research Council. That experience resulted in his appointment part-time to teach industrial hygiene in the University of Toronto in the fall of 1919 and shortly thereafter to the directorship of the new Division of Industrial Hygiene in the Ontario Provincial Board of Health. This Division was the first in Canada and the third in all of North America. In 1920, Cunningham completed the Diploma in Public Health course in the University of Toronto.[142]

Cunningham, a pioneer in industrial hygiene, viewed the subject in a very broad sense:

> It is impossible narrowly to confine the scope of industrial hygiene within the limits of actual industry, and while its interest is centered in humanity in its working capacity — on the human machine that is — it is imperative to remember that this machine, unlike the nonliving machine, never stops but continues to operate with a different purpose and under different conditions outside the plant. . . . Such study, involving investigation into the effect on health of things like sanitation and ventilation, hours and type of work, food and recreation, housing and general home surroundings, is the task of those scientists who are concerned with discovery of the laws of industrial physiology.[143]

Dr. J. Grant Cunningham

For Cunningham, industrial hygiene was an extension of the factory reforms of the nineteenth century resting on the foundation of the science of physiology rather than human benevolence.[144] Unfortunately, the depression of the 1930s restricted Cunningham's efforts until the demands of war in the 1940s opened up opportunities.

ALBERT E. BERRY 1894-1984

The other major figure whose career combined both practical work in the Department of Health and teaching in the School of Hygiene was Albert E. Berry. The sharp decline in deaths from water- and milk-borne diseases in Ontario was the result of Berry's efforts to promote the construction of water purification and sewage treatment plants, and the adoption of compulsory pasteurization of milk.[145] Berry was a pioneering environmentalist. His accomplishments over forty years from the 1920s to the 1960s earned him the title of "Ontario's Mr. Water".[146]

A graduate of the University of Toronto in civil engineering in 1917, Berry, following service in the military, joined the Division of Sanitary Engineering in the Ontario Provincial Board of Health and by 1926 was its head.[147] During this time, he completed a M.A.Sc. and Ph.D.[148] in the University of Toronto. He was appointed a part-time demonstrator in public health engineering when the School of Hygiene opened.[149] He taught in the School for more than forty years.[150] In 1933, Berry was responsible for the assumption by the Canadian Public Health Association of the responsibility for certifying sanitary inspectors in Canada.[151] In 1938, Berry oversaw the organization of the first formal postgraduate course in public health engineering.[152] (The instruction of engineers for the M.A.Sc. degree dates back to beginnings of postgraduate teaching in public health in the University of Toronto in 1914.)[153] Albert Berry's career was the best demonstration of how part-time instructors in the School of Hygiene both taught and put into practice the scientific knowledge to prevent the spread of infectious diseases.

DIPHTHERIA TOXOID

From the date when FitzGerald began the production of diphtheria antitoxin in late 1913 until the completion of the whole process of the research, manufacturing, field testing and general distribution of diphtheria toxoid in the 1930s took almost twenty years. That span of years demonstrated how much time was required to develop this pioneering scheme of mass immunization. An effective program, as FitzGerald's team learned through trial and error, depended on three things: scientific knowledge, human resources and organization. The ultimate success of the diphtheria toxoid immunization documented the value of the close relationship between the Connaught Laboratories and the School of Hygiene in the development and distribution of a biological product.

The key to the eventual success of the diphtheria toxoid campaign in Toronto and elsewhere in Canada was organization. One should not underplay the significance of the production in 1925 of diphtheria toxoid by the Connaught Laboratories after its discovery in France.[154] But once again, the existence of an active immunization against the disease alone was not enough.[155] In Toronto, Dr. Charles Hastings, the M.O.H., initially preferring to have

Dr. Albert Berry

family physicians carry out inoculations, soon realized the inadequacy of such an approach. Diphtheria continued to kill children. As one official later observed, "there was little evidence of any general immunization by the family physician and, . . . [because] many of the children in the schools came from families who did not have a family physician but received their medical attention through hospital clinics",[156] general immunization of school children had to be offered by the health department.

The campaign in Toronto began in December, 1926. Teams made up of a physician with five nurses moved from school to school. Even before the arrival of the team, teachers distributed pamphlets on the advantages of immunization and a consent form permitting the health department to perform the required test and inoculation. Parents who wished to have their child treated by the family physician were encouraged to do so. Only half of the consent forms were returned and about eight percent of the parents expressed a preference for their physician to administer the toxoid. At first, the campaign reached more than one third of the city's school population or approximately 40,000 children;[157] by 1934, over 100,000 children had been immunized.[158] One of the useful tools employed to minimize the number of adverse reactions to the toxoid was the reaction test. It identified the children who were liable to suffer severe after-effects. The toxoid was not given to these youngsters; luckily "this group did not contract diphtheria to any extent comparable to other children."[159]

The development of diphtheria toxoid held out the promise of bringing under control one of the principal killers of children in Ontario. However, there were many genuine difficulties with the toxoid. In order to identify and to minimize the risks, FitzGerald's team undertook elaborate laboratory and clinical studies to demonstrate the merit of diphtheria toxoid "on the basis of innocuity and immunising properties as a specific preventive against diphtheria."[160] McKinnon and Ross from the School's Department of Epidemiology and Biometrics collected data from the field trials in which they assessed and interpreted the efficiency of the toxoid.[161] Peter Moloney, the first scientist to produce diphtheria toxoid in North America at the Connaught Laboratories, hailed McKinnon's and Ross's work as a verification for the first time of the value of "a non-living antigen" in the prevention of a disease.[162]

In contrast to the experience in the United Kingdom, the Canadian campaign against diphtheria in the 1930s was far more effective. The credit for the adoption of mass immunization using diphtheria toxoid belonged to the staff of the University of Toronto School of Hygiene and the Connaught Laboratories. Largely because of the efforts of the team assembled by FitzGerald, Defries and Fraser, the difficulties of producing and distributing on a large scale a safe and useful diphtheria toxoid were overcome.[163] The manufacturing of substantial quantities of toxoid of the highest quality provided physicians with a reliable prophylactic. Between 1925 and 1936, the Connaught Laboratories sent out over three million units of the toxoid for general use.[164] The leadership provided by FitzGerald and his senior scientific staff in promoting the development of the toxoid was a key factor in the success of the program. It stood out as a model for the subsequent campaigns to control a wide range of contagious diseases around the world.

FITZGERALD, DEAN OF MEDICINE 1932-1936

The sixth Dean of the University of Toronto Faculty of Medicine since its re-establishment in 1887, FitzGerald succeeded Dr. A. Primrose.[165] At that time the position was a part-time one

Dr. J.G. FitzGerald, Dean of Medicine, University of Toronto 1932-1936

that rotated among the senior faculty. Nonetheless, FitzGerald's tenure, which coincided with the depression, sparked some serious reconsideration of the nature and orientation of medical education in light of economic and social trends.

At the close of his third year as Dean, FitzGerald presented a review of the evolution of the Faculty of Medicine. His comments revealed the "momentous changes" since 1887. The undergraduate medical course had grown from a duration of three to six years. The academic session was increased to eight months instead of six. Most noteworthy was the fact that in the beginning "there were no whole time teachers, or research workers in the medical sciences: these now number more than one hundred."[166] Reflecting this development was the existence in 1935 of eight laboratory departments in the faculty: Medical Research, Hygiene and Preventive Medicine, Biochemistry, Paediatrics, Pathological Chemistry, Psychiatry, Radiology and the Medical Art Service. Aware of the history of the faculty, FitzGerald wondered whether as a result of all the advances "we train better doctors, or train doctors better".[167]

FitzGerald raised a variety of questions about the whole process of medical education, especially the absence of health planning for manpower. He deplored "the absolute lack of any plan, in this and other countries, to adjust [the] supply of and demand for, medical graduates. . . . Why should universities in this province continue, at great expense, to train more physicians than are currently needed."[168]

There was no equivocation by FitzGerald about the direction that he believed medical education had to go. In his report for 1934 to 1935, he stressed the role of the community in paying, through taxes or donations, for the instruction of physicians. Because "the community must provide the funds", FitzGerald argued for the selection of candidates more "socially-minded" and with "some aptitude for the study and practice of modern medicine."[169] Of course, a primary concern of FitzGerald was to emphasize the "teaching of preventive principles and methods."[170]

FitzGerald's term as Dean drew to a close after only four years. Increasing involvement with the Rockefeller Foundation's attempts to improve medical education drew him away from the post in Toronto. In September, 1936, FitzGerald and Dr. C.E. Smith, a D.P.H. graduate of the School of Hygiene in Toronto,[171] embarked on a year-long survey of the teaching of preventive medicine in medical schools in North America, Great Britain, and Europe.[172] The same questioning of medical education initiated at Toronto by FitzGerald was directed towards a much larger international scene.

FITZGERALD AND THE EDUCATION OF HEALTH WORKERS

No discussion of the evolution of public health education programs in Canada or North America can be adequate without an examination of John FitzGerald's views on what he termed the problem of training health workers. Because of his international standing after 1920, FitzGerald increasingly devoted his time to the role of preventive medicine in the undergraduate medical curriculum. From 1932 to 1936, FitzGerald was Dean of the Faculty of Medicine in Toronto which provided him with more insight into the difficulties of introducing preventive medicine into the education of physicians.[173] From 1936 to 1937, on behalf of the Rockefeller Foundation, Dr. C.E. Smith of Stanford University School of

Medicine and FitzGerald studied undergraduate teaching in preventive medicine, public health and hygiene in the medical schools of the United States, Canada and twenty-four European countries.[174] As FitzGerald once remarked, he had "more than twenty years of consideration of this subject."[175]

For FitzGerald, public health education programs included not only physicians but health workers with university backgrounds in arts or science, engineering, agriculture, social science as well as nurses and trained sanitary inspectors, not necessarily graduates of a university.[176] There was a clear distinction between public health specialists who required postgraduate studies and practitioners with an undergraduate background in preventive medicine.[177] He recognized the need for non-medical health workers. Many medical practitioners were either unable or unwilling to do these tasks.

To some critics, the provision of special or postgraduate training of health workers in the School of Hygiene was an attempt to produce "superdoctors, or at least sub-doctors." One of FitzGerald's colleagues, Dr. Donald T. Fraser, responded to the criticism by pointing out the need for such specialists with graduate degrees in biometrics, bacteriology and serology, and physiological and industrial hygiene. In particular, he described the vital contribution of public health nurses who formed a major part of the student body in the School. These public health nurses, when properly educated, played an invaluable role in the delivery of municipal and rural health services. Fraser argued that the education of public health workers in a new country like Canada with its wide distribution of population, its various immigrant groups and its limited health resources such as hospitals in certain regions, dictated the adoption of a curriculum especially responsive to these social conditions.[178] The instruction of health workers had to reflect, as FitzGerald noted, "the character and extent of public health and social welfare organization and activities in any particular country."[179]

The instruction of medical students posed another set of complexities. FitzGerald appreciated the inherent difficulties in the teaching of preventive medicine to undergraduates in medicine. At the root of the problem, he concluded, was the way in which the subject of hygiene and preventive medicine had developed. It was boring. The original "environmental notions" upon which the field of public health had been built were responsible for retardation of the teaching of preventive medicine. In addition, FitzGerald noted how the major advances in public health of the previous decades owed little to traditional medicine but grew out of the discoveries in biology and chemistry as well as modern technology.[180]

Despite all these drawbacks, FitzGerald resisted strongly any move to downgrade preventive medicine from the status of a department or a chair. He attacked the advocates of such a proposal for their lack of reality. "The proponents of the view that preventive and social medicine is most likely to be developed vigorously and satisfactorily, if recognized as a distinct discipline in the medical school", FitzGerald stated in 1938, "are those who believe that preventive medicine, in many of its aspects, is a responsibility of practically every department of the medical school."[181]

One of the major ways FitzGerald hoped to overcome the indifference of medical students to preventive medicine was by taking them on mandatory "observational visits" to health departments. This exposure to school health services, public health clinics for children and general sanitation work was supposed to open up the eyes of future physicians to the practice of preventive medicine.[182] However, as one instructor in the process in Toronto has written, the desired objective was not always reached.[183] The problem of how to teach preventive medicine to medical undergraduates continued to be a concern.

By 1930, the University of Toronto School of Hygiene had established public health education programs tailored to the economic realities and social conditions of Canada. The School had become the staff college of Canadian health officers. It reflected FitzGerald's determination to co-ordinate research with the teaching of health workers at the undergraduate, postgraduate and graduate levels. Like their counterparts in the United States, many Canadian physicians were unwilling to enter public health work.[184] However it appears that the School enjoyed more success in attracting physicians to public health careers than its sister institutions south of the border. In 1949, Dr. C. Winslow, after a visit to inspect the School of Hygiene, marvelled at the high number of recruits to the field of public health in comparison with the American situation.[185]

As the School entered the troubled decade of the 1930s, the pioneering era of public health education was ending. Fraser, one of the founders of the School, noted this transition:

> The emphasis upon the subjects taught [in the curriculum for the D.P.H.] has shifted in a striking manner during recent years in Canada. The time alloted to the study of environmental factors or sanitation has become less, while the personal factors or preventive medicine has received greater emphasis. The emphasis has thus shifted from the study of the influence of the environment to that of the factors concerned in the physiology of the individuals—from sanitation to preventive medicine and physiological hygiene. This change has been brought about partly because of the appreciation of the achievements of sanitary engineering and partly because of the success resulting from the application of the knowledge acquired through research in the fields of infection and immunity, epidemiology, physiology, and nutrition.[186]

What Fraser was pointing out later emerged fully in the School with the proliferation of specialties in the 1930s and 1940s. A variety of new sub-departments arose in the areas of public health administration, hospital administration, public health nutrition, industrial hygiene, parasitology and virology. Eventually a whole series of diplomas came into being to reflect the growth of these new fields.[187] Of course, the intimate link between the Connaught Laboratories and the School of Hygiene with the practice of joint appointments of many scientists to both institutions was the source of the growth of new scientific expertise.

FITZGERALD AND HEALTH INSURANCE

More than just public health services were increasingly the concern of FitzGerald. By the end of the 1920s, he was a proponent of some form of health insurance. His role was primarily one of raising the issue to open discussions within professional circles. At the beginning of the decade, in his book on preventive medicine, he had called for basic health care for the young and their mothers.[188] In late November, 1928, FitzGerald in a speech at Winnipeg suggested that the time had come "to take the next step and make arrangements so that health supervision will be made available for persons of all ages and of any economic and social condition."[189] Curative and preventive medicine, he argued, should "no longer be separated, in so far as the state takes cognizance of them."[190]

In light of his outspokenness, FitzGerald received an invitation to appear before the House of Commons Select Standing Committee on Industrial and International Relations investigating unemployment and health insurance. In March, 1929, he went to Ottawa for the meeting. In his testimony before the standing committee, FitzGerald outlined his plan for any health insurance. He cited seven guiding principles:

1. the formation of insurance societies to provide medical benefits to the insured;
2. the negotiation of agreements between insurance societies and the organized medical profession relating to the provision of medical services;
3. insured persons to have freedom of choice in the selection of a doctor;
4. the capitation of fees paid to physicians;
5. the control of the medical services by the organized medical profession;
6. the inclusion of coverage for hospital treatment of the insured;
7. the systematic education of the insured population in the principles of preventive medicine.[191]

In many respects, FitzGerald's proposals were similar to the type of insurance plan developed in the 1930s by the Blue Cross in the U.S.

FitzGerald's major plea before the committee was to find out what was the state of the health of Canadians. To that end, he asked for the collection of data nationally on "the volume of sickness and invalidism in this country, either attended or unattended" by physicians.[192] In addition, he requested an assessment of the number of hospitals, then believed to be between 575 to 600 institutions with 55,000 to 65,000 beds, as well as the medical manpower which included about 8,000 physicians in general practice and another 1,000 in research, administration, teaching and public health. He wanted an estimate of the cost of all medical care from hospitalization to dental treatment as well as a summary of the voluntary health insurance schemes operating in the country in 1929.[193] One revealing statistic quoted by FitzGerald was the estimate from Dr. J.W.S. McCullough, Ontario Chief Medical Officer of Health, that all levels of government and voluntary societies covered about $34 million of the health costs while private citizens paid over $276 million a year.[194]

Closely related to his participation in the discussions on health insurance was FitzGerald's exploration of how different regions of the country tried to cope with the problem of delivering medical services in the 1930s to ordinary Canadians incapable of paying for such care. In the summer of 1932, FitzGerald travelled to the west to see first-hand the municipal physician system. This scheme had originated after the First World War in Manitoba where a rural municipality appointed a doctor paid out of local taxes to care for rural residents. In 1921, Saskatchewan followed the example. The municipal physician system that FitzGerald reported on was never a large program. In 1932, only twenty percent of Saskatchewan's rural inhabitants had access to a municipal physician. In Manitoba, the percentage was about one. Limited in its use, FitzGerald viewed the plan as "an interesting social experiment" and "a radical departure" from conventional private medicine born out of "sheer necessity."[195] FitzGerald's interest in alternatives to the existing structure of private medicine illustrated the ferment of the 1930s which prepared the way for the post Second World War health services.

THE C.P.H.A. AND THE SCHOOL

The commitment to public service, one of the three principles guiding FitzGerald's work in the Connaught Laboratories and the School of Hygiene, was evident in the role played by the faculty of the School in the public health lobby in Canada during the 1930s. That decade witnessed the steady erosion of many of the gains won after the First World War. The Department of Health in Ottawa was downgraded in 1928 when it was merged into the Department of Pensions and National Health.[196] A few years later, the federal government eliminated the grants for the control of venereal diseases. To arrest the deterioration and to promote the development of public health services, the faculty of the School campaigned through the Canadian Public Health Association to publicize public health problems and to pressure governments for better funding.

Not only government programs but also private initiatives in public health were threatened in the inter war years. During the "lean, very lean years" of the 1920s and "the unforgettable" 1930s, Defries, Fraser, Porter and McKinnon of the School of Hygiene preserved the survival of the national body of the public health profession in Canada.[197] For years, they kept afloat the beleaguered Canadian Public Health Association and The Public Health Journal. When the Association almost dissolved in 1928, the group in the School took over the responsibility for the publication of the Canadian Public Health Journal as it was renamed in 1929.[198]

For the next thirty-five years,[199] Defries, with the help of McKinnon and Phair in the first decade, was the editor and in reality the publisher of the Canadian Public Health Journal. Throughout the depression of the 1930s, the headquarters of the C.P.H.J. and later the Association itself was located in the School of Hygiene Building.[200]

The monthly editions of the Canadian Public Health Journal were a testament to the small number but vigorous efforts of primarily the faculty of the School to promote public health. Under the care of Defries, McKinnon and Phair, the journal's circulation more than doubled to over 3,100 in 1935 from around 1,500 in 1928.[201] During 1935, the journal printed eighty-five articles. It issued twenty-three editorials with titles including "Active Immunization against Diphtheria", "Administrative Aids to Rural Health Service", "Dominion Leadership in Public Health", "Foetal Mortality", "Minimum Standards for Health in Housing" and "Typhoid Fever and Gastro-Intestinal Infections."[202] An example of the type of campaigns promoted by the journal was the issue of the pasteurization of milk, which had proved so key to the production of a safe milk supply for the young. It was a preoccupation of the journal's staff. In 1938, the C.P.H.J. devoted fifteen articles to milk pasteurization and one entire edition in June.[203]

THE D.P.H. AND THE SCHOOL IN 1939

At the close of the 1930s, the program for the Diploma in Public Health in the School of Hygiene had expanded into a variety of courses, reflecting the widening spectrum of medical sciences and administrative expertise required by health officers. The School's year ran for a period of eight months from the last week of September until the middle of May with a three-month term of public health practice in a health department in the summer. There were four terms each of about two months in duration. These courses encompassed over 870 hours of instruction, primarily lectures, laboratory work and seminars.[204] The following subjects made up the curriculum: bacteriology, virology, immunology and serology, parasitology, public health chemistry, physiological hygiene, nutrition, industrial hygiene, biometrics,

The Public Health Journal

The Official Organ of the
Canadian Public Health Association

Editorial and Business Offices
40 Elm Street Toronto 2, Ont.

Editorial Board

SECRETARY—C. P. FENWICK

Executive Committee—G. D. PORTER, GORDON BATES, R. D. DEFRIES, A. GRANT FLEMING, C. P. FENWICK.

Section Editors:

Administration	M. M. SEYMOUR, Regina	W. J. BELL, Toronto
Child Hygiene	H. E. YOUNG, Victoria	J. T. PHAIR, Toronto
Epidemiology and Vital Statistics	A. C. JOST, Halifax	N. E. MCKINNON, Toronto
Public Health Engineering	T. J. LAFRENIÈRE, Montreal	A. E. BERRY, Toronto
Food and Drugs	H. M. LANCASTER, Ottawa	A. R. B. RICHMOND, Toronto
Industrial Hygiene	F. G. PEDLEY, Montreal	A. G. CUNNINGHAM, Toronto
Laboratory	G. B. REED, Kingston	C. E. ANDERSON, Toronto
Mental Hygiene	W. T. B. MITCHELL, Montreal	E. P. LEWIS, Toronto
Public Health Nursing	MISS F. H. M. EMORY, Toronto	(To be appointed)
Social Hygiene	A. M. DAVIDSON, Winnipeg	G. P. JACKSON, Toronto
Voluntary Agencies	MISS JEAN BROWNE, Toronto	

Selected Public Health Abstracts—RUGGLES GEORGE, Toronto *Book Reviews*—D. T. FRASER, Toronto. R. R. MCCLENAHAN, Toronto.

Provincial Correspondents:

British Columbia	—H. W. HILL	Quebec	(to be appointed)
Alberta	—M. R. BOW	P. E. I.	—I. J. YEO
Saskatchewan	—ARTHUR WILSON	Nova Scotia	—H. A. CHISHOLM
Manitoba	—A. J. DOUGLAS	New Brunswick	—WM. WARWICK
Ontario	—F. S. BURKE (Chairman).		

Subscription Rates: $2.00 per year in Great Britain and United States; $3.00 Foreign.

Change of Address: In all changes of address it is necessary that the old as well as the new address be given.

Reprint Rates will be furnished on application but where reprints are desired request must accompany manuscript.

Reproduction of contents may be made accompanied by acknowledgement to THE PUBLIC HEALTH JOURNAL.

1929 Masthead of the initial journal of C.P.H.A.

Canadian Public Health Journal

Owned and Published by the

Canadian Public Health Association

Editorial Board

SECRETARY—C. P. FENWICK

Section Editors:

Administration	J. W. McIntosh, Vancouver	W. J. Bell, Toronto
Child Hygiene	H. E. Young, Victoria	J. T. Phair, Toronto
Epidemiology and Vital Statistics	F. W. Jackson, Winnipeg	N. E. McKinnon, Toronto
Public Health Engineering	T. J. Lafrenière, Montreal	A. E. Berry, Toronto
Food and Drugs	H. M. Lancaster, Ottawa	A. R. B. Richmond, Toronto
Industrial Hygiene	F. G. Pedley, Montreal	J. G. Cunningham, Toronto
Laboratory	G. B. Reed, Kingston	A. L. McNabb, Toronto
Mental Hygiene	W. T. B. Mitchell, Montreal	H. C. Cruikshank, Toronto
Public Health Nursing	Miss R. M. Simpson, Regina	Miss F. H. M. Emory, Toronto
Social Hygiene	A. M. Davidson, Winnipeg	G. P. Jackson, Toronto
Voluntary Agencies	Miss Ruby E Hamilton, Toronto	
Publicity Methods	Miss Mary Power, Toronto	

Current Health Literature—D. T. Fraser, Toronto
Book Reviews—D. T. Fraser, Toronto and R. R. McClenahan, Toronto
News and Comments—P. A. T. Sneath, Toronto
Question-Drawer—A. L. McKay, Toronto.

Provincial Correspondents:

British Columbia—H. W. Hill; Alberta—M. R. Bow; Saskatchewan—Arthur Wilson; Manitoba—T. A. Pincock; Ontario—L. A. Pequegnat; Quebec—Paul Parrot; P. E. I.—I. J. Yeo; Nova Scotia—Geo. A. MacIntosh; New Brunswick— Wm. Warwick.
Chairman—Dr. F. S. Burke.

Subscription Rates: $2.00 per year in Canada, $2.50 in Great Britain and in United States; $3.00 in other countries.

Change of Address: In all changes of address it is necessary that the old as well as the new address be given.

The cost of reprints is per hundred as follows:

	2 pages	4 pages	8 pages	12 pages
Without covers	$2.50	$3.00	$4.00	$6.00
With covers	3.50	4.00	5.00	7.00

Where reprints are desired, request should accompany manuscript.

Reproduction of contents may be made only by permission of the Canadian Public Health Journal.

EDITORIAL AND BUSINESS OFFICES: 40 ELM STREET, TORONTO 2, Ont.

Change in name of journal circa 1929.

EDITORIAL SECTION

EDITORIAL BOARD

R. D. DEFRIES, M.D., D.P.H., *Chairman*

J. T. PHAIR, M.B., D.P.H., AND N. E. MCKINNON, M.B., *Associate Chairmen*

R. L. RANDALL, *Editorial Assistant*

G. D. PORTER, M.B., *Public Health Administration.*
A. L. MCKAY, B.A., M.B., D.P.H., *Epidemiology and Vital Statistics.*
A. L. MACNABB, B.V.Sc., *Laboratory.*
GORDON BATES, M.B., *Social Hygiene.*
E. W. MCHENRY, M.A., PH.D., *Food, Drugs and Nutrition.*
MARY POWER, B.A., *Public Health Education.*
A. H. SELLERS, B.A., M.D., D.P.H., *Books and Reports.*
D. T. FRASER, B.A., M.B., D.P.H., *Mental Hygiene.*
A. E. BERRY, M.A.Sc., C.E., PH.D., *Public Health Engineering.*
LAURA A. GAMBLE, REG.N., *Public Health Nursing.*
J. G. CUNNINGHAM, B.A., M.B., D.P.H., *Industrial Hygiene.*
JAMES CRAIGIE, M.B., CH.B., PH.D., D.P.H. ST. AND., *Current Health Literature.*

Staff of Canadian Public Health Journal in the 1930s.

epidemiology, public health administration, public health education, sanitation and clinical instruction in communicable diseases at Toronto's Riverdale Isolation Hospital.[205]

Entering the thirteenth year of its operation in September of 1939, the School of Hygiene had grown significantly since its inauguration. From a budget on paper that only revealed a portion of its financial resources of over thirty-two thousand dollars in 1927-1928, the School's expenditures had surpassed eighty-seven thousand dollars.[206] By the end of the 1939 to 1940 session, the School had graduated over one hundred and fifty students with the Diploma in Public Health.[207] In addition, the faculty of the School provided teaching for a variety of undergraduates and a growing number of graduate courses. With the postgraduate instruction, this constituted a body of over four hundred and forty students in 1938-1939[208] which more than doubled after 1945 with the extension of courses in preventive medicine to all undergraduates in medical school.[209]

The finest evaluation of the University of Toronto School of Hygiene during these troubled years came from a report to the Rockefeller Foundation on its support for the Schools of Public Health in Toronto and elsewhere that concluded, "the total result has been worth the expenditure."[210]

Scenes from the School of Hygiene Building in the mid 1930s.

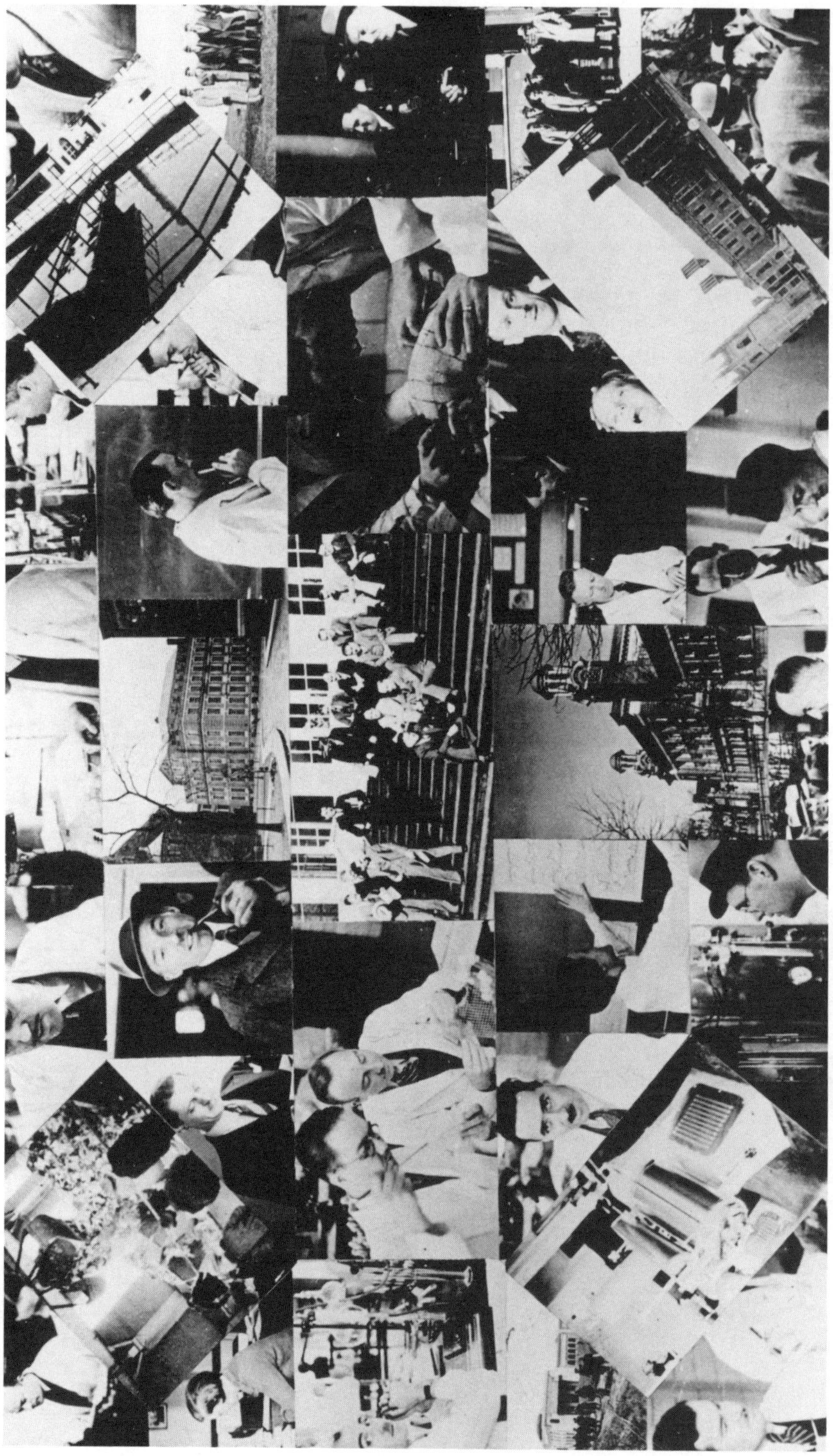

A collection of photographs on the course work and activities of D.P.H. students in the 1930s.

CHAPTER THREE

"VITAL TO THE WAR EFFORT":[1] THE UNIVERSITY OF TORONTO SCHOOL OF HYGIENE, ROBERT D. DEFRIES AND THE SECOND WORLD WAR

The growth of the School of Hygiene and its departments parallels the rapid development of Public Health.[2]

R.D. Defries in 1943

In 1940, Robert D. Defries was appointed the second Director of the Connaught Laboratories and of the University of Toronto School of Hygiene following the death of John FitzGerald.[3] Shortly thereafter, Donald T. Fraser was named the Associate Director of both institutions.[4] In reality both Defries and Fraser had taken over the *de facto* administration of the Laboratories and the School back in the 1930s. Thankfully, there was little need for them to adjust to their new positions. For there was to be little time to do anything else in the next five years except the effort to win the war.

The Second World War accelerated the evolution of the University of Toronto School of Hygiene. Within a span of six years, the School changed dramatically with the introduction of four sub-departments, three diplomas, a certificate, a field training centre and an Academic Council. Meanwhile, there was a jump in the number of undergraduates, postgraduates and graduate students. Moreover, the staff of the School provided special courses for industry, the military, Ontario health officers, public health nurses and other public health specialists. Some staff members served on important wartime committees advising the government, wartime industries and the military. Throughout these years, the faculty of the School undertook a variety of wartime research projects relating to the biophysical problems of servicemen in the Royal Canadian Air Force and the Royal Canadian Navy, chemical warfare, dietary standards for food rationing, industrial hygiene and medicine, and wound infections. There was wholesale conversion of the research in the School of Hygiene Building to solution of wartime problems. As never before or thereafter, the staff and facilities of the School of Hygiene and the Connaught Laboratories were integrated fully to manufacture biological products largely for the Canadian military. The School of Hygiene Building was a major wartime facility.[5]

WARTIME CHANGES TO HYGIENE BUILDING

Even prior to the advent of the Second World War, events in Germany touched the faculty of the School of Hygiene. In the 1930s, Don Fraser, in the Department of Hygiene and Preventive Medicine, involved himself in the plight of the refugee scientists forced to flee Nazi Germany. Appalled by the abusive treatment of his colleagues in Europe, Fraser helped to secure positions for some of them in Canadian Universities. He also extended assistance on a more personal level in terms of offering his hospitality and aiding these newcomers by rewriting their papers to make them suitable for publication in English language journals. One of the European refugee scientists brought to the Connaught Laboratories by Fraser, it appears, was R.F. Schnitzer, who worked on chemotherapeutic studies and later moved to the United States.[6]

From 1940 to 1945, the School of Hygiene Building, 150 College Street in Toronto, was a beehive of activities. At the war's beginning, it accommodated both the School of Hygiene as well as most of the administrative offices, the insulin plant and the production of other glandular products, and the filling and distribution of products of the Connaught Laboratories. In the six years of war, the staff of the Laboratories jumped from 252 members in 1939 to a wartime high in November, 1944 of 925 individuals. The increasing demands placed on the Connaught Laboratories led finally to the expansion of facilities at the Farm division near Dufferin Street and Steeles Avenue, and the purchase of the old Knox College at College Street and Spadina Avenue for the production of penicillin. Meanwhile, every possible square foot of space in the School of Hygiene Building was commandeered, even the corridors, for the production of biological products for the military. Obviously, some changes were necessary to the six-storey structure. Wartime economizing of fuel prompted the switch from oil-burning to coal-burning equipment in the product-manufacturing plants. The preparation of dried human blood serum required large amounts of high-pressure steam which led to the construction of a "new boiler room and a large steam plant in the courtyard between the centre and the north wings of the building at the sub-basement level." Also included in these renovations was the addition of more room in the sub-basement for the caging of small animals utilized by the different laboratory operations. In 1941, the two small rooms on the third floor used in FitzGerald's era for senior staff dining were converted to other uses. A new dining room was located on the fourth floor in the northeast wing; Defries later pointed out that the "new accommodation served both men and women." When there was need for still more space to house the plant for the production of dried human blood serum, a one-storey frame structure was constructed to the east and behind the Hygiene Building.[7] This "temporary structure" was still standing in 1986.

More than the floor space of the School of Hygiene Building underwent modifications to meet the demands of the war. The timetable of courses in the School changed. In 1940, to "make it more readily possible for practicing physicians to receive postgraduate training in public health", the courses for the Diploma in Public Health were rearranged into four terms of eight weeks allowing a physician to complete the requirements at different intervals in a period of more than a year.[8] With the increasing demand for trained health officers in the armed forces and on the homefront, the administration followed the example of the Faculty of Medicine in the acceleration of courses. By the session of 1943 to 1944, the D.P.H. course began in August and closed six months later in January.[9] The wartime shortage of senior staff forced also the abandonment of the tutorial system for the instruction of fifth-year medical undergraduates in the Department of Hygiene and Preventive Medicine. Lectures replaced these tutorials.[10] On top of the regular courses, the members of the School, as documented elsewhere in this chapter, assumed responsibility for the instruction of special courses for part-time health officers in Ontario, physicians in wartime industries and medical officers in the Royal Canadian Air Force. All of this increased teaching was undertaken by the School's faculty without the benefit of four senior professors away on military duties, and in addition to the heavy load of wartime research and the supervision of the manufacturing of essential biological products.

PREPARATION OF BLOOD SERUM

The processing of dried human blood serum for the treatment of wounded military personnel was, undoubtedly, the School of Hygiene Building's most vital contribution to the war effort. It involved two million Canadians from across the Dominion. It saved thousands of lives. Charles Best, the head of the School's Department of Physiological Hygiene, initiated the scheme. In 1941, he recalled its beginnings:

> The Department of Physiological Hygiene project for the preparation of human blood serum for military use was begun in the Departments of Physiology and Physiological Hygiene in October, 1939. The main part of the activities was carried on in the Department of Physiological Hygiene and the facilities of the Connaught Laboratories were from the first made available without cost to the project. The salaries of all the paid workers were secured from the Medical Research Best Fund, that is, the University Research Fund which was available for investigations in the Departments of Physiology and Physiological Hygiene. It was possible to demonstrate very quickly that serum was as effective as whole blood in the treatment of shock and haemorrhage in experimental animals . . . the first lots of serum were concentrated rather than dried. As soon as the drying apparatus, purchased in part by the National Defence funds, was available (summer of 1940), the serum was reduced to dryness.[11]

The project that began so simply soon grew into a major national enterprise.

The first donations of blood came from the staff in the School of Hygiene Building and thereafter from students in the University of Toronto. Initially, the operation was quite simple. Defries described the early days in the following way:

> An ordinary laboratory bench served in turn as a table for the assembling of equipment, a bed for blood donors, and a work bench for the processing of the blood. Of necessity, all these operations were included in one room in the School of Hygiene Building. The entire staff was composed of two or three persons who turned from one operation to another as the need arose. After drawing the blood it was typed and allowed to clot. From the clotted blood the serum was separated and the various sera were combined in groups in accordance with the particular blood type. Subject to satisfactory sterility tests, this material was filled into 250-cc. bottles of a kind readily available. The freezing and drying operations were carried on in a small section of the School of Hygiene Building, where space was provided for an alcohol-solid-carbon-dioxide freezing tray and for the pump and drying cabinet purchased with funds provided by the Department of National Defence.[12]

The original processing and drying of the serum took place in two rooms in the School of Hygiene Building. It utilized one vacuum pump and a drying cabinet. In 1941, three pumps were added and installed in the Farm section of the Laboratories, north of Toronto. All of the equipment shifted was used on a twenty-four hour basis. Still this was not enough. The expanding demand for blood serum resulted in the construction of a one-story building in the Courtyard behind the Hygiene Building and the installation of a big boiler to produce steam for the equipment. This facility augmented the weekly capacity to about twenty-five thousand 400-c.c. bottles. By the summer, the plants in the School of Hygiene Building and the Farm section were turning out five thousand bottles a week. The around-the-clock operation had a staff of one hundred and forty individuals.[13]

One of the most spectacular aspects of this story was the rising number of individual blood donations from Canadians in every province. From a total of 36,000 donations for the whole year 1941,[14] the donations between January and October of 1942 were 57,000. The maximum number of donations reached 77,000 from January to April, 1944.[15] To handle the immense growth, the processing of the blood was moved in stages to the old Knox College building between January and April, 1944.[16]

During the last twelve months of the war from May, 1944 to April, 1945, the project received an amazing total of over 890,000 blood donations. Throughout its history, the processing of dried human blood serum involved over two and a half million donations from Canadians. The operation in the Hygiene Building produced 436,000 bottles of serum, 51,000 administrative sets, 34,000 bottles of pyrogen-free sterile water and 23,500 vials of typing serum.[17]

WARTIME BIOLOGICAL PRODUCTS

Both the faculty and the School of Hygiene Building played an important role in the development and manufacturing of a variety of products vital to the preservation of the lives of Canadian airmen, soldiers and sailors, and saved the lives of thousands of wounded Canadians. Dr. James Craigie, head of the Sub-department of Virus Studies, working with American scientists, developed a typhus vaccine that proved effective against one of the most deadly diseases prevalent in wartime. The School of Hygiene Building housed the facilities used to convert the by-product of typhus-infected eggs from the Farm Section of the Laboratories into a vaccine.[18] At its height, there were one million doses of vaccine being produced each month by the end of the war.[19] Another essential product for the armed forces in combat was tetanus toxoid. Prepared successfully in the 1930s by P.A.T. Sneath, the toxoid was ready for use when war broke out. However, there were some adverse reactions to the tetanus toxoid which were minimized with the further research of Edith Taylor, Helen Plummer and Peter Moloney. To meet the request of the Canadian military for a reduction in the number of immunizations for soldiers, Don Fraser directed the preparation of a combined vaccine of tetanus toxoid with typhoid-paratyphoid vaccines. It was known as the TABT vaccine.[20] Fraser, Plummer, Moloney and Taylor were responsible also for the production of antitoxin for gas gangrene infections, caused by organisms named clostridia infecting wounds. This infection was a danger of the war, in the North African theatre and elsewhere.

Looking back to the experience of the First World War with the influenza pandemic that killed so many people, the staff of the Connaught Laboratories and the School assisted in the development of an influenza vaccine. The team from the Laboratories began their investigations in late 1940.[21] During the winter of 1942 to 1943, they launched an immunization program against "influenza A."[22] Dr. Ronald Hare, a lecturer in the newly formed Sub-department of Virus Studies, supervised the preparation of 200,000 doses of the influenza vaccine;[23] "the seed preparation, vaccine testing and lot making" were done in the School of Hygiene Building.[24] Hare was also responsible with a team of others for the production of penicillin on a large scale in the old Knox College building.[25]

For the production of forty-two products in 1945,[26] numerous men and women worked in the processing, filling and packaging plants of the Hygiene Building. To illustrate the size of

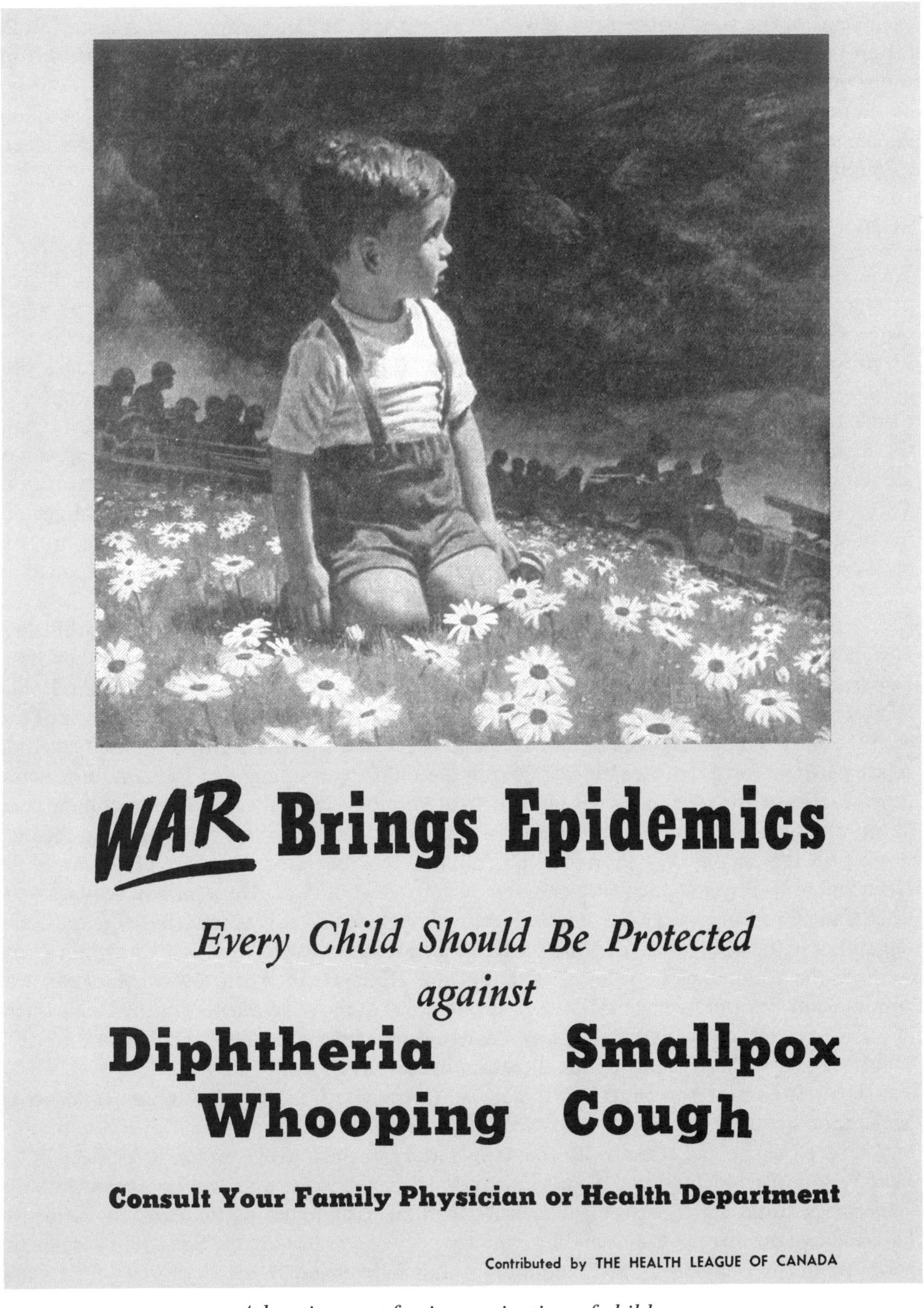

Advertisement for immunization of children

their task, at the start of the Second World War, the filling department, with a staff of 20 (almost all women) was located on the top floor of the north wing after moving in 1939 from the ground floor of the south wing. This unit "processed nearly two and one-half million containers" in a year.[27] With the addition of more products and larger volumes, the filling department of the School of Hygiene Building expanded rapidly into one of the larger assembly lines in wartime Canada.

SCHOOL'S STAFF AND STUDENTS IN THE WAR

While the School of Hygiene Building was the centre for the production of essential biological products for the armed forces, the faculty and students of the School enlisted to become health officers who provided vital services to treat and to bring under control the contagious diseases so prevalent in wartime: "overcrowding, often under bad sanitary arrangements, that develops in manufacturing centers, seaports, and close to large camps; the absorption of women, girls, and young boys into industry; the constant movement of the population; and the changed modes, habits, and tempo of living provide conditions conducive to the spread of communicable diseases."[28] What the Second World War brought about in the University of Toronto School of Hygiene was the transfer of senior faculty and students from teaching and learning about public health and preventive medicine to the practical application of these measures on the battlefields, in the military camps, and in the civilian sectors of Canadian society.

The immediate impact of the coming of war on the School was the departure within days of some of the senior faculty for duty in the armed forces. Dr. Milton Brown, a member of the Department of Hygiene and Preventive Medicine who had completed the Diploma in Public Health in the spring of 1939, joined the Canadian Army. He went to England by the year's end with the rank of colonel, in charge of Hygiene and Preventive Medicine with the Canadian Army Medical Corps. Brown participated in the military campaigns in Italy and northwest Europe. He was awarded the Order of the British Empire.[29] After the war, Brown collaborated in the writing of a chapter on his specialty for the official history of the Canadian medical services in the Second World War.[30] Dr. Donald MacLean, an assistant professor in the Department of Physiological Hygiene, served for the whole war. He went overseas with the First Canadian Corps as an assistant director of hygiene and saw action in Sicily and Italy. Beginning with the invasion of Normandy, MacLean stayed with the First Canadian Army through the campaigns in France, Belgium and Holland. In April, 1945, MacLean was appointed director of hygiene with the rank of colonel at the headquarters of the Department of National Defence in Ottawa. His war record earned him the Order of the British Empire.[31] MacLean's experiences changed the direction of his career in the School.

The third senior person to join the armed forces was Dr. Neil McKinnon. It was truly McKinnon's second world war. An associate professor in the Department of Epidemiology and Biometrics, he had served with the 48th Battery of the Royal Canadian Artillery in the First World War. In January, 1940, McKinnon left Canada for duty in England with the 15 General Hospital and then the 8 General Hospital. Appointed to the rank of major, he returned to a posting in Ottawa and by January of 1944 was back in the School to assume the headship of the Department of Epidemiology and Biometrics.[32]

Dr. Donald Solandt, acting head of the Department of Physiological Hygiene from 1941 to 1945, was a surgeon-commander in the Royal Canadian Navy who worked in the Naval Medical Research Unit on the "biophysical factors affecting the environment of seamen." The United States awarded him the Medal of Freedom with Bronze Palm for his contribution to the American military.[33]

Of course, many other staff served in the armed services. The head of the Sub-department of Public Health Administration, Dr. William Mosley, was a health officer in the Royal Canadian Air Force.[34] Dr. H.M. Barrett, an associate professor in the Department of Physiological Hygiene, did research on chemical warfare for the Department of National Defence.[35] A fellow in the Department of Hygiene and Preventive Medicine, Dr. Robert J. Wilson, joined the Royal Canadian Navy following the completion of a medical degree from the University of Toronto in 1942 while working on pertussis vaccine in the Connaught Laboratories.[36] Members of the technical staff of the School also enlisted: Walter Moore, a laboratory assistant in the Department of Epidemiology and Biometrics, went into the Royal Canadian Artillery;[37] Kenneth Roseblade, a senior technician in the Department of Physiological Hygiene, entered the Royal Canadian Navy.[38] Miss E.M.F. Bain, a secretarial assistant in the Department of Hygiene and Preventive Medicine, and W. Staples, a technical assistant in the Department of Physiological Hygiene were granted leave of absence for war duties.[39] One employee of the School of Hygiene Building, John Richards, who worked in the insulin plant, was killed in action while on bomber transport in the Mediterranean.[40]

An illustration of how faculty leaving for war service disrupted the School of Hygiene was the case of Dr. James M. Mather, a graduate of the University of Toronto Faculty of Medicine in 1936 who received the Diploma in Public Health from the School of Hygiene in September of 1939. After work with the Kellogg Foundation of Battle Creek Michigan, Mather was appointed on July 1, 1940 a lecturer in epidemiology with funds from the Rockefeller Foundation. Five months later, he resigned to assume the position of a sanitary officer in the Royal Canadian Air Force.[41] To complicate matters even more was the departure of Robert G. Struthers. A graduate in medicine of the University of Toronto in 1914 with a long career of medical missionary work in China, who finished his D.P.H. in the spring of 1943,[42] Struthers was appointed in April, 1943, to teach public health administration and to help run East York Health Unit. He resigned in September to assume special duties in the Royal Canadian Navy related to his command of Chinese dialects. Obviously, D.P.H. graduates of the School of Hygiene were sought after by the military.[43]

The University of Toronto School of Hygiene, through its faculty and especially its graduates, influenced the development of public health services in the Canadian armed services. In addition to the careers of Milton Brown, Donald MacLean and Neil McKinnon in the military, there were many others. For instance, P.A.T. Sneath, a 1927 D.P.H. graduate and thereafter a member of the School's faculty until 1937,[44] was an assistant director of hygiene in the Canadian Army before being succeeded by MacLean.[45] Another outstanding example was the military service of Dr. Alfred H. Sellers, a D.P.H. graduate in 1933 and a member of the Ontario Department of Health. He was in charge of the medical branch of the Royal Canadian Air Force from 1940 to 1946 where he rose to the rank of wing commander.[46] He developed the R.C.A.F.'s bureau of medical statistics.[47] Sellers' work in the R.C.A.F. illustrated how graduates of the School of Hygiene were able to put into practice an effective

Dr. Donald Solandt

system of immunization[48] and also to bring under control diseases like syphilis and gonorrhoea.[49] This type of experience was a model of what could be achieved in peacetime.[50]

RAYMOND PARKER 1903-1974

Not only did the war transfer faculty and technical staff to military service, it attracted individuals to work in the School of Hygiene. Such was the situation in the case of Raymond Parker. A Nova Scotian by birth, Parker, after finishing a Ph.D. in zoology and anatomy at Yale University in 1927, joined the Rockefeller Institute in 1930 where he developed techniques for the growth of cells in tissue cultures. His book, *Methods of Tissue Culture*, was a major addition to the subject. He was also the co-founder and a charter member of the Tissue Culture Association now based in Rockville, Maryland. In 1939, Parker joined an important American pharmaceutical company, E.R. Squibb & Sons of New Jersey, as head of its Virus Research Laboratory. However, he soon found that his preference was for academic research.

Then the Second World War intervened. "Being a Canadian, he felt that he might be able to make some contribution in war work", Defries explained in recommending Parker's appointment in the Connaught Laboratories. Parker came to Toronto in the late fall of 1941. He accepted the position at a salary of a little more than half of his previous one. His addition constituted an "important strengthening of our scientific staff", Defries wrote.[51] Parker became an important part of the new Sub-department of Virus Studies.[52] With Craigie and Hare, he did research on poliomyelitis and typhus. In particular, Parker developed a system for purifying and concentrating the typhus rickettsiae for the preparation of vaccine during the war years.[53] Later he played a major role in the production of poliomyelitis virus in tissue culture, an essential step in the preparation of the Salk-type poliomyelitis vaccine. Parker's pioneering work in tissue culture laid the foundation for modern medical research in laboratories around the world.[54]

FEMALE FACULTY AND STUDENTS IN THE WAR YEARS

With men going off to the military, the period from 1939 to 1945 highlighted the enormous contribution of women to the Connaught Laboratories and the School of Hygiene.[55] In fact, ladies had a key function in the teaching and research of the School of Hygiene from the beginning but they were often "out of the limelight." In wartime, two of the three senior faculty members, Frieda Fraser and Mary Ross, assumed increasing responsibilities within the School. In the Department of Epidemiology, almost half of the teaching staff in the fall of 1942 was female. Although not in the higher ranks of lecturer or assistant professor, women constituted half of the instructors in the less senior positions of associates or assistants. The newly established Sub-department of Nutrition was made up with the exception of the head, E.W. McHenry, of seven females. According to the Calendar for 1942-1943, there were twenty-four ladies teaching or associated in some capacity with the School of Hygiene out of a total of forty-six individuals.[56] With the exception of the senior faculty, they were paid less than male counterparts which was customary.[57] Most of these ladies were distinguished scientists with numerous publications.

Dr. Frieda Fraser, along with Mary Ross, Edith Taylor, Helen Plummer, Jessie Ridout, and Ruth Partridge, was one of the original faculty members of the School of Hygiene.[58] The

Dr. Frieda Fraser

sister of Don Fraser,[59] Frieda finished a B.A. in 1922 at University College, University of Toronto and then a M.B. in 1925.[60] Appointed to the Department of Hygiene and Preventive Medicine, she had reached the position of associate professor by the 1940s.[61] Her research into scarlet fever streptococcus toxin and antitoxin was important but eventually replaced by the introduction of sulfonamides and then penicillin, as well as "a gradual change in the clinical picture of the disease."[62]

One of the founders of the Department of Epidemiology and Biometrics, Mary Ross became the associate secretary of the School in early 1942 in order to allow Craigie time for his research on a vaccine for typhus. A "very effective teacher", Ross carried much of the instruction load while McKinnon was overseas in the military.[63] She assisted the other departments of the School in statistical studies as well as compiling details on the status of full-time health services in Canada.[64]

Completing a Ph.D. in 1924,[65] Edith Taylor joined the Sub-department of Chemistry in Relation to Hygiene in the early 1930s to work with Peter Moloney on immunochemistry and especially diphtheria toxoid.[66] Much of her time was spent in the Connaught Laboratories. She published a number of articles in scientific journals.[67] In the war years, Taylor made a major contribution to the improvement of tetanus toxoid and was part of the team producing gas gangrene antitoxin. Both of these products were very useful to the Canadian military. In recognition of her war work, Taylor received the Order of the British Empire in 1946.[68]

Many of the female staff of the School were effective team players who assisted in teaching courses or research. Helen Plummer, a bacteriologist with a Ph.D.,[69] was a member of the group that prepared the tetanus toxoid and the gas gangrene antitoxin.[70] Jessie Ridout, who completed a doctorate in physiology in 1939[71], aided C.H. Best with the processing of dried human blood serum.[72] Known as a "superlative teacher",[73] Ruth Partridge, with a Ph.D. in physiology, was part of the war research on naval medical problems in the Department of Physiological Hygiene.[74] Completing one of the first doctoral theses in nutrition,[75] Ethel Gavin worked with E.W. McHenry in nutritional studies until her tragic death in late 1942.[76] In addition to her duties during 1940 to 1941 as a class assistant in the Department of Hygiene and Preventive Medicine,[77] Dr. Laurella McClelland, a graduate of the University of Toronto Faculty of Medicine in 1938,[78] contributed significantly to preparation of an influenza vaccine under Hare and supervised the production of typhus vaccine for Craigie at the Farm Section of the Laboratories in the early 1940s.[79]

Some female faculty also participated actively in the war effort. A demonstrator in epidemiology, Dr. Charlotte Horner resigned in November, 1942, to enlist in the Royal Canadian Air Force as a medical officer.[80] Dr. Vera Binnington, a medical practitioner in the field of industrial hygiene, worked at the munitions plant in Ajax to the east of Toronto before completing the Diploma in Public Health in 1944.[81] Upon graduation, she was appointed an associate in Public Health Administration working in the East York Health Unit.[82]

There were few female graduates of the Diploma in Public Health course of the School of Hygiene during the war years. This was not unusual. Prior to the opening of the School in 1927, the University of Toronto granted the D.P.H. to only four women: the first was Dr. Rachel R. Todd in 1915; the second was Dr. Catherine F. Woodhouse in 1922; the third was Dr. Ann Curtin in 1924; and the fourth was Dr. Agnes Walker in 1927. From 1928 to 1938, only three females completed the course: Dr. Eva Mader (Mrs. C.N. MacDonald) in 1929; Dr. Ruth P. Dow (Mrs. Lewis Myers) in 1934; and Dr. A. Marguerite Swan (Mrs. D.C. Archibald) in 1938. In the six years of the Second World War, five women earned the D.P.H.: Dr. Eleanor Riggs (Mrs. B.M. Wood) in 1941; Dr. Charlotte M. Horner in 1943; Dr. Vera I. Binnington in 1944; Dr. Margaret Templin in 1945; and Dr. Jean Webb in 1945.[83] In contrast to the small number of female D.P.H. graduates, the School's faculty taught large numbers of public health nurses in the School of Nursing, over five hundred from 1939-1940 to 1944-1945.[84]

From 1939 to 1945, females formed an intrinsic part of the staff of the University of Toronto School of Hygiene. They taught courses, did pioneering research, took undergraduate, postgraduate and graduate courses, and performed essential technical and administrative tasks. The women of the School of Hygiene Building were vital contributors to the Canadian war effort.

At graduation exercises for their Ph.D.s, University of Toronto, 1939, Dr. Ethel Gavin, Dr. Mary Salter (psychologist) and Dr. Jessie Ridout.

Dr. Laurella McClelland

THE SCHOOL AND ONTARIO'S HEALTH OFFICERS

Just as the war erupted, the administration of the School of Hygiene was finishing the arrangements to upgrade the qualifications of health officers throughout Ontario. Late in the 1930s, senior officials with the Ontario Department of Health requested the assistance of the School. John T. Phair, Ontario's Chief Medical Officer of Health, who was also a clinical associate in public health administration in the School of Hygiene,[85] and his superior Bernard T. McGhie, the Deputy Minister of Health, wanted to modernize the province's public health services originally established in the 1880s.[86] They wanted to replace the part-time system of health officers with qualified physicians; in the whole of Ontario in 1939 there were only 14 full-time health officers at the municipal level.[87] When he was approached with a definite proposal, Defries, then Acting Director of the School, agreed to co-operate with the Department of Health:

> To enable medical officers of health to attend more readily the courses of instruction leading to a Diploma in Public Health, the School of Hygiene is prepared to re-arrange

Dr. John T. Phair, Ontario Department of Health (centre) near the north entrance of the Hygiene Building.

> the courses of instruction in such a way that the instruction can be given in four terms, each consisting of two months. . . . For the training of physicians who are being appointed from time to time as part-time health officers in the larger municipalities, the School of Hygiene would provide special facilities which would permit the immediate training of such physicians. . . . Such instruction would be personal and would not be part of the course leading to the Diploma in Public Health. . . (short courses of four or five days' duration would be of great value to the part-time health officers serving small urban or rural municipalities.)[88]

With Defries' willingness to accommodate the needs of the Ontario Department of Health, officials in Queen's Park acted. In 1939, under Section 37 of the Public Health Act, new regulations required minimal qualifications for health officers:

> No person shall be appointed as a full-time medical officer of health unless prior to his appointment he has secured a certificate or diploma issued by a Canadian university, following not less than one year's full-time postgraduate study of public health, or a similar qualification. . . . No person shall be appointed a part-time medical officer of health for a municipality with a population exceeding 4,000 unless prior to his appointment he has devoted not less than one month to a course of instruction designated by the Minister of Health, and completed to his satisfaction, or has had at least five years' experience as medical officer of health in a comparable municipality in the Province of Ontario. . . . Any part-time medical officer of health for a municipality having a population of less than 4,000 shall within one year after his appointment as a medical officer of health complete a course of instruction designated by the Minister of Health.[89]

Similar requirements were imposed on public health nurses and sanitary inspectors.

With an obvious sense of delight, John Phair reported the following year on the commencement of the courses:

> While these regulations were implemented in 1939, it was not until early in 1940 that arrangements were made with the School of Hygiene, University of Toronto, for the staging of the necessary courses of instruction.
>
> The first course held was one for part-time health officers. The course was of five weeks duration and was designed to meet the requirements of health officers in municipalities, both urban and rural, in which the population was 4,000 or over. A second course was held in August and September. Eight physicians attended and all satisfactorily completed these courses. Every effort was made to insure that the courses were both practical and informative and at the same time all aspects of a well planned community health programme were kept in their proper perspective. Lectures, discussion periods, demonstrations and field experience were happily combined. The fact that on both occasions the physicians attending formally expressed their approval of the Department's effort has been construed as justifying the setting up of what has appeared to some to be not only arbitrary but unnecessary standards.[90]

Phair explained also that the

> interest of the Department in securing for the health officer a background of administrative experience is not limited to supplying academic instruction only. An opportunity to see an effective but unextravagant community health service actually

> functioning is an essential requisite to any course on training. The Department, therefore, has subscribed whole-heartedly to the plan agreed upon by the School of Hygiene, University of Toronto, and the Township of East York, whereby funds should be jointly provided which would be sufficient to ensure a health programme designed to meet the needs of an urban community of 35,000-40,000 people.[91]

The founding of the East York Health Unit was the result of the input from local, provincial and medical interests as well as the Rockefeller Foundation.

ESTABLISHMENT OF THE EAST YORK HEALTH UNIT

Prior to the provision of major financing for public health services from the Canadian government in the late 1940s, the International Health Division of the Rockefeller Foundation was a principal source for the initiation of modern public health programs and the training of public health professionals, as well as improvements in medical schools in Ontario and elsewhere in Canada. The Foundation's grants established the School of Hygiene in the 1920s. Financing from Connaught Laboratories facilitated the northern addition to the structure. To support this expansion, the Rockefeller Foundation provided an endowment to support and even to enlarge the faculty in the difficult years of the 1930s. The Foundation also provided fellowships to enable physicians from across Canada to receive postgraduate instruction in the Diploma in Public Health course.[92] In 1935, the Rockefeller Foundation granted thirty-three thousand dollars over five years to assist the Ontario Department of Health in the formation of the Eastern Ontario Health Unit.[93] Naturally, when the provincial officials wanted to set up a similar unit close to the School of Hygiene near Toronto, they sought the support of the Foundation.

In conformity with its policy of encouraging governments at the provincial and state levels to assume more financial responsibility for public health services, the representatives of the Rockefeller Foundation approved a grant of twenty thousand dollars over two years. This was later extended when the Ontario health department's officials acquired authorization to cover fifty percent of the cost of the salaries and other expenses for a health officer and a nurse.[94] The need for a training facility in the School of Hygiene's program was an improvement recommended by the officers of the International Health Division of the Rockefeller Foundation:

> Although considerable progress has been made (in an effort to provide public health field experience for medical health officers, public health nurses, and medical students), opportunities for students to share in field experience have been slow in developing. Moreover, the urban and rural health organizations in the vicinity of Toronto, as now organized, are unsatisfactory for field training bases, and they do not lend themselves well to field studies of important diseases such as tuberculosis or syphilis, or to field investigations of such problems as nutritional deficiencies and mental hygiene.[95]

Under the agreement worked out by all parties, the School of Hygiene, with funds from the Rockefeller Foundation and the Ontario Department of Health, supplied a medical officer of health, an assistant health officer and a nursing supervisor estimated to cost eight thousand dollars in 1941. The Township paid for the rest of the expenditures, namely over eighteen thousand dollars which was the budget of the East York Health Department prior to the establishment of the unit.[96] Headed by Dr. William Mosley, the Unit was operational in January of 1941 with the hiring of another nurse, paid for by the Township, in addition to the supervisor of public health nursing, E. Wheler, provided by the School of Hygiene. D.B. Avison, a temporary appointee in epidemiology in the School helped to initiate school medical services.[97] At its inception, "the unit staff consisted of a health officer, a supervisor of public health nurses, 4 staff nurses, one sanitarian, and a secretary."[98] By the year's end, five child welfare clinics were functioning.[99] The departure of a succession of individuals for war service from the Unit hampered its early years. Nonetheless, the Rockefeller Foundation renewed the grant in November, 1943 to fund the East York Health Unit from 1944 to 1948.[100] Further progress had to await the return to peacetime.

The Rockefeller Foundation's support for the East York Health Unit was in addition to a further grant to the School of Hygiene during the war years to cover the expense of hiring more faculty members in the Departments of Physiological Hygiene, and Epidemiology and Biometrics. For a decade, these departments received an annual grant of four thousand and three thousand dollars respectively.[101]

SUB-DEPARTMENT OF PUBLIC HEALTH ADMINISTRATION

As a consequence of the opening of the East York Health Unit, Defries established a division of Public Health Administration within the Department of Epidemiology and Biometrics.[102] Its staff was made up of an associate professor, William Mosley, a 1937 D.P.H. graduate of the School of Hygiene and a former health officer in the Ontario Department of Health;[103] two associates, John T. Phair, Chief Medical Officer of Health in Ontario and Andrew McNabb, Director of the Division of Laboratories of the Ontario Department of Health; a lecturer in public health engineering, Albert E. Berry, Director of the Ontario Health Department's Division of Sanitary Engineering; an associate in public health nursing, Miss E. Wheler; and a laboratory assistant, Miss J. MacDonald.[104] No wonder this group was so well suited to teaching physicians who sought positions as health officers in Ontario. The functioning of the sub-department was just another conspicuous demonstration of the historically close link between the School of Hygiene and the Ontario Department of Health. The willingness of this department to allow its officers to offer part-time instruction in the School during the war years was another indication of that fact.[105]

INDUSTRIAL HYGIENE IN WARTIME

Another example of the ongoing inter-connections between the School of Hygiene and the Ontario Department of Health that intensified in the 1940s was the field of industrial hygiene under J. Grant Cunningham. After a decade of obvious difficulties for advocates of industrial health in the 1930s, Cunningham, a part-time instructor in the School and the head of the Division of Industrial Hygiene in the province, seized the opportunity presented by the war to drive home the importance of his medical specialty to the war effort:

> Under war conditions when raw materials are available, labour becomes the limiting factor in production. All measures are directed to maximum output and it is then better realized that general sickness is even more important than industrial accidents because of the much greater loss of time involved. Prolonged working hours are more likely to

> increase it, and many other conditions of work assume greater significance. For industrial operations of such a temporary and emergent nature, it is frequently more practical to control a health hazard by medical supervision of workers than by extensive alterations to process and equipment.[106]

Cunningham's appeal for a system of industrial hygiene attracted more than provincial involvement.

Suddenly with the coming war, the health of industrial workers in Canada was a national priority. The massive buildup of Canadian wartime production enabled the federal government to make certain demands of all factories. The federal health role in war industries grew out of Ottawa's inclusion of a clause in all federal contracts, lasting only for the duration of the war. Large factories manufacturing war products were required to insure that "sanitary arrangements and medical services in all plants should be to the satisfaction of the Department of Pensions and National Health. This necessitated inspection of plants in regard to ventilation, lighting, [and] testing of air for the presence of toxic substances such as Trinitrotoluene and Benzol. A special method was devised for this purpose and also for the chemical analysis of the blood of workers to detect absorbed Trinitrotoluene [used in the production of munitions]."[107] The promulgation of an Order-in-Council (P.C. 1550) on March 2, 1942 extended executive authority to the Minister of Pensions and National Health to institute medical or nursing services as well as establishing minimal nutritional standards for workers in war industries.[108] These policies had an immediate impact on the University of Toronto School of Hygiene which was approached to offer the postgraduate training to physicians so they could carry out the mandate of caring for Canadian war workers.

On the homefront in Canada, the rapid expansion of war plants to manufacture modern weaponry necessitated the emergence of medical specialists to treat or if possible to prevent the occupational diseases associated with war materials. For example, toxic solvents like benzol, trichlorethylene and carbon tetrachloride used in the manufacturing of aircraft were dangerous to human health. The making of trinitrotoluene (T.N.T.) in munitions plants was also harmful. Careful monitoring of workers exposed to these substances was essential to protect them from poisoning and damage to their skin, lungs, blood and liver. Likewise, the use of lead and radioactive materials in the assembly of precision instruments posed serious health problems not readily appreciated by the average medical practitioner.[109] The scope of these threats to human health was not appreciated in the early years of the war. In 1945, Cunningham reported that the "long range effects" of working conditions in some war industries

> are only now becoming apparent, e.g., in foundries the need for more than one "heat" a day results in increased exposure to silica dust. The recovery of scrap metal from storage batteries and lead glass has been associated with increased exposure to lead. Dermatitis from lubricating oils has considerably increased skin eruption among certain machine operators. In the manufacturing of artificial abrasives there has appeared an occupational lung condition which at this stage of investigation seems to have been associated mainly with increased exposure at electric furnaces due to continued increased production during the war.[110]

Not only fighting a war, but making the weapons to fight could be injurious to human health.

What J. Grant Cunningham had been advocating for decades, namely medical services in factories and the supervision of industries with occupational diseases, became a national concern in the 1940s. Even businessmen acknowledged the value of industrial health programs.[111] As chairman of the Canadian Medical Association's Committee of Industrial Medicine set up in 1941, Cunningham assisted in the formulation of hygienic standards for wartime workers published in a booklet that he wrote for industry. He was responsible for the formation of a Quebec and Ontario Industrial Medical Association of practicing industrial physicians.[112] On May 11, 1943, he presented a submission on industrial medicine to the House of Commons Special Committee on Social Security, recommending

1. That special provision be made whereby the maintenance of health and the control of general sickness of industrial workers are closely integrated with any health insurance plan adopted. This is additional to the treatment of disease when it supervenes, and to the protection for employees afforded by existing Factory and Workmen's Compensation Acts;
2. That all industries with more than one hundred employees be required to establish and maintain medical services for the improvement of health; Federal Order in Council No. 1550, under authority of the War Measures Act, now requires that in any war industry under contract to the Dominion Government, there shall be "medical, surgical, nursing and preventive services" to the satisfaction of the Minister;
   It is desirable that those working in factories and elsewhere, in groups of less than one hundred employees, receive similar benefit as it becomes practical;
3. That this health supervision provided by industry meet the requirements of the provincial health authorities on such matters as the extent of the program, the use of trained personnel, and securing the confidential nature of medical records;
4. That a part of the medical cost of health supervision in these groups of workers be paid, on a per employee basis, from the Health Insurance Fund, to each employer who meets the requirements.[113]

By stressing the importance of a system of health care for workers, Cunningham was expanding the scope of the provision by government of health services beyond the child to the adult population. Cunningham was an outstanding example of how part-time faculty of the School of Hygiene made significant contributions to the planning of health care services in Canada.

Throughout the war years, the School of Hygiene responded to the immediate need for plant physicians in Canadian industry by assisting with the Faculty of Medicine in the holding of special courses. In the fall of 1941, a three-day course offered instruction to forty-five practitioners.[114] A second course in January, 1942 was attended by forty-nine physicians. A third was given to sixty doctors in March, 1943. Drawn up and supervised by J.G. Cunningham and R.F. Farquharson of the Department of Medicine, these courses included a visit to an industrial plant.[115] Related to this type of teaching in the wartime was Cunningham's work in the Royal Canadian Air Force School of Aviation in Toronto where he participated in industrial health courses for personnel in the repair depots.[116]

The health problems of wartime workers drew members of the School of Hygiene into special research projects. In 1940, the staff of the Department of Physiological Hygiene investigated the "toxicity of benzol of petroleum origin."[117] A year later, a study was done into the "quantitative determination of certain substances in the urine of those exposed to this material."[118] Hugh M. Barrett, an assistant professor in the department and in charge of the industrial hygiene section of the Connaught Laboratories supervised studies in the "mechanism and treatment of phosgene poisoning", "toxic action of certain petroleum distillates containing benzene", "the carcinogenic activity of certain samples of coal tar", and the "metabolic fate of trinitrotoluene in the body."[119] With this type of problem-solving research going on in the School of Hygiene Building, the staff of the School was very much part of Canada's wartime industrial system.

The long-term response of the School of Hygiene to the need for specialists in industrial medicine was the establishment of the Diploma in Industrial Hygiene in February, 1943.[120] The D.I.H. was the second diploma to be offered by the School. Like the Diploma in Public Health, it was under the control of the Council of the Faculty of Medicine until the 1960s. The original course was based on the report of the Canadian Medical Association's Committee on Industrial Medicine chaired by Dr. J.G. Cunningham, the publications of the Council on Industrial Health of the American Medical Association, the syllabus of Professor R.T. Legge of the University of California and the course in industrial health developed by Dr. Cunningham and Dr. H.M. Barrett under the direction of Dr. C.H. Best.[121] Dr. D.Y. Solandt, who took over as Acting Head of the Department of Physiological Hygiene when Dr. C.H. Best left in 1941 to assume the directorship of the Banting and Best Institute, contributed to the formulation of the D.I.H. curriculum.[122]

The first course spanned one academic year of eight months which included lectures and laboratory work and a three-month session of field experience in industrial hygiene under the supervision of a recognized health department or industrial organization. Instruction was given in the Departments of Medicine, Surgery, Hygiene and Preventive Medicine, and Pharmacology of the Faculty of Medicine, and the Departments of Physiological Hygiene and of Epidemiology in the School of Hygiene. Only medical graduates were eligible for admission to study for the D.I.H. Graduates with a postgraduate qualification in public health could apply for exemption from half of the didactic and laboratory courses.[123] The University of Toronto's Diploma in Industrial Hygiene was the first postgraduate course in the field of industrial hygiene established in North America.[124]

The diploma's first graduate came at the very end of the war. Dr. J.J. Collins,[125] a D.P.H. graduate in 1944, received the Diploma in Industrial Hygiene in 1945.[126]

SUB-DEPARTMENT OF PUBLIC HEALTH NUTRITION

Like Public Health Administration, a separate unit to teach nutrition came into being in wartime as a result of the opening of the East York Health Unit[127], funded by the Rockefeller Foundation[128], that provided an area to do clinical work in nutrition. Established officially in March of 1941, the Sub-department's staff was made up of E.W. McHenry, head and associate professor, Miss A.E.C. Riggs, a clinical assistant, Miss E.G. Gavin, Miss J. Patterson and Miss H. Perry, research assistants, and Miss L. Barber, Miss J. Smith, and Miss E. James, technical assistants.[129] The prevalence of large-scale feeding in cafeterias, factories, military messes and daycare centres, as well as the adoption of food rationing, focussed national attention on the importance of nutrition. The headline of a leaflet circulated in 1943 by the Division of Nutritional Services of the Department of Pensions and National Health captured the emphasis given to nutrition: "EAT TO BEAT HITLER."[130]

Much of the credit for the emergence of nutrition as a respected science in Canada must be given to Earle Willard McHenry of the School of Hygiene. A 1921 graduate of the honour course in Chemistry in the University of Toronto, McHenry lectured to dental students while completing a M.A. degree awarded in 1923. The topic of his thesis, "Studies on the Composition of Saliva", was an indication of his future work. After some years of work with a cannery in Brighton, Ontario, and then with an American pharmaceutical company in New Jersey, McHenry returned to his alma mater to finish a Ph.D. in chemistry under the supervision of Lash Miller. His doctoral dissertation was a study of histamine. Brought to the Connaught Laboratories by J.G. FitzGerald in 1929, McHenry undertook work on the production of a variety of glandular extracts. He assumed the responsibility for the teaching of nutrition to medical students formerly offered by the Department of Biochemistry.[131]

McHenry's pioneering research in nutrition began in the winter of 1932-1933 with a small dietary survey of staff in the School of Hygiene Building. Over a year later, McHenry supervised his first graduate student. From 1934 to 1939, grants from the Connaught Laboratories and the Banting Research Foundation supported McHenry's investigations. During the 1930s, he produced forty-nine articles.[132]

Undoubtedly the depression and the advent of direct relief which furnished food were a fact of life for one-quarter to one-third of the population of Canada. This reality was a compelling reason for the growth of interest in nutrition. McHenry initiated the study of diets with general surveys in the 1930s to ascertain whether individual families received the proper intake of foods to sustain them. He saw the proverbial "silver lining in the cloud" of direct relief:

> Since many people are now dependent for food upon what is given to them here is an opportunity to place in perspective the advances made in nutrition in recent years. It is obvious that much can be done to supply adequate diets and to encourage proper use of the food furnished. There are probably many children securing proper amounts of milk today who would have received inadequate amounts if the purchase of milk depended on the family . . .[133]

To his credit, with further studies, McHenry charted the ugly reality of malnutrition in Canada during the 1930s. Referring to a national report on milk consumption, McHenry pointed to the inability of an average family in Toronto to purchase the recommended amount of milk for their children. McHenry reviewed the diet suggested by the Ontario Medical Association for a family of five, which was greater than the food allowance for those on relief in Toronto. This sum when extended over fifty-two weeks totalled 63 percent of an average family's yearly income, then estimated at $700. Such an amount was clearly beyond the means of most Torontonians.[134]

Concerns about the adequacy of food allowances for relief recipients prompted the Ontario Department of Public Welfare in the 1940s to commission a study of the subject by McHenry and his staff in the School of Hygiene. That report pointed out the special dietary requirements of children and pregnant women. It also stressed the need for a program to educate the public in how to choose the proper types of food.[135]

McHenry hoped to improve the nutritional standards for ordinary Canadians by teaching them how to use cheaper foods. However, the coming of the war demonstrated the extent of the serious shortages in the diet of most Canadians in the depression years.

Dr. Earle W. McHenry
1899-1961

"There has been for several years a growing interest in the subject of nutrition", McHenry announced in a speech to the Ontario Education Association in Toronto on April 8, 1942, "and during the past few months this interest has expanded very rapidly."[136] The year 1942 was indeed a momentous one for nutrition in Canada. McHenry played a key part in the emergence of the national preoccupation with nutrition. There was a flurry of activity by different levels of government. In Ottawa, the Department of Pensions and National Health created a Division of Nutrition Services. This new section reflected the enlarged wartime role of the federal government in the promotion of the health of workers in war plants. On March 2, 1942, under Order-in-Council (P.C. 1550), the Minister of Pensions and National Health was empowered to require food services in war industries to conform "to such nutritional standards as may be established."[137] Later in December, the Canadian Council of Nutrition, first organized in 1938, was established formally by Order-in-Council (P.C. 11144);[138] McHenry was an original member.[139] The Canadian military realized quickly the value of a proper diet. In December, 1941, McHenry joined the new standing committee on nutrition in the Department of National Defence as an advisor on the appropriate rationing for the armed services.[140] The data on the diet of Canadian men who enlisted in the army revealed the extent of hunger prior to the war; one federal official reported that "the average gain in weight in the first month" for recruits was seven pounds.[141]

Wartime rationing of food focussed attention on the significance of McHenry's work in nutrition. Early in 1942, the Wartime Prices and Trade Board imposed a quota on the consumption of sugar. Within a year, a system of rationing coupons was in place which regulated the individual Canadian's purchase of butter, coffee, tea and meat as well as alcoholic beverages.[142] McHenry served on the Nutrition Advisory Committee to the Foods Administration of the Board. He helped to set up a scale of minimal dietary requirements for the general population.[143]

Although these recommendations were never as stringent as the food controls adopted in Great Britain, there were problems in getting the population to adjust to the shortages of certain products. An editorial in the Canadian Journal of Public Health of January, 1943 — no doubt reflecting McHenry's views since he was on the editorial board—argued that the disruption of food supplies and rationing demanded the development of a comprehensive policy on nutrition:

> Stocks of meat are becoming low. The cheapest source of vitamin C, canned grapefruit juice is non-existent in Canadian grocery stores. All of this calls attention to the ramifications of nutrition and may even force a change in educational material. It will be of little avail to urge people to use foods which they cannot buy. It should not be forgotten that this is not a new situation, although the cause is now different. During the depression a large section of the population was unable to secure proper supplies of protective foods because of a lack of money. The spending power of Canadians has reached now the highest peak in history but supplies of food are short. An educational program will have lessened value unless it is made part of a national nutrition policy embracing production and distribution. The splendid success in actually improving nutrition in Great Britain under drastic war conditions has been due to the control of production, distribution and education under one ministry.[144]

This call for action was just one more example of how the faculty of the School of Hygiene, through the pages of the Canadian Journal of Public Health, influenced the development of federal and provincial policies.

McHenry and other members of the Sub-department of Public Health Nutrition did more than just writing and talking. They helped to improve the diet of many Canadians. Wartime demands for assistance in using nutrition to increase the performance of workers and the care of their children in nurseries and day care centres drew the staff into the practical side of nutrition. At the request of the Canadian Westinghouse Company in Hamilton, Dr. Eleanor Riggs, Miss Jean Patterson and Miss Helen Perry tested female employees for vitamin deficiencies. Some of the staff participated in a special noon lunch program for thirty boys conducted by the Kiwanis Club.[145] Special projects and services were undertaken for the federal government, the Ontario Department of Health and the military.[146]

As McHenry reported, an example of the nutritional studies done for the Canadian Army in 1942 and 1943 was the examination of "a group of 100 girls who are living under controlled conditions. These girls were examined after entrance to the Army in May and June and will be re-examined three months later. During this time they will be on army rations."[147]

In 1943 and 1944, Dr. Earle McHenry, Dr. Jean Leeson (a clinical assistant), and Miss Helen Perry, a research assistant, helped the Ontario Department of Welfare in the planning and inspection of meals for Wartime Day Nurseries and also for Day Care Centres for school age children.[148] Dr. Leeson and another research assistant, Miss Helen Ferguson, investigated the diet of patients in Ontario mental hospitals and the effects of supplemental dosages of vitamin C.[149]

The establishment of the East York Health Unit enhanced the work of McHenry's sub-department. It allowed him and his staff to gain clinical experience in the testing and the evaluation of human nutritional habits. A nutritional survey of 850 students in East York Collegiate Institute was undertaken in 1941 and 1942. Dr. Eleanor Riggs, a graduate in Medicine from the University of Toronto who completed a D.P.H. in 1941[150], was responsible for the physical examination of female students. She paid special attention to the eyes of "each student for possible evidence of deficiencies of vitamin A and riboflavin."[151] Miss Helen Perry, a graduate of Acadia University in Arts and Household Economics with graduate training and work as a nutritionist in Massachusetts[152], "did measurements of capillary fragility and of haemoglobin." Miss Jean Patterson, a research assistant in nutrition, measured the dark adaptation of students.[153] Even before the completion of the survey, Dr. Riggs had resigned and her replacement was Dr. Jean Leeson who had a medical degree from the University of Toronto in 1939 as well as postgraduate clinical training in nutrition at Toronto General Hospital and The Hospital For Sick Children.[154] The findings of this pioneering study appeared in 1943[155] and 1944.[156]

In January, 1944, another survey re-examined 75 of the students studied earlier to assess the impact of rationing. "This study is of particular interest", Defries reported, "because rationing of several foods, meat for example, was in operation in 1944 but not in 1942. In addition there had been considerable instruction concerning nutrition in the school and the community. The conclusion was that food rationing "as it existed in January, 1942, had no harmful effects upon the nutrition of the examined group."[157]

Even the research carried out had a very direct relationship to the Canadian war effort. McHenry and an assistant, Miss Alma Owens, investigated the B vitamin content of the different kinds of bread sold to the Canadian consumer in wartime:

> This was done by incorporating the bread into diets resembling human food intakes in general composition, with the bread in an amount proportional to six slices for 2,500

> calories. On this basis it was found that this amount of bread would supply for growing animals optimal amounts of the B vitamins in the case of whole wheat bread, somewhat less than optimal in the case of Canada Approved white bread, definitely less than optimal in the case of ordinary white bread.[158]

Another member of the department, Miss Evelyn Simmons, examined the calcium content of meals and of specific types of food for the Committee on Food Analysis of the Canadian Council on Nutrition.

A more basic type of scientific research in McHenry's sub-department centred on the biochemical and physiological functions of the B vitamins. The objective of McHenry's work was to achieve a better understanding of the role of certain vitamins in human metabolism, that is all of the chemical and physical processes by which animal and human bodies turn food into energy.[159] The Division of Natural Sciences of the Rockefeller Foundation provided initial funding for this research of six thousand dollars for two years starting July 1, 1940, and thereafter an additional appropriation of thirteen thousand five hundred dollars for three years from July 1, 1942. In December of 1944, the Foundation extended its financing to ten thousand dollars for a two-year period from July 1, 1945. In renewing the grant, an internal assessment of McHenry's work on B vitamins underscored its worth:

> The sequence of events in the intermediary metabolism of carbohydrates, proteins, and fats has long remained obscure, but in recent years experimental work has shown that several of the B vitamins are necessary for these syntheses. It is this latter aspect of vitamin research with which Dr. McHenry is concerned. Other workers have shown that rats can synthesize fats from protein, but Dr. McHenry finds that fat synthesis from protein can occur only when B_6 is supplied; and it seems likely that this vitamin is necessary for normal metabolism of protein. Similarly the synthesis of fat from carbohydrate is dependent upon thiamin; and other members of the B complex, if present, will augment the amount of synthesis. On the other hand, biotin, while causing fatty livers, actually does not increase the percentage of body fat, as compared with the amount of body fat produced by all of the isolated B vitamins except biotin.[160]

By the end of 1944, McHenry's Sub-department of Public Health Nutrition had grown to a staff of twelve with a total budget of approximately twenty-three thousand dollars. The funding came almost entirely from grants provided by the Rockefeller Foundation, the Nutrition Foundation Incorporated, the Department of National Health and Welfare and the Connaught Laboratories. As Dr. Defries pointed out to President Cody in December of 1944, all the grants, research, and teaching in the Sub-department were an indication of the "substantial character" of nutritional studies in the School of Hygiene.[161]

VIROLOGY

In early 1942, the Sub-department of Virus Studies (renamed by 1944 the Sub-department of Virus Infections), the forerunner of the School's Department of Microbiology established in 1956, came into existence in the School of Hygiene.[162] During its first year, it was a small operation. Dr. James Craigie was named head in February, 1942.[163] Dr. Ronald Hare and Dr. Raymond C. Parker were lecturers. Craigie, Hare and Parker taught students in the D.P.H. course as well as other graduates. Lectures, demonstrations and laboratory exercises concentrated on the "nature of viruses, methods of virus study, propagation of viruses, [and the] economics of virus disease." The two textbooks used in courses, Dr. C.E. van Rooyen's and Dr. A.J. Rhodes' *Virus Diseases of Man* and Dr. R.C. Parker's *Methods of Tissue Culture*, were written by individuals who were or were to be associated with the School of Hygiene and the Connaught Laboratories.[164] The School's Sub-department of Virus Studies, organized by Dr. James Craigie, pioneered in initiating research on human viruses and the teaching of virology in Canada.[165]

After a year of operation, Defries reported on the work of the new sub-department:

> Miss E.M. Clark and Mrs. M.E. Malcomson have continued their studies in typhus fever under the direction of Dr. James Craigie. Miss Clark has made an important contribution in the elaboration of a method of assessing the antigenicity of typhus vaccine and has also carried forward other studies on the development and variation of *R. prowazeki* in embryonated eggs. Mrs. Malcomson has continued her studies on the in vitro reactions of *R. prowazeki* with special reference to the complement-fixing antigens. The urgency and number of problems in relation to typhus vaccine have restricted the research activities to this field and it has not been possible to carry forward studies in phage typing in relation to the epidemiology of enteric fever. Mr. J.W. Fisher has completed his studies in poliomyelitis. The initial objective of this work, the development of a sensitive method of detecting the presence of poliomyelitis in the gastro-intestinal tract, was achieved.[166]

The international significance of the work on a typhus vaccine was recognized following the war when Craigie received the United States of America Typhus Commission Medal and the Medal of Freedom (U.S.A.).[167] This was a very auspicious introduction to the future of such work in the School of Hygiene.

PARASITOLOGY

The fourth sub-department generated by the war years was parasitology. Although it had been a part of the curriculum for the Diploma in Public Health from the beginning, it was only in the Second World War that the science of parasitology achieved a distinctive status within the School of Hygiene. "Interest in parasitology", Defries reported in 1943, "has increased since Canadian troops have become engaged in theatres of war where parasites and other tropical diseases are prevalent."[168]

Almost thirty years earlier, Defries, as the first student to take courses for the Diploma in Public Health, received instruction in parasitology from Edmund Walker.[169] A medical graduate who became a respected entomologist, Walker began giving courses in parasitology at the University of Toronto in 1906.[170] Seven years later, he joined the Faculty of Medicine as an assistant professor of zoology.[171] In the 1920s, Walker directed studies in parasitology as one of the three mandatory laboratory subjects for the D.P.H. program.[172]

Even before the opening of the School of Hygiene, Dr. Donald Fraser, in the Department of Hygiene and Preventive Medicine, taught a course in parasitology.[173] The School's second Calendar listed an introductory laboratory course of ninety hours in parasitology.[174] In 1932, Dr. P.A.T. Sneath, a D.P.H. graduate of 1928, took over the teaching of the course from Fraser. Sneath, with medical experience in the British Colonial Service in Tanganyika (now

Tanzania), was well-equipped for the job. In 1937, he resigned from the School to resume working in Africa.[175]

With the departure of Sneath, Fraser was looking for a replacement when he was appointed an examiner for the final Senate oral examination of a student, A.M. Fallis. A student of E.M. Walker, Fallis completed a Ph.D. thesis in 1937 entitled "A study of the helminth parasites of lamb in Ontario." Much later, Fallis described the circumstances surrounding his joining the School of Hygiene:

> Following the examination the candidate found himself walking across the campus in the company of Dr. Fraser and others. Dr. Fraser remarked that Dr. Sneath was returning to Africa and asked Fallis if he would be interested in giving some lectures on parasitology to the 1938-1939 Diploma in Public Health class. . . . Cordial discussions followed and it was agreed that Fallis would give the course at no cost to the University.[175]

Fallis' full-time employer was the Ontario Research Foundation, then located conveniently across Queen's Park from the School of Hygiene. His first course was "basic in nature and stressed preventive rather than curative measures." Lectures on the clinical aspects of parasitology were given by Dr. Wallace McClure, a medical missionary in China who in the late 1930s was in charge of the Diagnostic Laboratory for Parasitology and Bacteriology in the Ontario Department of Health.[177]

Dr. A. Murray Fallis

The first notice of a distinctive course devoted to parasitic diseases in the School of Hygiene's curriculum appeared in the report of the Director of the School for 1941-1942 under the title of "Medical Zoology and Entomology."[178] When the Sub-department of Parasitology was established in 1944, Dr. A.M. Fallis and Dr. E. Kuitunen were members of this new division.[179] In 1944, the Calendar reported that lectures in parasitology were given to students in the Diploma in Public Health, public health nursing, and fifth-year medical students. Dr. Fallis, an associate professor (part-time) and Dr. Kuitunen, a fellow, taught three courses: 1) an introduction to parasitology with a laboratory course of thirty-three hours that identified the life cycles and control of human parasites; 2) a lecture course of ten hours on parasitic diseases dealing with the pathogenesis, symptomatology, diagnosis, pathology, and epidemiology of diseases caused by parasites; 3) advanced course of ninety hours made up of lectures, laboratory work, demonstration and seminars designed for those specializing in parasitology or tropical hygiene.[180]

Ella Kuitunen's appointment to the staff of the School of Hygiene was another example of the support extended by Dr. Donald Fraser to young scientists. Originally from Estonia, Kuitunen completed a Ph.D. thesis on fish parasites in 1938 at the University of Toronto. Due to the ongoing depression of the late 1930s, she was unable to find employment after graduation. According to Fallis, "Dr. Fraser was kindly disposed toward helping promising individuals. He arranged a fellowship for her in his department in 1940 with the support of the Connaught Laboratories." Kuitunen lived up to Fraser's expectations in her research on fish parasites, pinworms in children and the parasitic infections of Canada's aboriginal people in the north.[181]

THE NEW DIPLOMAS

The background to the establishment of the Diploma in Dental Public Health revealed the significant contribution of the School of Hygiene to the development of public health in Quebec prior to 1945. In the 1930s, most of the physicians who headed the health units set up across Quebec received their D.P.H. from the University of Toronto School of Hygiene.[182] When Dr. Jean Gregoire, Deputy Minister of the Quebec Ministry of Health decided to form a Division of Oral Hygiene, he turned to the School and the Faculty of Dentistry in the University of Toronto for help. Dr. Gregoire wanted special postgraduate training in preventive dentistry and public health for the director of the new division, Dr. A. Reny, a graduate of the School of Dentistry in L'Université de Montréal. In a letter of October 9, 1942, to President H.J. Cody, Defries described what happened:

> It was explained to Dr. Gregoire that there was no course leading to a diploma in this field of public health work and that it was not possible to register a dentist in the course leading to the Diploma in Public Health which is provided for physicians by that Faculty. In discussing the matter with Dean Mason it was possible for Dr. Reny to register in the Faculty of Dentistry for the Degree of B.Sc. (Dentistry). . . . Dr. Reny will receive certain of the courses which are being given to the physicians proceeding to the Diploma in Public Health and other courses will be arranged for him. It is possible that he will spend at least half his time in the School of Hygiene.[183]

Defries then raised the possibility of the provision of a Diploma in Dental Public Health similar to the D.P.H. to be controlled by the Faculty of Dentistry. In response, President

Cody applauded the move. He wrote to Defries: "I think there are real possibilities of public service here. I am glad that you have begun this work in the case of Dr. Reny, and as a result of your experience with him this year, you may be able to set up a regular diploma course in this field."[184]

Over a year later, the Senate of the University of Toronto established on April 14, 1944, a Diploma in Dental Public Health under the control of the Faculty of Dentistry. The first recipients of the D.D.P.H. in 1945 were Dr. S.L. Honey and Dr. F.A. Kohli.[185]

Responding further to the need for specialists within the field of public health, the School of Hygiene in 1944 inaugurated under its own authority a Diploma in Veterinary Public Health.[186] The first graduates of this program finished their studies after 1945.

Another example of the development of a new course added by the School near the war's end was the Certificate in Public Health. Its establishment was a recognition of the role of non-medical graduates in public health.[187] The goal of the studies for the Certificate was "to provide knowledge of public health and to afford special training in one of the following subjects: nutrition, vital statistics, public health education, laboratory diagnostic services."[188]

COUNCIL OF THE SCHOOL

The war years witnessed the formal restructuring of the School's administrative structure with the establishment of a Council in June of 1943.[189] The Council's first meeting was held on Friday, March 3, 1944, in the Library of the Hygiene Building. The original membership of the Council included the Director, the acting Secretary and Secretary as well as the heads of Departments and Sub-departments: Doctors R. Defries, M. Ross, J. Craigie, D. Fraser, N. McKinnon, P. Moloney, W. Mosley, E. McHenry, D. Solandt and M. Fallis. The other members were the President of the University, the Deans of the Faculties of Medicine, Engineering, and Dentistry, the School of Graduate Studies, and the Directors of the School of Nursing, Physical and Health Education, and Social Work as well as the Principal of the Ontario Veterinary College.[190]

The Senate Statute set up a standing committee of the Senate, called the Committee of Hygiene Studies, composed of the Chancellor, the President and seven other members of the Senate. At the beginning, the Council of the School had a committee on curriculum, and another on applications and admissions.[191]

Within a few months of its inauguration, the new Council was busy at work. At a meeting on Wednesday, May 17, 1944, the Council discussed, according to Defries,

> a proposal that the courses of instruction leading to the Diploma in Veterinary Public Health and to the Certificate in Public Health, as offered to graduates in Arts and Science, be given in a period of six months in the place of eight months as provided by the regulations. It is proposed that by extending the daily hours of instruction approximately the same number of hours of instruction could be provided in the six months as in the period of eight months. The courses, therefore, would be accelerated rather than shortened. This plan is recommended as a means of meeting the postwar situation in the anticipated demand for a large number of personnel with suitable training for public health appointments both in Ontario and in the other provinces of Canada. The Department of Health of Ontario has placed before the School of Hygiene its anticipated needs and has urged that the provision be made for the training of the maximum number

> of physicians, dentists, veterinarians, engineers and other essential personnel for health departments.[192]

The Council's establishment and functioning was just another indication of the School's maturation and its preparation for the postwar period of expansion.

RELATIONS WITH CANADIAN PUBLIC HEALTH ASSOCIATION

Possibly one of the most important national roles performed by the staff of the School of Hygiene from 1939 to 1945 was to be an effective lobby for the expansion of public health services in Canada. As already pointed out in the previous chapter, Defries, Phair, McKinnon and other faculty rescued the Canadian Public Health Association and its Journal from dissolution in the late 1920s. In the 1930s, with the Journal's editorial offices located in the School of Hygiene Building, the C.P.H.A., then operating in the office of the Canadian Health League on Avenue Road in Toronto[193], survived the depression because of the voluntary efforts of members of the School. By 1943, both the editorial offices of the Journal and the national headquarters of the Canadian Public Health Association were housed at 150 College Street in the School of Hygiene Building. The Journal and the Association were now an intimate part of the School. That same year witnessed the change of the official name from the Canadian Public Health Journal to the Canadian Journal of Public Health.[194]

As in the previous decade, the war years complicated the efforts to continue publication of the Journal. In 1942, Defries announced that Mr. R.L. Randall was largely responsible for the composition of the C.J.P.H.[195] Randall was the first full-time office assistant of the Journal. In 1943, Defries reported on the difficulties facing the editors of his monthly:

> Contributions from medical officers of health are much less frequent, as those who formerly contributed valuable articles now have little or no time for their preparation — even formal reports of health departments have been reduced to "dry bones." The provincial and federal governments no longer have the opportunity to conduct studies, because of the depletion of their staffs. Your editorial board is similarly handicapped.[196]

Despite these problems, circulation of the Journal, aided by the various provincial health departments who paid for the subscriptions of their health officers, was 3,395 at the end of December, 1942. The subscribers included 1,800 physicians, 400 public health nurses, 450 other public health workers, 200 scientific libraries in Canada and the U.S.A., 75 hospitals and 275 agencies, companies, and institutions.[197]

Defries and his editorial board had to confront the question of how to keep up with the changing character of the public health profession without alienating long-established readers. "We realize that local medical officers of health", Defries stated in 1942,

> may sometimes find the [C.J.P.H.] disappointing because of the absence of papers that they would term practical and of reports of work in the field from health and other departments. They may feel that papers in bacteriology and immunity, presenting laboratory methods and other advances, are of little practical value. Such a view, however, does not constitute a substantial reason for the exclusion of such papers from the [C.J.P.H.]. It must be appreciated that new methods of control of diseases in the field are dependent upon work in the laboratory, and today the health officer needs to be acquainted with the laboratory. So, too, in the field of vital statistics, papers often may

Canadian Journal of
PUBLIC HEALTH

Volume 34, 1943

INDEX

	PAGES		PAGES
January	1- 50	July	299-346
February	51- 96	August	347-392
March	97-146	September	393-432
April	147-192	October	433-480
May	193-250	November	481-528
June	251-298	December	529-582

CANADIAN PUBLIC HEALTH ASSOCIATION
150 COLLEGE STREET
TORONTO, ONTARIO

The modern title of the journal appeared in 1943.

Canadian Journal of Public Health

THE DEPARTMENT OF NATIONAL HEALTH AND WELFARE

FOLLOWING the establishing of three new departments in the Federal Government—National Health and Welfare, Veterans' Affairs, and Reconstruction—the functions of the Department of Pensions and National Health were assigned to two of these departments. The Honourable Ian Mackenzie, formerly Minister of Pensions and National Health, was appointed Minister of Veterans' Affairs; and Dr. R. E. Wodehouse, formerly Deputy Minister, was appointed a member of the Canadian Pension Commission in the Department of Veterans' Affairs, and liaison officer between that department and the Department of National Health and Welfare.

The duties and powers of the new department include "all matters relating to the promotion or preservation of the health, social security and social welfare of the people of Canada over which the Parliament of Canada has jurisdiction." This is truly a great charter, reflecting the recognition by the government of the interrelation and interdependence of the two vital fields of health and welfare.

The Honourable Brooke Claxton, Minister of the new department, is an experienced Parliamentarian and deeply interested in health and welfare. After outstanding service overseas in the last war, for which he received the Distinguished Conduct Medal, he resumed his education at McGill University. Upon his graduation with honours in 1921, he practised law and in 1939 was appointed a K.C. He is an associate professor of commercial law at McGill University. In 1940 he was elected to Parliament as member for the Montreal constituency of St. Lawrence—St. George, and in 1943 was appointed Parliamentary Assistant to the President of the Privy Council. Mr. Claxton has had extensive experience in international affairs, having served as a Canadian delegate to the British Conference on Commonwealth Relations in 1935, 1939 and 1941, and to the Institute of Pacific Relations in 1942. He represented Canada at the first session of the Council of the United Nations Relief and Rehabilitation Administration in 1943 and participated in the sessions held in Montreal last September. He was a government delegate at the International Labour Conference in Philadelphia in April 1944.

On the occasion of the 1944 annual meeting of the Canadian Public Health Association, which was held shortly after his appointment as Minister, Mr.

38

An editorial from the C.J.P.H. in January, 1945 with list of staff.

> seem to consist largely of tables and findings that have no immediate application to the health officer's work. The [C.J.P.H.], however, must be something more than a "trade" publication. This is said not to defend the absence of more "practical" papers but to support the inclusion of laboratory, statistical, and other communications.[198]

Defries' comments in the early 1940s were the first of a succession of debates to erupt in the profession during the next several years on the role and scientific character of public health work.

Besides the publication of the Journal, Defries and his editorial board were the publishers for the Canadian Public Health Association of a number of manuals. By 1945, over 1,800 copies had been distributed of the *Manual of Sanitary Inspectors*, first published in 1937 to assist sanitary inspectors seeking certification by the C.P.H.A. A guide to a "Standard Milk Ordinance" setting out the legislation required to control milk was another publication. There was also an exercise book to instruct medical undergraduates in the proper way to fill out "Medical Certification of Deaths."[199] In 1940, the Association published a history of the development of public health in Canada edited by R.D. Defries.[200] All of these printed works and the Journal show the determination of Defries and his colleagues in the University of Toronto School of Hygiene to promote public health services across the country.

THE SCHOOL AND HEALTH CARE PLANNING

In the early 1940s, Defries and other members of the School of Hygiene through the Canadian Public Health Association launched the planning of and then lobbied for the establishment of a modern system of public health services across the country. This effort dated back to the controversy surrounding the inadequate state of health services in the previous decade. In 1939, the Dominion Council of Health requested that the C.P.H.A. appoint a committee to compile as much information as possible concerning the expenditure of local and provincial health departments and the number of full-time local health services. As late as that date, there were no accurate data on public health activities in Canada.[201] The task of assembling these details was assumed by the Department of Epidemiology and Biometrics of the School of Hygiene.[202] A questionnaire was sent to local and provincial health departments soliciting general facts on the number and qualifications of full-time and part-time personnel in each organization as well as the budget. This survey found only 85 municipalities with full-time health officers throughout Canada in 1938. Half the Canadian population was without a permanent health officer. Of the total of 21.7 million dollars spent by all provinces on public health services, less than ten percent ended up in the prevention of disease. The compilers of the study, specifically Defries, Ross, Davey and Moore of the School of Hygiene, lost no time in making the reader aware of their principal recommendation by presenting their conclusion in the opening rather than the closing paragraph: "It is clearly recognized that in so far as the provision of adequate public health services is concerned, ways and means must be found whereby the federal government may make to the provincial government grants-in-aid for public health purposes."[203]

Even before the publication of the 1938 survey, Defries and the leadership of the Canadian Public Health Association announced the passage of a series of resolutions at the annual meeting of the C.P.H.A. in Toronto from June 1 to 3, 1942, laying down the Public

Health Charter for Canada. The Association's Journal explained how the Charter consisted of "the points which are basic to a sound public health program in these days of stress." While acknowledging the progress in environmental sanitation, the editorial attacked the practice of pouring crude sewage into the sources of drinking water. It deplored also the lack of "healthful" housing for Canadians. Universal pasteurization of milk was endorsed. There was a call for "properly planned programs of maternal and infant care." The Charter called for the mass immunization of children against smallpox and diphtheria. The Association's public health charter urged an all-out campaign against tuberculosis and the free and humane treatment of the victims of T.B. It recommended the "Dominion Government again assume leadership in the field of venereal disease control and re-establish the policy of grants-in-aid which, for some years, served so useful a purpose in the control of venereal diseases by enabling education of the people and provision of facilities for diagnosis and treatment." A country-wide system of school health services for all students in primary and elementary school was another major proposal. No doubt influenced by war-time developments in nutrition and industrial hygiene, the Charter backed the adoption of a national nutritional policy and an industrial health system to care for workers.

To implement these proposals, the Canadian Public Health Association's Charter pointed to the need for full-time public health services and the availability of diagnostic and treatment centres for every Canadian. In order to achieve this standard of health care, the Association urged the federal government to offer grants-in-aid for local health services. Of great significance was the endorsement by the Convention of the Canadian Public Health Association at Toronto in June, 1942, of national health insurance as a means to further the nation-wide provision of medical, dental and nursing services.[204]

Almost a year after the passage of the Public Health Charter, Defries appeared on Friday, May 21, 1943 before the House of Commons' Special Committee on Social Security. Very appropriately, Defries presented the official brief of the Canadian Public Health Association to the Committee. The submission constituted the Association's nine-point plan for health insurance in Canada which visualized:

1. The benefits of health insurance afforded to every citizen of Canada;
2. The provision of adequate local health services for every community by physicians, dentists and nurses, and full-time local health departments;
3. The family as a unit, which would receive continuous health services and treatment when required from the physician of choice, with adequate diagnostic facilities and the services of specialists provided to assist the family physician;
4. The administration of health insurance federally through a Division of Health Insurance in the Department of National Health . . . thus permitting of the development of health insurance and public health in a co-ordinated and effective plan;
5. The administration of health insurance provincially through a Health Insurance Commission, or, preferably, through a Division of Health Insurance in the Provincial Department of Health, thus permitting of the closest relationship on the forwarding of a broad program of health;
6. The administration of health and public health locally through the suitable division of each province into districts or regions organized as full-time health units for the

provision of local health department services and for the local administration of health insurance;

7. The provision of grants-in-aid to provincial governments to further the control of such national problems as tuberculosis, venereal diseases and mental illness, and to permit of establishing full-time health units to serve all parts of each province;
8. The provision of assistance, through fellowships, for the training of public health personnel including medical officers of health, public health nurses, sanitary engineers, and sanitary inspectors;
9. More adequate provision for medical research in Canada.[205]

Here was the postwar plan for Canada's health care system.

WAR EFFORT OF SCHOOL OF HYGIENE

Like the First World War, the Second World War engendered the development of Canadian public health services. Unlike the First World War, the opportunities opened up by the Second World War enabled the public health lobby, whose leadership was largely made up of the senior faculty of the School of Hygiene in Toronto, to build a truly modern public health system across the country.

Defries and the staff of the Connaught Laboratories and the School of Hygiene responded to the wartime demands from 1939 to 1945 in a spectacular fashion. The Hygiene Building at 150 College Street in Toronto became the centre of a national war industry. Within its walls, an assembly line turned out millions of units of various drugs, sera and vaccines. Without any doubt, these biological products saved thousands of lives in Canada and elsewhere. The sera and vaccines from the Connaught Laboratories were distributed internationally. In the early 1940s, Dr. Andrew J. Rhodes, the Director of the School of Hygiene from 1956 to 1970, first encountered the name of the Connaught on the labels of containers of dried human blood serum while working as the head of a diagnostic laboratory in a hospital in the English midlands.[206]

The School of Hygiene was also an educational resource for military medicine. Senior faculty on wartime leave of absence directed the organization of public health services in armed forces. The operation of the academic programs of the School changed to meet the needs for health officers in the army, navy and airforce. The administration of the School offered accelerated courses to medical undergraduates and postgraduates as well as nurses in the period after 1940 until the end of the war. The establishment of new diplomas was another indication of willingness of the School's staff to offer the specialized education for experts in fields like industrial hygiene and veterinary public health that emerged in the war years.

Similarly the research projects assumed by the scientists in the School and the Connaught Laboratories illustrated how those involved in what appeared to lay persons as esoteric work could be reoriented to deal with very practical problems in occupational and environmental health. The numerous wartime investigations of the members of the Department of Physiological Hygiene showed the undisputed value of understanding the impact of technology on the humans working in munitions factories or aircraft plants.

But perhaps the most lasting contribution of the members of the School of Hygiene during the Second World War was in health planning. Defries and his colleagues through the

Canadian Public Health Association constituted a lobby for better health programs. Their efforts extended back to the 1920s but met with little success. The war created an opportunity to raise the issue of improving health standards, first in the military and then in the civilian population. This campaign led to development of major policies. For example, the "Public Health Charter" promulgated by the C.P.H.A. in 1942 urged the federal government to extend grants to local public health departments in order to establish a national standard of services. This policy became the National Health Grants Program in 1948. The C.P.H.A., by proposing the adoption of health insurance in the early 1940s, helped to put the idea on the national agenda decades before its establishment. Most importantly, during the years from 1939 to 1945, the faculty of the School of Hygiene exercised a national leadership in the manufacturing of biological products, research, teaching and planning that clearly demonstrated how public health matters were "vital to the war effort."[207]

CHAPTER FOUR

"A UNIQUE PARTNERSHIP":[1] THE UNIVERSITY OF TORONTO SCHOOL OF HYGIENE, THE FACULTY OF MEDICINE AND THE CONNAUGHT MEDICAL RESEARCH LABORATORIES, 1945-1955

A unique development has been in progress in the University of Toronto during the past forty years. Two institutions, the Connaught Medical Research Laboratories and the School of Hygiene, have been established and developed as partners in the fundamental objective of advancing preventive medicine and contributing to health, not only of our own population but also the world at large. The Connaught Medical Research Laboratories, by conducting research, by preparing essential products (many of which are the results of research) and by sharing through the School of Hygiene in the training of our public health personnel, are making a notable contribution to the health of the Canadian people.[2]

R.D. Defries in 1955

After enduring a depression and a war, R.D. Defries and the faculty of the School of Hygiene participated in the transformation of Canadian health care in the decade following 1945. The members of the School helped to plan the growth of modern health services and taught many of the health professionals who staffed that expanding system. In less than five years there were more graduates with the Diploma in Public Health than in the first ten years of the School's operation. Five new departments emerged to extend the departmental structure to eight. The Sub-department of Virus Infections made substantial advances in research and teaching which laid the foundation for the establishment of the Department of Microbiology headed by Dr. Andrew Rhodes in 1956. Of special significance was the formation of the Department of Hospital Administration and the creation of the School's fifth diploma, the Diploma in Hospital Administration, which signalled Defries' determination to broaden the School of Hygiene's role beyond its purely public health orientation to a more comprehensive medical care concept. While this period in the School's evolution broke new ground, the 1945 to 1955 era demonstrated also the value of John FitzGerald's original idea of linking research, teaching and public service in the unique partnership of the School and the Laboratories. It was under Defries as the second and last director of both institutions that this unique partnership achieved its fullest development.

POSTWAR EVOLUTION OF SCHOOL

The years 1945 to 1950 constituted a watershed for the University of Toronto School of Hygiene. With an enlarged teaching role, the number of full professors and departments rose. The formation of a Department of Hospital Administration marked the movement to a broader understanding of health care delivery. Funding from the budget of the University replaced increasingly the financing from American foundations and the Connaught Laboratories (Defries changed the name to the Connaught Medical Research Laboratories) for the expansion of instruction. The initiation of National Health Grants by the federal government resulted in the growth of the budget for research. Internationally, the School gained a reputation for high standards when the American Public Health Association recognized it as one of the ten accredited Schools of Public Health in North America. These years witnessed also the involvement of faculty members in different international health bodies such as the World Health Organization and the Pan American Sanitary Bureau. Moreover, the number of students from other countries taking their instruction in Toronto was another strong indication of the long tradition of excellence associated with the School of Hygiene throughout the world.

In September of 1946, the opening of L'École d'hygiène de l'Université de Montréal for the education of French-speaking health officers meant that the Toronto School was no longer the primary centre for public health education programs in all of Canada.[3] In addition, the growth of provincial health systems made possible by the National Health Grants resulted in the emergence of a variety of other centres across the country for the planning and research once almost exclusively concentrated in the School of Hygiene of the University of Toronto.[4]

In the latter part of the 1940s, the reports of C-E.A. Winslow, an American public health authority, portrayed the chief characteristics and assessed the stature of the University of Toronto in comparison with its sister institutions. At the request of the Surgeon-General of the United States, a committee on professional education of the American Public Health Association inaugurated the evaluation of Schools of Public Health in North America. "At that time postgraduate instruction in public health was offered in thirty-four institutions in the United States and Canada", R.D. Defries explained later, "and the degrees, diplomas and certificates offered were so diverse that serious confusion existed on the part of the civil service agencies and other bodies concerned with the appointment of public health personnel." Toronto was one of the ten schools granted accreditation in 1946.[5] Similarly when the School's Department of Hospital Administration came into existence, the Association of University Programs in Hospital Administration[6] accepted it as one of the Charter members.

From an examination of Winslow's initial evaluation in November 1945 to his third one in December 1949, one can appreciate the rapid growth in the size of the faculty of the School of Hygiene. Winslow's first assessment in 1945 listed four professors and nine associate professors with their teaching fields. R.D. Defries was Director of the School and Professor of Hygiene and Epidemiology. Other professors were N.E. McKinnon (Epidemiology and Biometrics), D.Y. Solandt (Physiology), D.T. Fraser (Hygiene and Preventive Medicine), and associate professors W. Mosley (Public Health Administration), D.L. MacLean (Physiological Hygiene), H.M. Barrett (Physiological Hygiene), J. Craigie (Virus Infections), M.H. Brown (Hygiene and Preventive Medicine), F.H. Fraser (Hygiene and Preventive Medicine), and F.O. Wishart (Hygiene and Preventive Medicine).[7]

Four years later, another evaluation of the School for the American Public Health Association's accreditation committee reported that the faculty of the University of Toronto School of Hygiene consisted of twelve professors and five associate professors. Winslow provided a list of the members of the faculty with the teaching specialty which demonstrated some of the newer sciences taught in the departments: R.D. Defries (Director, and Public Health Administration), Harvey Agnew (Hospital Administration), M.H. Brown (Microbiology and Public Health Administration), A.M. Fallis (Parasitology), D.T. Fraser

(Microbiology), F.H. Fraser (Microbiology), D.L. MacLean (Epidemiology and Biostatistics), E.W. McHenry (Nutrition), N.E. McKinnon (Epidemiology and Biostatistics), P.J. Moloney (Chemistry), C.E. van Rooyen (Virology), D.Y. Solandt (Physiological Hygiene) and Associate Professors L.O. Bradley (Hospital Administration), W. Mosley (Public Health Administration), R.C. Parker (Experimental Cytology), A.J. Rhodes (Virology) and F.O. Wishart (Preventive Medicine).[8]

By the end of Defries' tenure in 1955, there were eight departments: Hygiene and Preventive Medicine, Epidemiology and Biometrics, Physiological Hygiene, Chemistry in relation to Hygiene and Sanitation, Public Health Administration, Public Health Nutrition, Hospital Administration and Parasitology. The one sub-department was Virus Infections.[9]

BUDGET OF THE SCHOOL

As Director of the School of Hygiene, Defries proved to be a master of financial ingenuity. He tapped a number of sources within and without the University to pay for the expansion of the School. This is probably why he called the budget of the School "somewhat complicated."[10] From 1945 to 1955, Defries reported an increase in the total salaries of the School from about $120,000[11] to over $177,000.[12] A similar rise occurred in the School's research funding which jumped from $6,692 in 1947,[13] the first year this spending was identified distinctly, to $71,643 in 1955.[14] Significantly, these figures do not include the support directly from the Connaught Medical Research Laboratories where Defries was the Director, or the research grants from outside agencies to the staff of the Connaught who taught in the School. The budget of the School was, in fact, composed from a variety of sources. The other significant detail in the finances was the growth of support for the School from the general funds of the University of Toronto from under 20 percent of the School's budget in 1945 to over 60 percent a decade later.[15] All of the changes in the financial structure charted the transition of the School from its beginnings as a Rockefeller School of Public Health to an independent division of the University of Toronto.

At the end of the 1940s, the ten-year period of grants for faculty salaries from the International Health Division of the Rockefeller Foundation ended. In 1949, Defries summarized the changes during that period and especially the increase in the financing from the University:

> When the grant [from the Rockefeller Foundation] was first provided in the session 1939-1940 the staff of the Departments composing the School included: six professors; five associate professors; four assistant professors; and three lecturers. In the estimates for the session 1949-1950, provision was made for: nine professors; eight associate professors; six assistant professors; and three lecturers.
>
> The University has continued to increase its support of the School of Hygiene providing $36,000.00 more than was provided in 1939-1940. The income from the Rockefeller Endowment Fund has been reduced this year by an estimated $5,600.00 which amount has had to be met from other sources. There has been a very substantial increase in the amount for research work, which, in the Session 1949-1950, will be $89,000.00. The total budget for the coming year is $241,000.00 in contrast with approximately $100,000.00 in 1939-1940.[16]

Eight months earlier, in trying unsuccessfully to get support for new enterprises, Defries detailed succinctly the new relationship with the Rockefeller Foundation:

> When the School of Hygiene was established through the interest of the Foundation the endowment fund provided more than half of the total expenditures. Today the endowment fund is providing about twenty percent of the budget. To the endowment income has been added by the Foundation the grant of $17,000 for Faculty Salaries, of $5,000 for the East York-Leaside Health Unit, and of $4,500 for the Nutrition Study. With these additional amounts, the Foundation's contributions provide approximately twenty-five percent of the budget.[17]

By the 1950s, over sixty percent of the finances of the School came from university funds. In terms of its budget, by 1956 the School of Hygiene had been integrated into the administrative and financial structure of the University of Toronto, and separated formally from the Connaught Medical Research Laboratories.

The Canadian office of the International Health Board of the Rockefeller Foundation closed in 1953. From 1940, the Rockefeller representative used a suite close to the main entrance of the School of Hygiene Building. Until 1950, Dr. W.A. McIntosh occupied the position. His successor was Dr. D. Bruce Wilson, a graduate of the School's D.P.H. program in 1928, who was the second and final representative of the Foundation stationed in Toronto. An era had ended.[18]

ADMINISTRATION OF SCHOOL

Like the rest of the university and the society of that era, the School of Hygiene under R.D. Defries was a hierarchical organization based on rank. At the top was the Director; then came the chief administrators, D.T. Fraser, Associate Director, and D.L. MacLean, the Secretary, followed by the heads of the departments, the senior scientists, the junior scientists and professors, the senior technicians, "the non-commissioned officers" of the institution, the technical staff, and lastly the cleaning and maintenance staff. A formal distance separated the ranks; the School's administrators followed the custom of addressing staff by using the appropriate titles, such as doctor for scientists and Miss or Mrs, depending on the individual female, for the ladies of the faculty. All decision making was centralized in the offices of the Director and Secretary. Defries used the Council of the School to implement policies set by himself through its several committees on admissions, the curriculum, timetables and grading. Nonetheless, "a sense of family" where everyone knew his or her place in the hierarchy prevailed in the relationships among the social strata in the School.

A lifelong bachelor and a devout Christian, Defries displayed a fatherly concern for all his staff. Yet he maintained a formal deportment. All but a handful of very senior professors addressed him always as Dr. Defries or referred to him as R.D.D. in conversations about the Director. While he might consult the senior members, there was no doubt that Dr. Defries was "the boss."[19]

Defries' description of the method in which the budget was put together shed light on his style of managing the School:

> In the School of Hygiene the budget is prepared by the Director and is discussed in detail with the head of each department. Knowing the amount of money available from various sources, it is possible to indicate to the head of each department what may be planned.[20]

When the Office of the President requested the completion of a report on each staff member, Defries received permission for himself and the Secretary of the School to fill out the assessments "after full discussion with the head of each department." This procedure was Defries' policy of "the continuation of the centralizing of the administration" in the School.[21]

In a distinctive fashion, Sidney Smith, the President of the University of Toronto from 1945 to 1957, displayed his customary warm yet formal relationship with the Director of the School of Hygiene and its faculty. The correspondence of Smith with Defries was correct but Smith exhibited a genuine interest in the problems of the School. The President sat on the School's Council and participated in its discussions. Defries kept him informed about the illness of certain professors.[22] On different occasions, the President helped to settle internal differences within the School in a generally comfortable way for all sides.[23] Sidney Smith's genuine concern for the future development of the School was apparent in the lengthy discussions about a successor to Defries. In response to fears about the possible closure or reduction of its status,[24] Smith assured one graduate of his determination to strengthen and "enhance the role of the School."[25]

STUDENTS AND COURSES

Like the rest of the University of Toronto, the School of Hygiene experienced a surge in enrolment after the Second World War lasting into the 1950s.[26] Veterans, aided by government grants, were a dominant component of the classes. To accommodate the demand immediately following the war, the School operated two D.P.H. courses in the session of 1945 to 1946; thirty-four physicians took the program beginning in September and another thirty-one in the subsequent April.[27]

The core of the School's postgraduate teaching was the Diploma in Public Health. In 1947, the curriculum of the D.P.H. consisted of one thousand and forty hours of instruction with courses in bacteriology (108 hours), immunology and serology (60 hours), parasitology (48 hours), virus infections (30 hours), biometrics (109 hours), epidemiology (110 hours), communicable diseases (14 hours), physiological hygiene (41 hours), industrial hygiene (46 hours), public health services (210 hours), public health education (30 hours), sanitation (66 hours), chemistry in relation to hygiene (66 hours), and public health nutrition (51 hours). Dr. C-E.A. Winslow, in his evaluation of the School's program, noted that "the offering in the fields of Microbiology, Serology and Virus Infections is more extensive than any other school except Hopkins."[28]

The longest course was public health administration given by Defries and Mosley and dealt with ten subjects: general public health administration, administration in clinical specialties in public health, public health law, social and economic factors, nursing, mental health, planning and housing, history of public health, dental health and hospital administration. Two specialists from outside the School lectured on the social and economic factors in health, H.M. Cassidy of the School of Social Work in the University of Toronto provided four lectures on welfare services. Dr. Fred W. Jackson, in 1947 the Deputy Minister of Health and Welfare in Manitoba, and later the head of the division of health insurance studies in the Department of National Health and Welfare, offered a series of lectures on medical care and health insurance. The report of the American Public Health Association's

Postgraduate students in D.P.H. Class of 1946 at the beginning of the session.

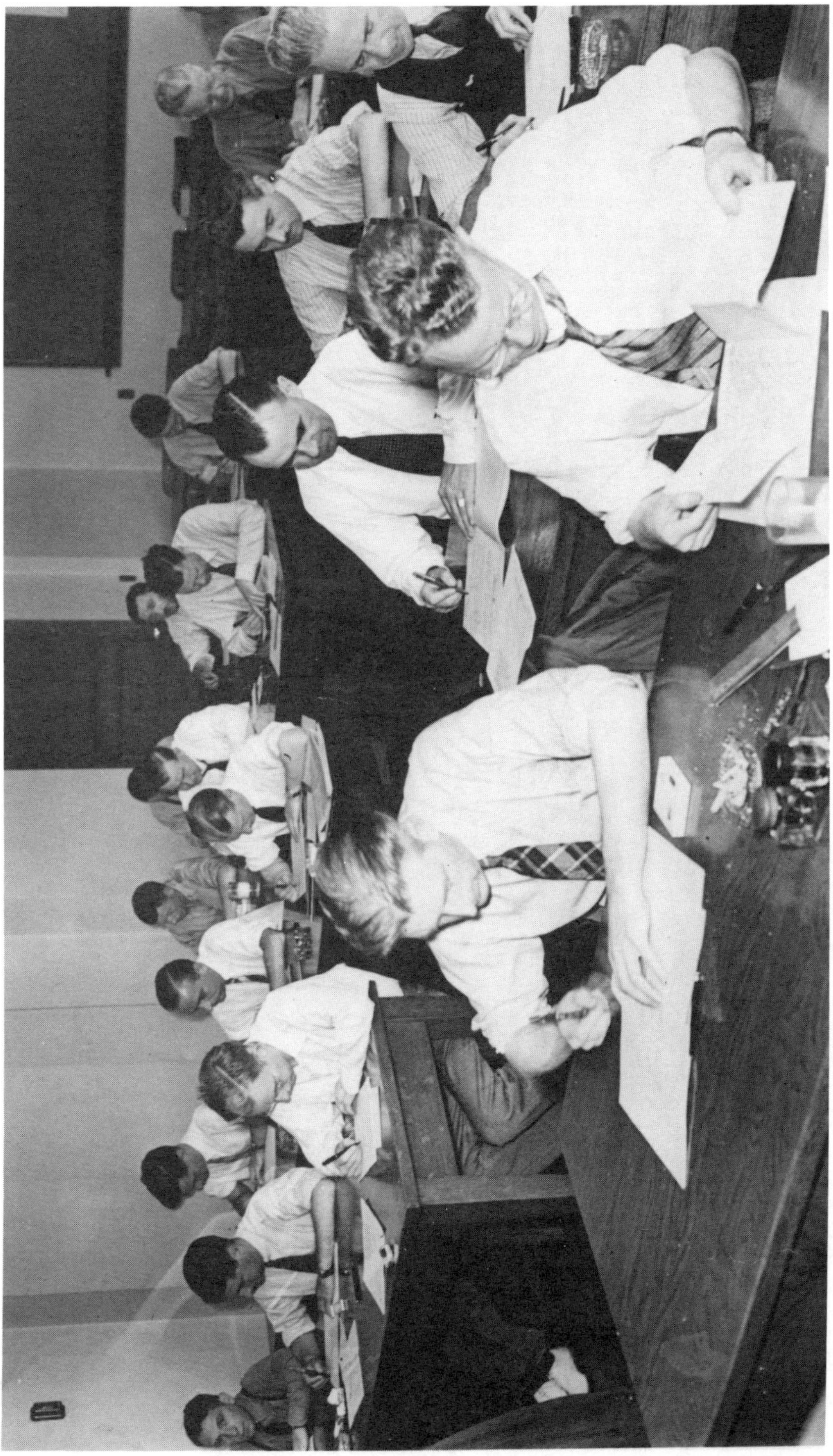

Students in D.P.H. Class of 1946 writing exams. Note the prevalence of cigarettes.

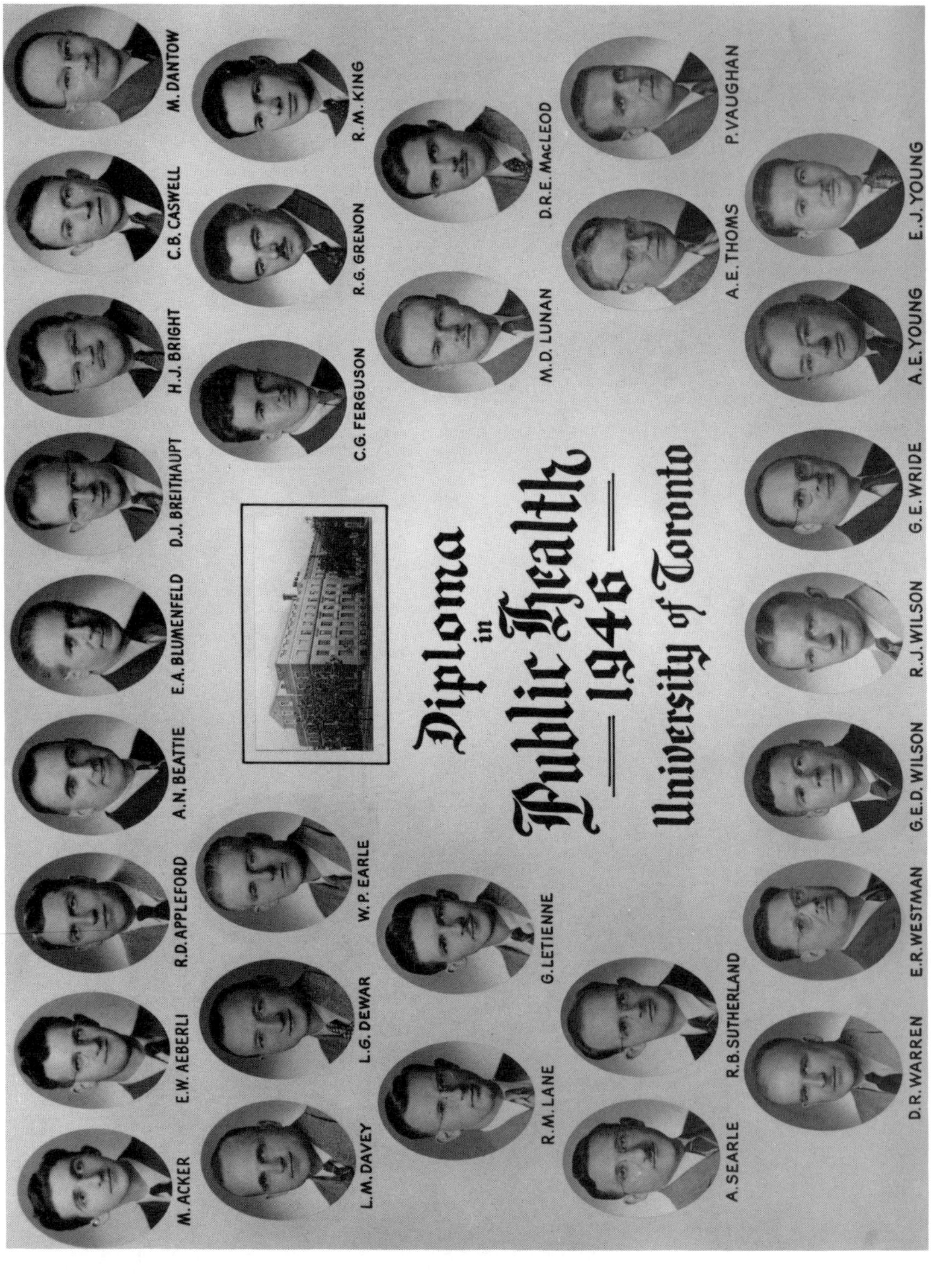

D.P.H. Class of 1946

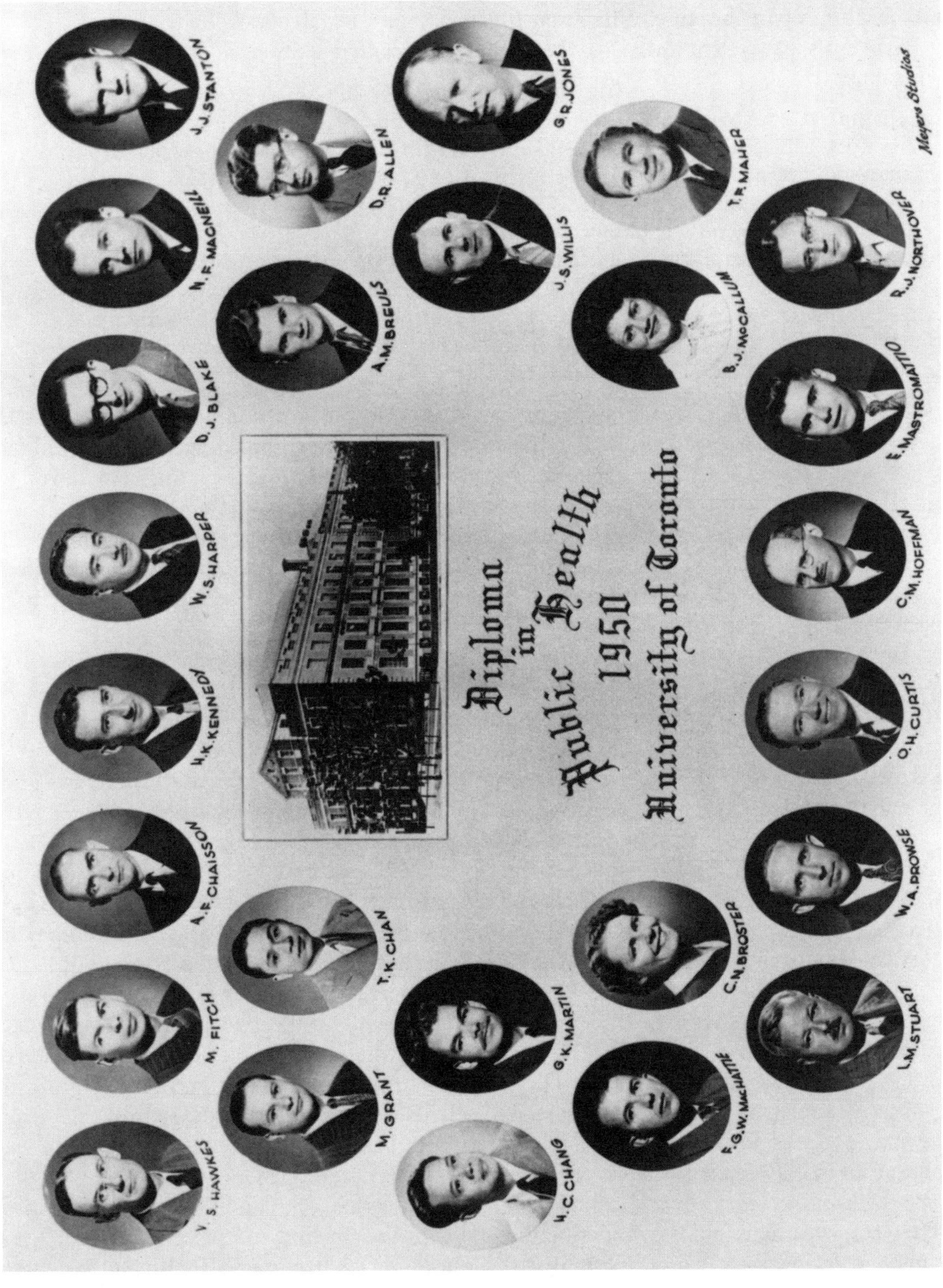

D.P.H. Class of 1950

accreditation visit was critical of the small amount of time alloted to the study of the role of public health nursing because of its importance in health departments.[29]

Winslow's assessment in 1947 of the D.P.H. program in the School of Hygiene was very favourable:

> In general, the curriculum at Toronto represents the first attempts to provide a complete uniform balanced curriculum for the D.P.H. (or M.P.H.). As such, it deserves the serious study of other schools, which may not want to go quite so far, but which may gain valuable hints from this program as to basic essential subjects of interest to all health workers. The general emphasis of the program — as at Columbia, Michigan and Yale— is on the training of the health administrators; but the influence of the Connaught Medical Research Laboratories has determined a second — and almost equally powerful — emphasis on Microbiology. In the teaching of such subjects as Nutrition and Physiological Hygiene the practical application of theoretical knowledge to the practical problems of the field is specially noteworthy.[30]

Winslow's third evaluation in 1949 reiterated his admiration for quality and scope of the instruction in the School's courses. He singled out for praise a course in virology offered by Dr. C.E. van Rooyen and Dr. A.J. Rhodes. "In view of the rapid progress in this field, it would seem that a course of this type has very special values."[31]

What impressed Winslow was the large number of new recruits and young medical graduates entering the D.P.H. course in Toronto in comparison to the situation in the United States. "This is perhaps", he remarked in his report, "due to the greater prestige of public service in the British social tradition."[32]

An example of the type of students in the D.P.H. course was the class of 1949. Twenty-six physicians entered the program for the Diploma in Public Health in September, 1948.[33] Twenty-two graduated. This group reflected the impact of veterans on the School. Half of the class had served with the Royal Canadian Army Medical Corps, the Royal Canadian Navy or the Royal Canadian Air Force. They were familiar with military medicine.[34] There was one female in this bastion of males, Eva Susan May, whose married name became McMaster. Six of the postgraduate students were from outside Canada. Four came from China: D.O. Chan, A.O.T. Cheung, T.H. Chiang, and J.J. Fang; Dr. Cheung and Dr. Chiang practiced in Ontario. P.K. Ratnasingham from Ceylon (now Sri Lanka) returned home to be a Medical Officer of Health.[35] K.W.C. Sinclair-Loutit from England received also a Diploma in Industrial Health in 1950,[36] and then went on to a career with the United Nations.[37] R.D. Barron came back to the School of Hygiene to succeed D.L. MacLean as the Secretary.[38] George Moss was the Medical Officer of Health of Toronto in the 1970s.[39]

Besides the students in the D.P.H. course during the session 1948 to 1949, there were additional postgraduates enrolled in the School's other programs. For the Diploma in Hospital Administration, a total of eleven individuals registered in the course. Four dentists were taking courses for the Diploma in Dental Public Health. Three veterinarians were in the program for the Diploma in Veterinary Public Health. Three engineers were working on the Master of Applied Science specializing in sanitary engineering; one candidate was from India. There were three individuals completing the work for the Certificate in Public Health: J.H. Doughty, a senior statistician with the British Columbia Department of Health and Welfare; Y.C. Ma, with the National Epidemic Preventive Bureau in Peking, China whose "chief interests have been connected with the chemistry of blood protein and latterly with antibiotics"; and Doris L. Noble, a nutritional consultant with the British Columbia Department of Health and Welfare.[40]

Not all students registered in the School of Hygiene were in programs proceeding to a degree or a diploma. For example, from 1950 to 1953, twenty-five special students with undergraduate degrees studied in the School.[41]

FELLOWSHIPS

A variety of awards helped students to attend the School of Hygiene. The oldest was The Hastings Memorial Fellowship established in 1929 to honour Dr. Charles J.C. Hastings, the Medical Officer of Health of the City of Toronto from 1910 to 1929. Valued at $1,500, it was awarded in 1932 to A.H. Sellers, in 1935 to A.E. Allin, in 1938 to L.E. Ranta, in 1946 to J.M. Parker, in 1949 to E. Kovacs, and fittingly in 1953 to J.E.F. Hastings, the great nephew of Charles Hastings. The Connaught Laboratories set up in 1943 The FitzGerald Memorial Fellowship and The Colonel Sir Albert Gooderham Memorial Fellowship in Preventive Medicine to commemorate the first Director and the benefactor of the Laboratories. The value of each was $2,400 in 1953.[42]

From 1947 until 1951, the W.K. Kellogg Foundation provided scholarships in hospital administration. Earlier in 1942, it had provided a fund of $10,000 to assist certain students in the form of grants or loans.[43]

The year 1948 marked the end of an era with the passing of the fellowships in public health from the Rockefeller Foundation and the Connaught Laboratories. During the first twenty years of the School's operation, there were at least one hundred and sixty-six Rockefeller Fellowships[44] and sixty-eight Connaught Fellowships.[45] The introduction of the National Health Grants Program by Ottawa made provision for the financing and assistance of the education of public health professionals.[46] Moreover, the introduction of fellowships by the World Health Organization constituted another source of support for foreign students who wanted to study in the School of Hygiene.[47]

GRADUATE EDUCATION

In the postwar period, the School of Hygiene was a major centre for graduate public health education in Canada. The faculty of the School supervising the M.A. and Ph.D. research and dissertations of students in the School of Graduate Studies taught a number of graduate students from other parts of the University as well. For example from 1946 to 1953, twenty-six candidates from the Ontario Agricultural College for the Master of Science in Agriculture received instruction.[48] Seventy engineers earned a M.A. Sc. with a specialization in sanitary engineering in the fifteen years following 1940.[49] During the decade after 1945, there were forty-seven M.A. and twelve Ph.D. degrees awarded in the School in the fields of epidemiology, parasitology, microbiology, nutrition and physiological hygiene.[50]

STUDENTS FROM OUTSIDE OF CANADA

The background of the postgraduates in the School of Hygiene revealed the rising number of individuals from outside of Canada coming to Toronto for postgraduate education in the fields of public health. In the five years following 1945, the faculty welcomed students from China, Hong Kong, Ceylon (now Sri Lanka), Syria, Nigeria, Haiti, Jamaica, Yugoslavia, England, Ireland, Wales and the United States.[51] Of significance was the role of the School in providing instruction to public health specialists from developing countries. In the 1950s, The Colombo Plan funded by the Canadian Government paid for the cost of educating these officials.[52] Much earlier, the Massey Foundation of Toronto in 1946 helped five students, including four engineers from India, to attend the School.[53]

THE CONNAUGHT AND THE HYGIENE BUILDING

Forced by the exigencies of the Second World War, the Connaught Laboratories had developed by 1945 to a stage unimaginable by John FitzGerald and R.D. Defries over thirty years earlier. The growth of research which increased the number and variety of products distributed by the Laboratories prompted Defries in 1946 to change the name to the Connaught Medical Research Laboratories (C.M.R.L.), "thus indicating clearly their fundamental interest in research."[54] At the war's end, the Connaught Laboratories' staff numbered about 800 people, more than three times the pre-war level.[55] With the return to peacetime operations, there were 488 employees in March, 1947, 159 of whom worked in the School of Hygiene Building.[56]

The expansion of the 1940s doubled the floor space available to the Laboratories to over 150,000 square feet,[57] about one third of it located in the School of Hygiene Building. Meanwhile, administrative changes in the Toronto area resulted in the formation of three divisions by 1946 in addition to the Western Division organized in 1935 in British Columbia. Located in the old Knox College building at Spadina Avenue and College Street, the Spadina Division accommodated administrative services, the filling, packaging and distribution of products, the production of penicillin, general research facilities, and the processing of blood serum.

The Farm, originally donated in 1915 by Colonel Albert Gooderham situated at Steeles Avenue West and Dufferin Street, north of Toronto, had increased to 147 acres and had been designated the Dufferin Division. It was the centre of the postwar growth of the Laboratories. The School of Hygiene Building on College Street in Toronto was named in April, 1946, quite logically, the College Division with the transfer of many operations to the Spadina Division, a few blocks west.[58]

Throughout the administration of R.D. Defries, the University of Toronto School of Hygiene was an academic extension of the Connaught Medical Research Laboratories. In terms of staff and research, the Laboratories made it financially feasible for the School to function. Defries was unequivocal on that aspect. In June of 1947, he wrote:

> In reviewing research work maintained in the Laboratories, mention must be made of grants given to the departments of the School of Hygiene, amounting to $19,000 annually, to permit of studies to be conducted in those departments. These grants represent but a small part of the assistance given by the Connaught Medical Research Laboratories to the School of Hygiene. Of major importance is the assumption of a large part of the salaries of many of the members who constitute the teaching group, and the maintenance of the Library in the School of Hygiene building entailing the expenditure of approximately $8,000 a year, which is essential to the students and to the work of the School. In addition, the Laboratories have defrayed the expenses of the animal room and

> cafeteria and have provided laboratory facilities for teaching purposes. In 1928, Connaught Laboratories fellowships in public health were established and since that date sixty-two fellowships, each of $1,500, have been provided for the training of physicians nominated by provincial departments of health, in order that these physicians may serve as medical officers of health. It is fair to say that the School of Hygiene could not be maintained as presently organized if support were not available from the Laboratories. The original thought of the founder of the Laboratories, Dr. FitzGerald, has therefore been developed in which medical public service has been rendered through the distribution of essential products and the distribution of these has maintained a programme of research and has made possible an intimate relation with teaching. In this way the Laboratories are unique in their relationships and undertakings.[59]

Even after the formal separation of the School and the Laboratories in 1955, the Connaught Medical Research Laboratories remained a valuable source of funding for the School of Hygiene.[60]

The School of Hygiene Building exemplified the integral connection of the School of Hygiene with the Connaught Medical Research Laboratories. Renovations in 1946 accommodating the needs of the School for more classrooms, laboratories, and offices[61] resulted in the School of Hygiene occupying about 21,000 square feet in the structure or less than one third of the space. The Connaught Medical Research Laboratories used the remaining 51,000 square feet. Most of the cost for the maintenance of the Building and the equipment from refrigeration machines to air compressors, elevators, sterilizers and incubators as well as the share of the cost of utilities came from the budget of the Laboratories. Moreover, the Connaught Medical Research Laboratories provided a library available to the students of the School and subsidized food services in the cafeteria for students and staff and in the senior lunch room for scientists and heads of departments.[62]

Even with the shifting of many of the activities of the production and distribution of products to the Spadina Division in 1946, the Hygiene Building was the centre for the manufacture of insulin. Here four huge tanks[63] located on the second floor of the southeast wing processed the crude insulin extracted from the pancreas of thousands of cattle and pigs that flowed into collection tanks in the basement.[64] The insulin plant was a "self-contained unit."

During the 1950s, the capacity of the insulin plant in the School of Hygiene Building that commenced production in the late 1920s had expanded enormously. By 1952, the annual output of insulin had grown more than five times since 1936.[65] In addition, better procedures for extraction and purification were introduced. In 1954, over 1,400,000 pounds of pancreas from abattoirs across the country were used. A year later, the insulin plant began working on a 24-hour basis five days of the week.[66] An article described the plant's operation:

> It occupies three floors, extending to a sub-basement, connected by narrow circular stairways. The process works downward: On the top floor is the machine grinding animal pancreas, which flows like molten cooked liver into glass-lined tanks of acid alcohol on the floor below. The murky material is filtered, centrifuged and dried, becoming lighter and lighter in colour until the final product, a white flour-textured powder, is put into sterile solution and bottled for distribution to hospitals and druggists. Connaught obtains about three quarters of a pint of insulin from three tons of pancreas. The waste is made into fertilizer and dog food. To test the potency of its insulin Connaught uses three thousand mice every two weeks.[67]

More than any other product, the manufacture of insulin was an integral part of the School of Hygiene Building for over fifty years.

HYGIENE AND PREVENTIVE MEDICINE

The oldest department in the School of Hygiene, namely Hygiene and Preventive Medicine, traced its origins back to the establishment of the modern Faculty of Medicine of the University of Toronto in 1887. It was responsible for providing instruction in the wide spectrum of sciences and subjects emerging in the general field of public health during the early twentieth century. Becoming a joint department of the Faculty and the School in the 1920s, FitzGerald, Defries and Fraser developed within the structure of Hygiene and Preventive Medicine the sciences of immunology, microbiology and parasitology. This tradition of innovation continued in the post-1945 era with the reorganization of the instruction of medical students. The department's members taught most of the undergraduate courses in the School, teaching to a wide variety of students from other faculties and schools within the university. Because the budget of the department came partially from the Faculty of Medicine and also the Connaught Laboratories, there was an understandable tension about the objectives of Hygiene and Preventive Medicine. Forty percent of the budget was designated for the teaching of medical students. Ironically, this department that had launched so many other disciplines on their way to departmental status was itself to be merged into another department in 1956.[68]

From 1927 until 1955, the Department of Hygiene and Preventive Medicine provided the largest number of offerings to the most students in the School of Hygiene. First, second, third and fourth year medical students received instruction in lectures, tutorials, field visits, demonstrations and laboratory exercises dealing with an eclectic area of public health, sanitation and preventive medicine. In addition, there were courses on bacteriology, immunology and serology, virus infections, hygiene and preventive medicine, infection and immunity, and microbiology. Undergraduates taking these subjects were from the School of Nursing, the School of Physical Health and Health Education, the Faculty of Arts and Science, the Faculty of Household Science and the Faculty of Pharmacy (until 1953 it was the Ontario College of Pharmacy). Candidates in the D.P.H. program took ninety hours of teaching in bacteriology. A course of seventy-five hours was provided to graduate engineers as part of their requirement for a Master of Applied Science degree that specialized in sanitary engineering.[69] During the 1953 to 1954 session, the department taught over eight hundred and seventy individuals in thirteen courses.

The biggest change in Hygiene and Preventive Medicine was the reorganization of the whole undergraduate medical program and the introduction of social medicine into the curriculum which resulted in the adoption of some innovative approaches. Instead of concentrating the teaching of preventive medicine in the last year, Fraser, Brown and others decided to offer instruction in each of the four years.[70] Their objective was clear:

> Briefly stated, the purpose of these courses is to present to the student the problems and practices of preventive medicine. The chief emphasis in this presentation is laid upon the means by which the general practitioner may most effectively practice preventive medicine; the duties and obligations towards society imposed upon the physician by

> Legislative enactments; the role he plays in, and the assistance he may derive from organized preventive medicine.[71]

Instructors discussed with the classes the impact of social security measures and medical care insurance on general practice. Students visited homes with public health nurses in East York "to observe the social and economic aspects of health."[72]

A fascinating attempt to introduce social medicine into the undergraduate medical experience was the Department of Hygiene and Preventive Medicine's experiment with summer internships for a third-year student in the East York-Leaside Health Unit. Dr. M. H. Brown sponsored the project and it was directed by Dr. W. Mosley, the M.O.H. of the area and his assistant, Dr. J.M. Parker, in 1948. The purpose was to provide future physicians with a "view of life" in order to make them aware of how they might co-operate with local health departments to improve standards of health in a community. Rather than getting only a theoretical classroom examination of preventive medicine, an aspiring practitioner was exposed to the realities of sickness in the lives of individual human beings. Reporting on his activities in the Health Unit during the summer of 1948, one student described how he learned first-hand of the impact of tuberculosis on individuals and "the limitations of a purely epidemiological approach" that failed to identify all victims of the disease. A survey of houses without plumbing and sewage facilities, and tours with sanitary inspectors, brought home the influence of the social and economic problems on the health of a community. The work of the public health nurses, child health centres and immunization clinics "likewise showed how sociology may help us to see medical practice in a new light and more fully exploit its possibilities as an instrument of social welfare." Never as widespread as some might have wanted, the summer internship projects nonetheless illuminated the willingness of the members of the Department of Hygiene and Preventive Medicine to explore ways in which medical education might make students more sensitive to the social realities in which they would be treating human beings.[73]

Another example of the department's experimentation in teaching social medicine was its joint undertaking with the Department of Medicine in the Faculty in 1953 to bring medical undergraduates into contact with the realities of health care through a program of visitation to the homes of patients from the Out-Patient Department and public wards of the Toronto General Hospital. Thirteen students in third year volunteered to participate in the elective course.[74] The scheme received the financial support of the Rockefeller Foundation. It involved also a member of the Social Service Department of the Hospital.[75]

Despite all of these changes in the curriculum, the serious problem of teaching preventive medicine to medical undergraduates persisted.[76] Some students objected to the study of old-fashioned ideas that stressed the role of water and sewage systems as well as other sanitary procedures.[77] Yet the efforts to improve the course in Toronto were impressive. After studying other medical schools in North America, the Dean of the Faculty of Medicine in British Columbia, Dr. C.E. Dolman, reported, "I found no place in the United States where Schools of Hygiene or of Public Health were attempting more in undergraduate education than is being done in Toronto."[78]

Research by the staff of Hygiene and Preventive Medicine centred on applied immunology. Dr. D.T. Fraser directed the projects. All of his work utilized the facilities of the Connaught Laboratories. For example, Dr. M.H. Brown, an assistant director of the

Laboratories, studied the production of B.C.G. vaccine for tuberculosis.[79] Dr. Frieda Fraser investigated antibiotics. Dr. F.O. Wishart continued his work on "recall doses" of diphtheria and tetanus toxoid. Dr. R.J. Wilson examined the growth requirements of *H. pertussis.*

Graduate students in the department completed a number of dissertations in the field of microbiology.[80] Some of them made use of the electron microscope in their research. For instance, Miss Sheila Toshach completed a thesis on the *C. diphtheriae* phages that contained one of the first electron micrographs of these agents.[81] Hygiene and Preventive Medicine had the third largest number of graduate students of the various departments and sub-departments in the School.

Much of the orientation of the research and teaching of the faculty within Hygiene and Preventive Medicine can be understood by their positions in the School of Hygiene after 1955. Three of the senior ranks, "Frieda H. Fraser, F.O. Wishart, and Helen C. Plummer", as the Calendar of the School reported, moved into the Department of Microbiology in 1956; Fraser and Wishart as professors and Plummer as an associate. Brown and Wilson ended up in the Department of Public Health; Brown as the head and Wilson as associate professor.[82] Brown had succeeded Dr. D.T. Fraser as the head of the Department of Hygiene and Preventive Medicine when Fraser died in July, 1954, on an official visit to Santiago, Chile.[83]

EPIDEMIOLOGY AND BIOMETRICS

Each of the departments in the School of Hygiene by the 1950s reflected very much the character and academic interests of the individual who was the head. There was no better illustration of that fact than Neil McKinnon who began lecturing in the Department of Epidemiology in 1928. Long associated with the Farm Division of the Connaught Laboratories where he was resident supervisor in the 1930s, McKinnon, on his return from military service in 1944, was appointed the head of Epidemiology, a post previously occupied by Defries.[84]

In McKinnon's graduation yearbook, a very appropriate quotation in terms of his future vocation appeared below his photograph: "I am earnest; I will not equivocate; I will not excuse; I will not retreat a single inch and I will be heard."[85] He certainly was heard. A man with strongly expressed views, McKinnon had an impact on his students and colleagues. He was viewed as an iconoclast. McKinnon challenged prevailing assumptions. His frankness and sharply critical approach was his attempt to force individuals to think on their own.

Neil McKinnon's writings projected his colourful personality. In a series of articles examining the reduction in mortality in Ontario from 1900 to 1942, he questioned the apparent explanation for the increasing control of infectious disease. At the beginning, McKinnon stated clearly his perspective:

> Muddling along, as we are, it is common practice to re-orient ourselves periodically in relation to the past, measure our progress, if any, and re-examine our objectives. The term "muddling" is not used in a derogatory sense or with intent of criticism of the present or the past; nor does it imply that the existing public health structure is faulty and should be wrecked and re-built. It is but a term somewhat descriptive of conditions that have existed or exist because they were or are inescapable for a time, being inherent in the scheme of things. Official public health departments as we know them today are of very recent development in the scheme. They did not begin at the beginning, but, as they came

Dr. Neil McKinnon
1894-1985

into being, one after another, they assumed responsibilities for functions which, in some form, had been carried on for decades and centuries and ages by the family, the community, the tribe, and the sect, by charity, organized or unorganized, by other governmental departments of earlier development, other agencies, etc. Had our public health departments existed at the beginning and been responsible for the scheme of things, they might have had no disease and no untimely death in the plan. Had they been of early development when populations were small and life of a more simple order, if life ever really were of a more simple order, they might have functioned in a different way and have encompassed in their field all the health and all the disability and all the conditions which influence health favourably and unfavourably. But they came late and inherited from the past not only diversified functions and responsibilities but traditional restrictions and limitations and, too, practices dictated by expediency and compromise, all as part of our common human lot. They inherited, as well, a vast amount of disease and untimely death. They did not inherit any superhuman capacity to alter the scheme of things or any special privilege to act as agents freed from the bonds of human relationships and considerations. From their late beginning, official public health agencies have broadened, attacking major problems as they became manifest, as necessity required, as sometimes acting on sound professional advice and sometimes harassed by that malign influence, the misguided propagandist, promoter and publicist

> motivated by commercial, political or personal considerations or even by ill-founded enthusiasm based on bias and misconceptions.[86]

McKinnon acknowledged a sizeable reduction in mortality for all age groups in the era from 1900 to 1942; a two-thirds drop in deaths for the age group under 30 years, one-half for those between 30 and 39 years and a one-third decline in the 40 to 49 year age group. However, McKinnon wondered whether "muddling along. . . has something to its credit—or does the credit rightly belong to the scheme of things?"[87]

In reviewing the statistics, McKinnon argued that there was a "persistent maintenance" of the high rates of the incidence of disease up to 1936 in Ontario and that "neither medicine nor public health had achieved any reduction in this mortality over the years." The sharp fall of deaths in all age groups, McKinnon suggested, was "due to chemotherapy and later to antibiotics." On closer examination, McKinnon was not dismissing entirely the value of public health services and medical treatment as much as he was pointing out the other reasons such as "better community, shop and home sanitation" for the drop in deaths. For example, in analyzing the fall in the mortality of Ontarians from tuberculosis, McKinnon stated that the "value of treatment in improving the outcome of the individual case may be accepted but this is quite different . . . from accepting extension of treatment, in quantity or quality, as the explanation of the marked decline."[88] McKinnon was looking at the wider social context of disease. In the case of deaths of children from measles, whooping cough and respiratory ailments, McKinnon showed how the incidence of those diseases remained the same while the fatalities from them had fallen significantly. His hypothesis attributed the decline in mortality "in part, to an absolute and proportionate reduction in physically substandard children—children debilitated by neglect, by chronic or complicating disease, or by other causes. It is not suggested that this is the complete explanation; as in other mortality declines, e.g. scarlet fever and tuberculosis, much remains obscure."[89]

Neil McKinnon continued his provocative approach in studying cancer mortality in different Canadian provinces and other countries with and without control programs. As expected, his findings, as he described them, excited "vigorous emotionally-based opposition from some clinicians."[90] Breast cancer and all other cancer mortality from 1921 to 1947, he concluded, remained the same in all provinces regardless of the existence of special treatment facilities.[91] McKinnon extended his comparison of Ontario's mortality rates from cancer with those in England and Wales, and Massachusetts; there were no differences in cancer deaths in any of the jurisdictions. For McKinnon, this fact proved the folly of "heavy expenditures that have been made with the objective of 'controlling' cancer except in so far as the failure to achieve effectual 'control' broadens our understanding of cancer and demonstrates that 'getting cancer early' does not effectually 'control' mortality. The ability to cure locally malignant lesions is not to be misinterpreted as an indication of equal ability to cure metastasizing cancer."[92] Explicit in all of these studies was McKinnon's determination to place medicine and public health on a factual and scientific basis.[93]

McKinnon's trenchant views permeated the teaching of the Department of Epidemiology and Biometrics. He described his philosophy of instruction thus:

> An attempt is made to learn something of disease that mars or shortens man's life. This attempt is made by critically studying the past and current experience rather than by

> reciting the dicta of hope, belief, propaganda, authority or expediency. The emphasis in the study is the study itself, the seeking for facts and understanding rather than the finding of it, greatly at variance with preconception though the findings often prove to be. It is hoped that the candidates will have learned to discriminate between the true and the false in such material. It is held of the utmost importance that the student should learn something of how to find, identify and study, in his own setting, the problems that will confront him in his daily work, whether he is engaged in public health itself or in any other field of medicine. Further, it is considered most important that he will so study his problems personally before he launches into otherwise ill-founded attempts for their treatment, correction or control. It is hoped, too, that the student will emerge with reasonable confidence that he can thus meet his problems intelligently, professionally, honestly and efficiently, and that he will thereby contribute to the advancement of both medicine and public health, and even with pleasure to himself.[94]

In contrast to the drab statistics which were the basis of his investigations, Neil McKinnon enlivened the subject of epidemiology with a passion for truth.

Graduate work in Epidemiology and Biometrics was not a priority. From the 1920s to the middle of the 1950s, there were only two Ph.D. and a similar number of M.A. candidates who were in most cases members of the staff. McKinnon made no apology for this record:

> It is true, too, that I have regularly discouraged such candidates because, once students have grasped certain fundamentals, as provided for in the D.P.H. course, they can do much more productive work in the field, in a provincial division of Epidemiology or Vital Statistics, or in Medicine itself, than by staying here. They can there effectively train themselves *by doing* — the ideal way; in so doing they can add not only to the scanty store of knowledge but also to the development of investigation which should be a very large part of public health and medical work. The situation is somewhat comparable to that in Medicine where the great mass of graduate training is not under the School of Graduate Studies.[95]

Obviously, McKinnon had little interest in expanding theoretical studies.

Yet there was a member of the department who attracted large numbers of graduate students from other departments. His name was David B.W. Reid, always known as Bill Reid. A native of Winnipeg and a graduate of McGill University in psychology who did graduate work there and later at Columbia University in New York City, Reid was a statistician during the war years for the National Research Council in Ottawa. Afterwards, he went to study statistics at the Virginia Polytechnical Institute. Appointed to the School in the spring of 1946, Reid received part of his salary from the Connaught Medical Research Laboratories.[96] His reputation as a good instructor in statistical methods attracted fourteen Ph.D., seven M.A. and six other students to his course in the session of 1951 to 1952. Reid was teaching also in the Department of Mathematics.[97] Even McKinnon boasted in 1956 that because of Reid's popularity among graduate students, Epidemiology and Biometrics "has given instruction to more students in the School of Graduate Studies than, I would think, has any other department in the University."[98] Along with others in the department, Reid provided assistance on statistical methods for many research projects in the Connaught Medical Research Laboratories.[99]

Dr. Donald R.E. MacLeod, originally an associate in Epidemiology and Biometrics, contributed significantly to the research in the Laboratories. Born in Formosa, MacLeod graduated from the Faculty of Medicine of the University of Toronto in 1938. He continued his studies, earned a B.Sc.(Med.) in his alma mater and then worked in the field of bacteriology in the Banting Institute. Enlisting in the military, MacLeod served overseas as a bacteriologist. After graduating with a D.P.H. from the School of Hygiene in 1946, he joined the School and the Connaught Medical Research Laboratories.[100] In the 1950s, MacLeod participated in the research on the various strains of polio viruses in the Canadian Arctic and Toronto's sewage as well as directing the production and testing of Salk poliomyelitis vaccine in 1954.[101]

By the middle of the 1950s, the staff of the Department of Epidemiology and Biometrics consisted of eight people: N.E. McKinnon (head), D.L. MacLean (the secretary of the School and a professor of public health), D.R.E. MacLeod (assistant professor), D.B.W. Reid (assistant professor in biometrics), Mrs. M.R. Richardson (fellow in epidemiology), Miss S. McCausland (technician), Mrs. R.E. Haddon (laboratory assistant) and Miss D.L. Muller (secretary).[102]

PHYSIOLOGICAL HYGIENE

Largely as a result of its vital role in assisting the armed services and wartime industries, the Department of Physiological Hygiene was the largest department in the School of Hygiene in the years following the Second World War. The Calendar for 1945-1946 shows twenty-two members including nine research fellows. The teaching faculty offered eleven different types of courses ranging from elementary to advanced instruction in human physiology, physiological hygiene and industrial hygiene to medical, nursing, physical education, and engineering students as well as postgraduates enrolled in the Diploma in Public Health and the very specialized Diploma in Industrial Hygiene.[103] Closely tied to the Faculty of Medicine's Department of Physiology and the Banting and Best Department of Medical Research, the staff members of Physiological Hygiene were in fact part of a much larger research enterprise within the University of Toronto.

As noted elsewhere, the departure of Dr. Charles Best to direct the Banting and Best Department of Medical Research following Banting's death in 1941, as well as the leave of absence for war duties given Dr. Donald MacLean, had left the leadership of the department in limbo. In the interim, Dr. Donald Solandt was chosen acting head.[104] An associate of Best, Dr. D. Solandt was an internationally respected scientist who did significant wartime research for the Royal Canadian Navy. MacLean's decision to accept an appointment as professor of public health was probably based on his experience in the Canadian Army. MacLean's change in specialization prompted Defries to confirm Dr. D. Solandt in 1946 in the position of head of the Department of Physiological Hygiene.[105]

Under Solandt's general direction, a number of research projects were undertaken. A variety of organizations, both public and private from Canada and the United States, supported these investigations: the National Research Council of Canada, the Division of Industrial Hygiene of the Ontario Department of Health, the City of Toronto, the Connaught Medical Research Laboratories, the Rockefeller Foundation, the National Foundation for Infantile Paralysis of New York Incorporated, the Abrasive Grains Association and the Illuminating Engineering Society for New York City. Solandt's work for agencies outside the university created public support for the School's interest in the influence of environment on health. He was a consultant on lighting to the World Health Organization, the American Public Health Association and the Illuminating Engineering Society of New York. He was an advisor to the Canadian and American Governments on the ecology of the Arctic. As a representative of the School of Hygiene on the Committee for Atmospheric Pollution in Canada, he helped to draw up plans to control pollution in Canadian cities. Solandt's expertise made him a frequent speaker at conferences studying vision, arthritis (Solandt did research on nerve-muscle physiology) and human ecology. No wonder Physiological Hygiene had so much success in attracting funds.[106] A report in 1949 called the research in the department the "most important" in the School, "unmatched in terms of its comprehensiveness and fundamental approach."[107]

CUNNINGHAM AND THE DIPLOMA IN INDUSTRIAL HYGIENE

All of the courses in industrial hygiene benefited from the continuing participation of Dr. J. Grant Cunningham. Using his role as Director of the Division of Industrial Hygiene in the Ontario Department of Health, Cunningham involved a number of officials in the instruction, especially Dr. F.M.R. Bulmer and Dr. R.B. Sutherland who helped in giving the course to D.P.H. candidates.[108]

The Diploma in Industrial Hygiene (D.I.H.) was a very specialized program, and from 1945 to 1955, only seven individuals graduated with the D.I.H.[109] Dr. Peter Vaughan was one of the graduates. A graduate of the McGill Medical Faculty, he finished his D.P.H. in the School of Hygiene in 1946 and then completed the D.I.H. in 1947. Vaughan, who had a pilot's license, retired in 1981 after serving 16 years as the chief medical officer of Air Canada and the Canadian National Railways. In 1969, he was the fifth Canadian to be elected a member of the International Academy of Aviation and Space Medicine.[110]

ENVIRONMENTAL HEALTH

The undergraduate and graduate courses stressed the development of an understanding of the field of human ecology long before that approach became popular. This emphasis, a report to the Rockefeller Foundation stated, was "an extension of the basic teaching programme initiated under the leadership of Professor C.H. Best, founder of the department."[111] High praise for these courses came also from Dr. C-E.A. Winslow in his accreditation report for the American Public Health Association in 1947. In comparison with all the other Schools in North America, Winslow singled out Toronto's instruction in physiological hygiene and industrial hygiene for "a balance between basic research . . . and vital contact with practical field problems" as well as the thorough coverage of the physiology of respiration, illumination, sound, radiant effects and the evaluation of sensory performance under differing environmental conditions.[112]

RESEARCH

In the early 1950s, researchers in the Department of Physiological Hygiene investigated the impact of a wide spectrum of environmental factors on human beings. "These include studies", Defries declared in his annual report,

> on the effects of noise on personnel in industry; the visual importance of the various spectral components of white light; the visual importance of the dimensions of spatial orientation of light sources; the role of lighting in the development of ocular defects in school children; the effect of long-term and short-term exposures to alumina fume on the pulmonary mechanism, and on existing and concomitantly induced silicosis in experimental animals; the sources, identity, concentration and physiological effects of atmospheric pollutants in the urban atmospheric environment, with special attention to the olfacient pollutants; the mechanism of specific and localized motor nerve inactivity induced in experimental animals by systematic lead intoxicant, and the relation of this phenomenon to the typical palsy of plumbism in man; and studies of the effects of analogous chemical intoxicants in human subjects.[113]

These research projects demonstrated how the staff employed physiological, biophysical, medical, public health and engineering sciences to examine the environment and occupational hazards threatening human health.

One of the fascinating results of the various studies was the design and construction of special technical equipment to collect data. Joseph Slovik, a machinist, assisted by other technicians under the supervision of the chief technician, John Horwood, a long-time member of the department's technical staff, developed several pieces of equipment. During the session 1950 to 1951, they built a vision tester for certain health units.[114] The following year, Horwood and Slovik assembled an "electrostatic precipitator to eliminate fume particles from the atmosphere introduced into the control chambers used in the study of aluminum oxide fume effects on experimental animals." Special photographic apparatus was devised to record histological details in this experiment.[115] John E. Goodwin, a professor in the department, and John B. Gallager, a research associate, constructed a special electronic device to collect details on noise and its relation to fatigue and deafness.

Perhaps the most intriguing mechanism was the olfactometer, an apparatus utilized to study odours:

> This equipment is designed to direct either a stream of odourless humidified air into the nose of the subject or to direct a controlled quantity of an odour to the subject's nose. The change from odour to odourless material can be made without the subject's knowledge and changes can also be made in the interval of time during which odour is supplied. By this method it has been possible to study the detection of odour with a number of subjects. It appears that duration of odour and concentration of odour are interchangeable variables. It also seems that ability to detect odour decreases with increasing age. If accumulated data establish the method as reasonably satisfactory, it is planned to extend the studies to surveys of odour in urban areas.[116]

The facts collected by this and other devices were evidence for the growing concern with pollutants in the urban environment during the 1950s.

ATMOSPHERIC POLLUTION

Like so many other problems in Canadian public health, pioneering work on atmospheric pollution originated in the School of Hygiene back in the 1930s. Hugh M. Barrett, an associate in the Department of Physiological Hygiene in the 1930s, conducted the first study of pollution in Toronto between late 1932 and 1936.[117] (Barrett went on leave of absence to do

Olfactometer

war-related research in the early 1940s and then resigned in 1946 to remain with the Department of National Defence as superintendent of research at its experimental station in Suffield, Alberta.)[118] At that time, there was an increasing suspicion that smoke had an adverse effect on the health of urban dwellers. The Toronto study was modelled on investigations in Pittsburgh from 1911 to 1914, British cities and other American centres as well as European and Japanese urban areas. To measure pollution in Toronto, the researchers used "funnel-shaped gauges of enamelled iron" with a "catchment area" of four square feet that collected solids in a twenty-litre bottle beneath the gauge in locations across the city. The four sites were near large slaughter houses and stockyards at Keele and St. Clair Avenue; in the downtown business core surrounding the neighbourhood of Union Station close to the intersection at King Street and University Avenue; the School of Hygiene Building surrounded by a residential neighbourhood at College Street and University Avenue; and on the property of the Connaught Laboratories Farm six miles north of Eglinton Avenue. Not surprisingly, the data showed pollution to be the greatest in the downtown business core at King Street and University Avenue. "The amount of pollution settling in Toronto", Barrett concluded from the data, "is as great as has been found in badly-polluted areas of Great

Britain." With some variations during seasons of the year, the impurity in Toronto's air was similar to five American cities; "Total solids deposited at the three locations within the city averaged 341, 358 and 610 tons per square mile annually, compared with an annual deposit of 133 tons found at the gauge located outside the city." The outstanding conclusion of Barrett's research was that "the greater part of Toronto's pollution is of non-industrial origin."[119] Shortly after the publication of this study, the more immediate wartime considerations pushed any interest about urban pollution into the background.

By the 1950s, the renewed concern about increasing pollution resulted in a major study by the Department of Physiological Hygiene financed by a grant of $7,100.00 from the City of Toronto.[120] An Air Pollution Board chaired by Professor E.A. Allcut set up a system of eighteen stations to monitor dustfall, two stations to measure suspended particulate material in the air and one station to record sulphur dioxide concentrations.[121] "By comparison with previous records, referring to Barrett's study in the 1930s, the data proved that "Toronto cannot claim any vast improvement over the last twenty years in contrast to the improved situation in some other large cities on this continent."[122]

The Department of Physiological Hygiene's research on air pollution illuminated the potential controversy in all scientific research which had obvious economic, social and political implications. The faculty and administration of the School were conscious of the fact that scientific information formed only part of the development of a public policy. In his 1954 report, Defries addressed directly the quandary facing scientists and citizens:

> The population of large cities is becoming increasingly conscious of the pollution of the atmosphere by smoke, dust and gases arising from industrial activities. With the development of industry in Canada, it is obvious that the control of atmospheric pollution will become of greater importance. It is obvious also that limitations placed upon industry must be enacted with a full appreciation of the problems which industry must face in controlling atmospheric pollution. As citizens, we desire unpolluted, clean air; but as members of a society dependent upon industrial activity, there is of course, some minimum condition which we must accept as reasonable.[123]

This modern conundrum about what was an acceptable risk was to become an increasing focus of the debate on environmental and occupational health issues confronting members of the School in the succeeding decades.

ALBERT FISHER

The death of Donald Solandt at the end of March, 1955 after a lengthy illness raised concerns about the future of the Department of Physiological Hygiene. Luckily, Dr. Albert M. Fisher, a long-time member of the Connaught Laboratories was available to take over as acting head during Solandt's long sickness.

Fisher's career illustrated the interplay between the Connaught Laboratories and the School of Hygiene. Although he began work in the School of Hygiene Building in the early 1930s, Fisher was not associated formally with the School until 1945.[124] With a B.A. in chemistry from the University of Toronto in 1931, Fisher completed a M.A. thesis in his alma mater in 1932. That same year, he joined the Connaught Laboratories to work with the chemist in charge of insulin, Dr. D.A. Scott. Fisher, with another researcher Dr. Arthur F.

Charles, formulated a new international insulin standard, the first insulin standard in crystalline form. In 1934, Fisher received his Ph.D. from the University of Toronto; the topics of his thesis were "I. An attempt at peptic synthesis of insulin. II. Peptic hydrolysis of insulin. III. The insulin content of the pancreas of cattle of various ages. IV. The absorption of insulin on charcoal. V. Blood coagulant from beef lung. VI. The preparation of some unsymmetrical acid anhydrides and their behaviour with benzene and aluminum chloride." The following year, Scott and Fisher investigated the importance of zinc, nickel, cobalt and cadmium in the crystallization of insulin and the role of zinc when added to protamine and insulin in the prolongation of hypoglycaemia. Their research helped to improve Protamine Insulin introduced by a Danish Scientist, Dr. H.C. Hagedorn and led to the distribution in 1936 of Protamine Zinc Insulin by the Connaught Laboratories. Scott and Fisher were also responsible for the development of crystalline insulin which replaced amorphous insulin by 1940.[125] Defries praised Fisher for his work on insulin: "As a colleague of Dr. D.A. Scott he made a highly important contribution to the development of Insulin and the patents which are now in effect are the patents relating to the work of Scott and Fisher."[126] During the Second World War, Fisher directed the preparation of dried human blood serum in the School of Hygiene Building. In 1948, Fisher was promoted as an administrative and research associate of the Laboratories. He managed the expansion of exports of products, especially penicillin and insulin to European and South American countries. Fisher was appointed in 1950 an assistant director of the Connaught Medical Research Laboratories. That same year, he assumed an expanding role in the School of Hygiene.[127]

After serving as a lecturer in the 1945 to 1946 session and then as associate in the Department of Chemistry in Relation to Hygiene in the 1946 to 1947 session, Fisher was promoted to associate professor in the Department of Physiological Hygiene.[128] Three years later, he took over as acting head when D.Y. Solandt became ill. After Solandt's death, Defries recommended Fisher's appointment to the headship of Physiological Hygiene in a letter to President Sidney Smith. He pointed out how Fisher had turned down a more attractive offer as an example of his "fundamental desire . . . to contribute to the advancement of public health in Canada."[129] This was not to be the only time Fisher helped the department and the School through a difficult period. Over fifteen years later, he assumed again the acting headship.[130]

CHEMISTRY IN RELATION TO HYGIENE AND SANITATION

In the reorganization of the School of Hygiene after the Second World War, Chemistry in Relation to Hygiene achieved full departmental status.[131] Moloney, Taylor and Fisher worked primarily in the Connaught Laboratories.[132] Professor Moloney, an internationally respected scientist in immunochemistry, contributed significantly to the development and testing of a variety of vaccines, toxoids and other products, most notably insulin and diphtheria toxoid.[133]

The 1947 evaluation of the School of Hygiene by C-E. Winslow praised Moloney's "unique contribution":

> Only at Harvard is any serious instruction in sanitary chemistry offered to the M.P.H. candidates and there the application is directly to problems of sanitary engineering, and

> the course taken only by a few students. The presence of a 66 hour required course at Toronto is no doubt due to the traditional interest in this field in England. The spirit and content of the course, is, however, by no means traditional. It does not deal with the chemical tests as tools but with chemical processes involved in milk analysis and water analysis, the control of chlorination, the tests for fluorides and the like as examples of a theoretical approach and as materials for developing habits of critical analysis and evaluation of results.[134]

Although the department's name may have appeared to be an anachronism, Peter Moloney displayed a determination to make the courses relevant and responsive to the needs of Canadian society in the postwar expansion.

There were two courses given to students in diploma programs, the Certificate in Public Health and the M.A.Sc. in sanitary engineering. An elementary course of thirty-three hours focussed on "the problems of water and milk and with certain aspects of sanitation." An advanced course of sixty hours included lectures and laboratory exercises, and stressed the principles and methods of public health chemistry.[135]

By the fall of 1950, Moloney's department included two new members. In the previous year, Kenneth H. Geiger became a senior research fellow. He was an engineer with a M.A.Sc. in chemical engineering from the University of Toronto who had worked on the production of penicillin.[136]

Dr. Anthony Tosoni was appointed an associate in 1950. A student of Moloney, Tosoni, with a Ph.D. in biochemistry, did pioneering research on a method to crystallize penicillin.[137] In the war years, Tosoni had worked on the production of gas gangrene antitoxin and the extraction of insulin. He and Moloney had developed two new penicillins, "the ethyl tyrosine and isoamyl esters, both capable of producing effective prolonged levels of penicillin in the blood."[138]

In February, 1951, the decision was made to change the name of the department to Chemistry in Relation to Hygiene and Sanitation. Defries explained the reasons for this move in a letter to President Sidney Smith:

> Dr. A.E. Berry has for years been responsible for the instruction in sanitation including engineering. As there is no Department of Sanitation in the School, Dr. Berry was attached to the Department of Public Health Administration. (A student in looking through our calendar for the subject of sanitation would not find it presented in a department as is customary in schools of hygiene but would locate it in the Department of Public Health Administration.) In order to give greater prominence to the subject of sanitation particularly for students who wish to proceed to the Certificate in Public Health in the field of sanitation, I would recommend that the teaching of sanitation be transferred to the Department of Chemistry in Relation to Hygiene and that the title of the Department be the Department of Chemistry in Relation to Hygiene and Sanitation.
>
> This recommendation is the first step in providing for more adequate instruction in sanitation and the relating of this to the work given in sanitary chemistry by Dr. Moloney. This year we have three students proceeding to the Certificate in Public Health specializing in sanitation. Two are graduates of the Ontario Agricultural College and one from the University of British Columbia in science. Although the number of students may be small, yet an important contribution will be made to the public health teaching in Canada by making better provision for instruction in sanitation in the School . . .[139]

The postwar explosion of industrial plants discharging dangerous wastes and suburban housing with inadequate sewage systems re-focussed concerns about the importance of sanitation and sewers to a healthy environment.

One illustration of how research in Chemistry in Relation to Hygiene and Sanitation addressed the pollution problems of the 1950s was the work of Dr. Edith Taylor. She studied the impact levels of nitrates on well water in order to identify the contamination arising from the increased use of septic tanks in the mushrooming suburbs of Toronto.[140] Alarm about the deterioration of the quality of water in Ontario because of inadequate water and sewage treatment resulted in the banning of septic tank systems in new housing developments and the formation of the Ontario Water Resources Commission in 1957.[141] This decision was largely due to the efforts of the associate professor of sanitation (part-time), Dr. Albert E. Berry.

ONTARIO'S MR. WATER

Albert Berry, the Director of the Division of Sanitary Engineering in the Ontario Department of Health, was for years a part-time instructor in the school before his transfer to the Department of Chemistry in Relation to Hygiene and Sanitation with its renaming. At the same time, D.S. Caverly, a part-time instructor in sanitation, was appointed also to the renamed department.[142] Berry taught numerous health officers and sanitary engineers who were to witness the development of modern water and sewage treatment systems in Ontario and elsewhere in Canada. From 1940 to 1955, Berry, in co-operation with the Faculty of Engineering, supervised the graduate education of seventy engineers who earned the degree of Master of Applied Science.[143]

By the late 1950s, Albert Berry led a campaign to focus public and political concern on the long-neglected issue of water pollution. Inaction during the 1930s led to a further deterioration of sewage and water treatment plants. Then the war, combined with the postwar boom in suburban housing and the growth of industries, produced enormous amounts of untreated human effluents and industrial wastes. These discharges posed a serious public health threat. In October, 1953, Berry appeared before the Dominion Council of Health in Ottawa to highlight the urgency of the situation which raised provincial, national and international questions of responsibility. Of the over 1,500 water works systems in Canada, only 770 municipalities maintained sewer systems; and only 365 jurisdictions provided more than just primary treatment of effluents. According to Berry, there were four categories which required attention:

1. The discharge of raw or improperly treated sewage into waterways;
2. The dumping of wastes into creeks and streams;
3. The unwillingness of municipalities to finance the construction of treatment facilities;
4. The increasing problem of the disposal of industrial wastes.

In proposing to control water pollution, Berry called for "increased education" of ratepayers in the value of sewage treatment plants, the provision of financing from provincial and federal governments to municipalities for the construction of sewage systems, the development of "some better method of financing" for these projects and the possibility of a provincial agency to supervise the operation of existing sewage treatment facilities.[144] As a result of Berry's efforts, the Ontario Water Resources Commission came into being in 1957.[145] Berry's lengthy involvement with the School of Hygiene dating back to the 1920s demonstrated how yet another member of the School's faculty not only taught but also made major contributions to the improvement of public health and the environment. No wonder Berry earned the title of "Ontario's Mr. Water."[146]

DEFRIES AND PUBLIC HEALTH ADMINISTRATION

One department, Public Health Administration, reflected the lengthy experience and ideas of R.D. Defries. He was a pioneer in the establishment of the Canadian health and welfare system. Long before the term was fashionable, Defries was a "health care planner." The Canadian Journal of Public Health, which Defries and a handful of others saved from extinction in the late 1920s and the depression of the 1930s and kept alive in the war years, was a primary medium for the promoting and planning of Canadian health services. "Over the years the Journal . . . constitutes", Defries stated in 1945, "a record . . . of the movement that led to the creation of a national department of health in Canada, the development of the movement for social welfare, and the foundations on which have been built the modern programs in venereal disease control, industrial hygiene, mental hygiene, public health nursing, and public health engineering."[147] In fact, Defries, through the Canadian Public Health Association housed in the School of Hygiene Building in the 1940s and 1950s, was a persuasive lobbyist for national and provincial health policies.

The extent of Defries' influence was evident in his role as the scientific advisor to the Dominion Council of Health. At the fifty-fourth meeting of the Council held in Ottawa from June 7 to 8, 1948, which was devoted to the implementation of the National Health Program that Defries had promoted, all but four of the thirteen members of the D.C.H. were graduates of the School of Hygiene's Diploma in Public Health course.[148] The large number of federal, provincial and municipal health officials who were part-time faculty members of the School, documented the close working relationship with health departments. The Department of Public Health Administration mirrored the state of Ontario's system of Medical Officers of Health. Almost all of the faculty within the Department of Public Health Administration had major responsibilities in other departments of the School or the Connaught Medical Research Laboratories. Many of the teaching staff were employed by the Ontario Department of Health, municipal health departments and the Department of National Health and Welfare. The Calendar for 1953-1955 listed thirteen special lecturers: Doctors G.C. Brink, W.G. Brown, A.R.J. Boyd, D.V. Currey, G.A. Edge, L.E. Elkerton, F.W. Jackson, G.W.O. Moss, L.A. Pequenat, J.T. Phair, D.S. Puffer, C.E.A. Robinson and A.H. Sellers.[149] In addition, a number of visiting lecturers with a specific background had provided lectures on certain topics.[150] For instance, Professor M.G. Taylor of the Department of Political Economy provided lectures on health insurance.

Of great significance was the part played by John T. Phair, the Deputy Minister of Health and Hospitals in Ontario. A part-time instructor in the School of Hygiene beginning in the 1930s, Phair worked with Defries in the 1940s and 1950s as a strong advocate of modernization of health services. Dr. Phair included the School in his plans for modern health services. Phair was an example of a civil servant who used political pressure shrewdly to advance the interests of better health care for the general population.[151]

THE DIPLOMA IN VETERINARY PUBLIC HEALTH

The role of various specialists in the public health system demanded that the School of Hygiene provide courses tailored to the requirements of different professionals. The Diploma in Veterinary Public Health (D.V.P.H.) was this type of program. Most of its students were graduates in veterinary medicine from the Ontario Veterinary College, then a part of the University of Toronto, but now a part of the University of Guelph. Dr. V.C.R. Walker directed the D.V.P.H. The courses were given by the faculty of the School of Hygiene, the Faculty of Medicine, the Faculty of Arts, the School of Social Work and the Ontario Veterinary College. The subjects in the curriculum were bacteriology, immunology, virus infections, parasitology including entomology and helminthology, epidemiology, physiological and industrial hygiene, nutrition, public health chemistry, public health administration and an emphasis on food control, sanitation, public health education and social science.[152] By 1955, there were sixty-three graduates with the D.V.P.H. from the School of Hygiene.[153]

HEALTH EDUCATORS

The development of a course of instruction for health educators within the Department of Public Health Administration was a further indication of the growing specialization of the School's involvement in modern health services. In 1950, Dr. C.E.A. Robinson became an associate in charge of teaching of health education. Miss M. Cahoon was hired also as a fellow to assist Robinson.[154] Students wishing to become health educators required an undergraduate degree and completed a variety of courses in a one-year program.[155]

Within the department, there was also a course of forty hours for D.P.H. candidates.[156] It covered the principles and methods in health teaching, public speaking, the use of radio, newspapers, magazines, slides, films, and graphic arts[157] in the promotion of official and voluntary health work. There were, in addition, practical exercises in running health education campaigns in the East York-Leaside Health Unit.[158]

EAST YORK-LEASIDE HEALTH UNIT

Originally handicapped by the departure of its leading personnel for war services, the East York Health Unit became fully operational after 1945. In early 1947, the Town of Leaside joined to form a more effective local jurisdiction:

> The new consolidated health unit has provided a large industrial area, and a substantial upper-middle class residential area, in addition to increasing the unit's population to a total of 60,000 to 65,000 inhabitants. Furthermore, the formation of the enlarged unit area qualified the municipalities to participate in Provincial Grants-in-Aid towards support of full-time health services in Ontario.[159]

Students from both the Schools of Hygiene and Nursing received practical experience, working in the Unit for a month or more. The budget of over $72,000 in 1947 was drawn mostly from the municipalities of East York and Leaside but also the Province of Ontario, and the School of Hygiene with a contribution from the Ontario Department of Health and the International Health Division of the Rockefeller Foundation. The staff of the Unit consisted

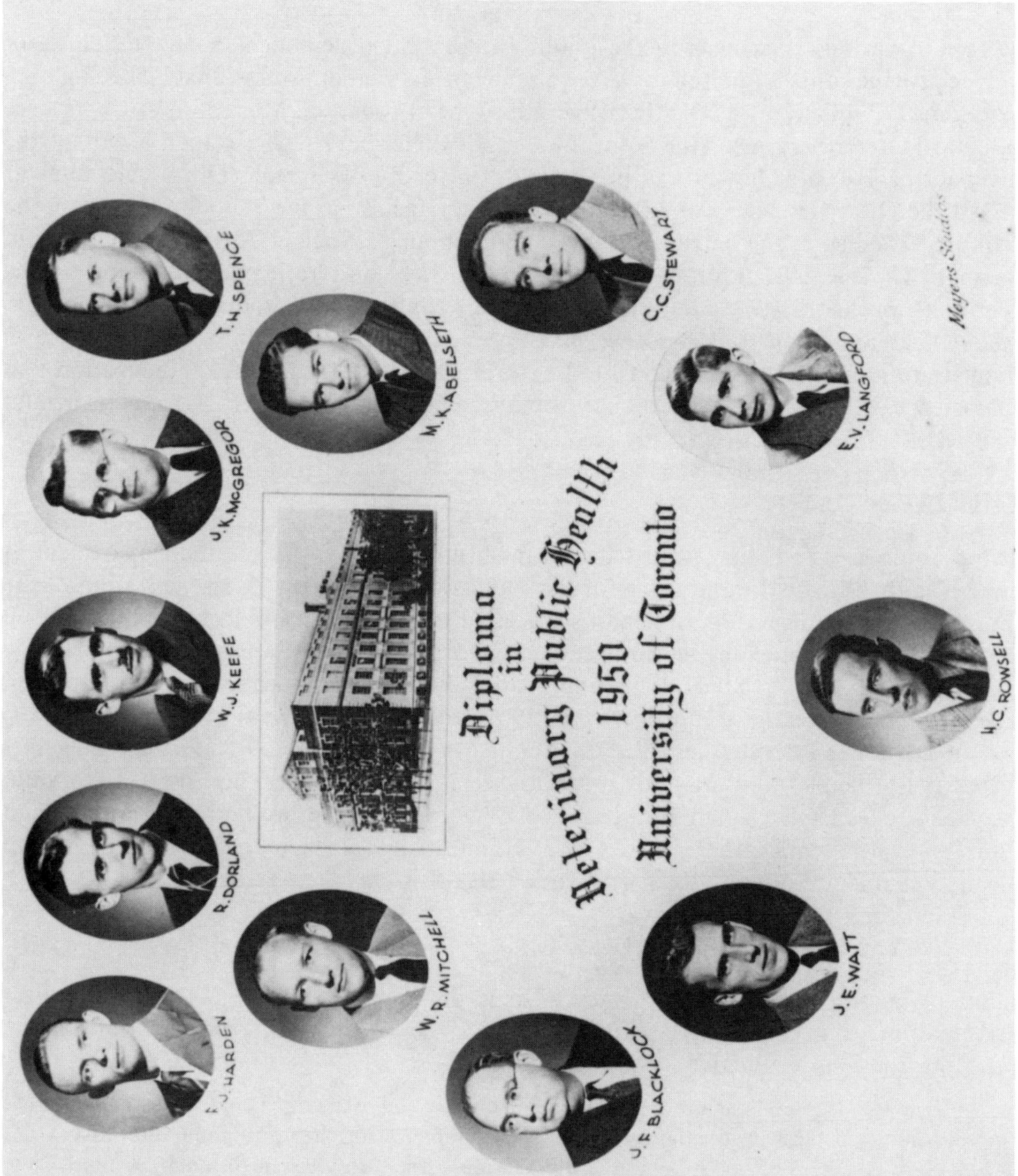

Veterinarians who graduated from the School.

of a health officer, an assistant health officer, a supervisor of public health nurses, 8 nurses, 2 sanitary inspectors and 3 secretaries. The Unit operated two dental clinics, several child care centres, immunization clinics and school health services. Special investigations, which were one of the principal reasons for establishing the Unit, included a study of the nutritional and physical character of 500 pupils as well as the lighting in their classrooms and a survey of the mental hygiene of 300 pupils in their schools and homes.[160] The Unit provided an opportunity to devise the best method for conducting public health education campaigns.[161]

MEDICAL CARE ADMINISTRATION

The dramatic rise of private and public medical care programs in the 1940s changed the Canadian system of health services. Defries recognized the significance of these activities which he outlined in a letter to the Canadian representative of the Rockefeller Foundation in 1948 which requested funding for the establishment of medical care studies:

> There has been considerable development of plans for prepaid medical care in the various provinces by both official and voluntary agencies. . . . A great impetus is now being given to planning [health services] by the offer of the Government of Canada of substantial financial assistance in the form of annual public health grants to the provinces. . . . The prerequisite is a comprehensive survey to be conducted by each province presenting its public health and hospital resources and the extent of its need in these fields and in providing more adequate medical care for its citizens.
>
> In several of the provinces, provincial associations of physicians have already offered plans for pre-paid medical care. In addition, many large industries have made provision for medical and hospital services for their employees. In Canada, the Blue Cross Hospital Plan is providing hospital services to a large section of the population in a number of provinces; the Ontario plan, for example, has now enrolled over one-third of the four million persons in Ontario. In Saskatchewan, a province-wide hospital service has been provided on a compulsory contributory basis, and a similar plan is being introduced for the citizens of British Columbia.[162]

A direct illustration of how the School's administration followed this pattern of prepaid plans was the establishment of industrial medical services in 1943, later expanded to the other divisions of the Laboratories. Dr. F.O. Wishart operated the scheme from a room in the Hygiene Building. In April, 1946, the employees of the Laboratories received Blue Cross Hospital coverage and later medical care insurance through Physicians' Services Incorporated.[163]

In October, 1948, the Rockefeller Foundation awarded $17,000 to the School after the establishment of instruction and studies in Medical Care Administration.[164] Defries hired Dr. Gordon H.M. Hatcher to teach and to study medical care problems in Canada even before the grant was authorized by the Rockefeller Foundation. Hatcher graduated in medicine from McGill University in 1944, served in the Royal Canadian Army Medical Corps and then earned a Diploma in Public Health from the School of Hygiene in 1947.[165] He taught full-time in the School until 1955 when he resigned as an assistant professor to become Project Director for Community Research Associates of New York in Hagerstown, Maryland.[166]

An important part of the instruction was the use of a number of authorities on medical care and health insurance. One was Dr. F.W. Jackson, a D.P.H. graduate of the School in

1929 and Deputy Minister of Health and Welfare in Manitoba before joining the Federal Department of National Health and Welfare as the Director of Health Insurance Studies. He gave a series of eight to ten lectures yearly.[167] Another contributor was Malcolm G. Taylor, who had been the Director of Research and Statistics in the Saskatchewan Health Services Planning Commission.[168] Taylor later was appointed to the Department of Political Economy in the University of Toronto where he finished a book on health insurance.[169] Many years thereafter, Taylor completed a major study of the evolution of health insurance in Canada.[170] From its inception, medical care studies relied on a variety of instructors from other departments and schools within and outside the University of Toronto.[171] That pattern of teaching reflected Defries' growing understanding of the economic, political and social features of health care planning and services.

Hatcher conducted, with assistance from the Rockefeller Foundation, a series of studies examining the health systems in Newfoundland, Saskatchewan, Alberta and British Columbia. He also visited American Schools of Public Health to observe their courses in medical care.[172] Interestingly, the federal Department of National Health and Welfare in the early 1950s refused to grant funds for the payment of the salaries of professors engaged in medical care studies because of "the different political pressures by various provinces."[173] Hatcher published later the results of his research and visits in two informative articles which provided a picture of the state of medical care in relation to public health practices and group hospitalization insurance in the different provinces in the middle of the 1950s.[174]

Besides his research and the teaching of postgraduates, Hatcher was involved in the instruction of medical undergraduates within the Department of Hygiene and Preventive Medicine. The differing interests of the School of Hygiene from the Faculty of Medicine came to light in the teaching of medical care studies. As a field of investigation and education in North America, medical care had evolved by the early 1950s into two different spheres; one area, namely the administration of medical services and facilities, had become the preserve of Schools of Public Health, while the development of a course in social medicine that sensitized medical students to the sociological and economic factors in illness was the domain of clinical medicine taught in departments of preventive medicine.[175] "There has been a reluctance on the part of conservative faculties [of medicine] in Canadian schools to venture into [the environmental and social influences on disease]", a representative of the Rockefeller Foundation pointed out without naming the institutions, "largely due to a fear that such a program might distract from sound physiological teaching of medicine." Despite these reservations, the Dean of the Faculty of Medicine, the Head of the Department of Hygiene and Preventive Medicine and the Professor of Medicine promoted the inclusion of programs stressing social medicine in the undergraduate curriculum.[176]

END OF DEFRIES ERA

The evolution of the teaching and research in the Department of Public Health Administration was a testament to Defries' willingness, despite the limitations of his own experience in public health administration, to plan for the development of new areas in Canadian health services encompassing both curative and preventive medicine. Rather fittingly, the appointment of Dr. John Hastings in 1953 as a fellow in medical care administration was evidence of the linkage between the past and the future.[177] Hastings, the great nephew of Dr. Charles Hastings, Toronto's Medical Officer of Health from 1910 to 1929 who was responsible for the international reputation of the City of Toronto in public health, undertook research on the operation of the Workmen's Compensation Board, and medical administration.

By the middle of the 1950s, the Department of Public Health Administration offered a variety of courses in six general areas:

1. Introduction to and history of public health and welfare services;
2. Theory, method and practical aspects of managing a health department;
3. Survey of municipal, provincial and federal public health activities as well as related programs in hospitals, housing and welfare;
4. Discussion of international and foreign public health practices, especially the work of the World Health Organization founded in 1945;
5. Public health education and medical care administration;
6. Veterinary public health practice including food sanitation.

Defries had participated in the evolution of each of these fields.[178]

Defries, always aware of the values of bringing in new people, displayed a remarkable foresight in introducing social and economic aspects of health care that revealed a growing appreciation of the health needs of ordinary Canadians.

Dr. MacLean and Dr. Defries with a visitor to the Hygiene building.

CHAPTER FIVE

THE SCHOOL'S DEPARTMENT OF HOSPITAL ADMINISTRATION, 1947 TO 1955

Considering the hospital field both here and internationally, the past quarter century has seen more progress in hospital work, in better qualified personnel, in technical procedures, in plant and equipment, in organization, and in the protection of the public, than ever before in any comparable period.[1]

Dr. G. Harvey Agnew, in 1953

"For a number of years there has been a growing and ever more widely expressed opinion that public health agencies and hospitals should work more closely in meeting their common problem."[2] So declared the Deputy Minister of Health for Saskatchewan in June, 1952 at the beginning of an address before the Canadian Public Health Association meeting in the Fort Garry Hotel, Winnipeg. What was of historical note about these remarks was their focus on a significant change in health care underway across Canada, a change which health planners in the University of Toronto School of Hygiene had helped to initiate and then to direct. The speaker, Dr. Frederick Burns Roth, had been a member of the second class of postgraduate students in the newly organized course in Hospital Administration of the School of Hygiene. In the 1960s, after years as a pioneer in the delivery of health services in Saskatchewan, Roth joined the faculty of the School to become Agnew's successor and the first full-time head of the Department of Hospital Administration.[3]

Roth's comments in June, 1952, focussed attention on two major trends. Firstly, there was the increase in federal and provincial expenditures on health services after 1945. Federally, the adoption of the National Health Grants Program which Defries and others in the C.P.H.A. had lobbied for made possible a level of funding for provincial public health services that guaranteed a minimal standard of care.[4] The second trend identified by Roth was the dramatic increase in hospital financing. Public health agencies and hospitals, Roth argued in reiterating the views of other health care advocates, had to work together to achieve "better health services" without the traditional regard for the separation between preventive and curative medicine.[5]

The response of R.D. Defries to the needs of Canadian society was well exemplified by his decision to establish a Department of Hospital Administration and a Diploma in Hospital Administration in 1947.[6] It was a significant departure from the traditional instruction which concentrated on public health services. In characteristic fashion, Defries chose the best man in Canada to head his new venture, G. Harvey Agnew. His appointment was another example of a full-time professional joining the academic staff (on a part-time basis) to head a department that prepared students for management positions in hospitals and other medical care facilities. Once again, Defries showed leadership in the development of the education of health professionals in North America.

G. HARVEY AGNEW 1895-1971

Torontonensis, the yearbook of the graduates of the University of Toronto, carried under G. Harvey Agnew's picture in 1918 the rather appropriate quotation which was indicative of his career and organizational talents, "He hath made many friends."[7] A native Torontonian who was born on July 26, 1895, Agnew attended Humberside Collegiate Institute. He served in the Royal Canadian Army Medical Corps in the First World War. Agnew received a M.B. degree in the University of Toronto in 1918 and a M.D. in 1923. Unable to proceed to studies in Great Britain because of a dock strike in New York, he completed his internship in the city's Harlem Division of the Bellevue Hospital. Later he did postgraduate work in London and Vienna. Married in 1921 to Helen Moore, Agnew practiced from 1921 to 1928 as a physician in Toronto Western Hospital. In 1928, he became a demonstrator in the Department of Clinical Medicine in the University of Toronto Faculty of Medicine. In January, 1928, Agnew

Dr. G. Harvey Agnew during the First World War.

assumed the directorship of the newly formed Department of Hospital Services in the Canadian Medical Association, a post he held until 1945.[8] The C.M.A.'s decision to establish this division was "to develop an accreditation program independently of the American College of Surgeons", which was to improve professional procedures and standards in Canadian hospitals.[9] John FitzGerald, Director of the University of Toronto School of Hygiene, was a member of the small committee that helped to organize the C.M.A. department.[10]

Harvey Agnew was a pioneer in the study, management and planning of hospitals in North America. In Canada, one of his first major contributions was to compile data about hospitals. "It was amazingly difficult", he later remarked, "to get lists of hospitals." He and Dr. Helen MacMurchy of the federal Department of Pensions and National Health published in 1929 the first directory of Canadian hospitals; there were 886 hospitals with 74,882 beds and an estimated annual expenditure of $35,000,000.[11]

Two years later, Agnew, then the Associate Director of the Canadian Medical Association, was the author of a medical survey that illuminated some of the problems in the country's medical care. It was based on the 1,400 completed questionnaires from physicians across the Dominion. Some 9,000 had been sent out. This study presented details on the practice of medicine, the population per doctor (1 practitioner per 1,221 persons), and the income of physicians. In response to the question of the need for a health insurance system, the report noted the differing viewpoints:

> Judging by the comments made, many men are of the opinion that the present system of practice is not ideal. Severe condemnation of contract practice is made by several. Health insurance and other forms of state medicine are considered by many in their replies, some expressing a doubt as to the wisdom of adopting such a system, while others feel that it would be a panacea enabling the physician to give good service and at the same time minimize the burden to him of the patient who cannot or will not pay.[12]

Agnew's investigation illuminated the shortage of hospital accommodation, particularly in public wards. In 1931, there were 898 hospitals "of which 485 are public general hospitals" and only 36,523 of the 77,120 hospital beds available nationally were for "public general hospital usage." Agnew's survey also produced data on specialists, laboratory and X-ray facilities and medical education. Although limited by the number of respondents, Agnew's survey was a pioneering examination of Canada's health system.[13]

Principally because of Agnew's conviction that hospitals required a more effective lobby nationally, the Canadian Hospital Council came into existence in 1931; it was renamed the Canadian Hospital Association in 1953. Interestingly, impetus for this development grew out of the holding of the American Hospital Association's annual convention in Toronto in September of 1931. Agnew's Department of Hospital Services in the C.M.A., itself funded by the Sun Life Assurance Company, provided office and secretarial assistance in the early years of the C.H.C.[14] The organization's first secretary was quite naturally Agnew who served until 1950. From 1938 to 1950, he was also the editor of the *Canadian Hospital*.[15]

From the beginning, Agnew confronted the typically Canadian clash of strong regional and organizational rivalries in the Canadian Hospital Council. He managed to minimize these differences and to forge a concensus. The sharpness of the opposing interests within the national body was reflected over the issue of whether private or public funds "should bear the

Dr. G. Harvey Agnew

cost of caring for the indigent." There was a major crisis facing hospitals overwhelmed by the needs of the unemployed in the 1930s. Agnew recollected how only the withdrawal of a resolution endorsing the government's full responsibility for the hospitalization of all Canadians saved the C.H.C. from being split during its second meeting in Winnipeg in 1933.[16]

AGNEW AND HOSPITAL INSURANCE

In the 1930s, Agnew established himself quickly as an expert on the Canadian system of hospitals and especially of insurance for hospitalization. On the one hand, although he did not want to "rock the boat" of current medical and hospital practices, Agnew, on the other hand, was conscious of the danger of ignoring human needs in the depression. In late October, 1931, Agnew addressed a symposium on hospital services held by the Section of Preventive Medicine and Hygiene in the Toronto Academy of Medicine in which he pointed to the pressure for changes:

> Those who assert that there is no public clamour for "state medicine" do not realize the profound changes appearing in western Canada, the attitude of labour and of the farmer groups, and the recent endorsation of the principle of the nationalization of medicine by our Federal Liberal party. To the best of my knowledge our medical organizations are taking no partisan attitude on this question, either for or against; to do so at this stage is not their province. But they would be sadly remiss in their duty did they not endeavour to acquaint the medical profession with present day facts and prevent it being unawares, as was the profession in Great Britain a few years ago.

Agnew continued his speech by noting how the "entering wedges of health insurance" were already a reality:

> From the viewpoint of hospitalization, we find pensioners and those suffering from war disabilities cared for by the government; psychiatric patients are hospitalized by the provinces; our western provinces have developed "union" hospitals; in Saskatchewan all tuberculosis patients are entitled to free hospital care, the government apportioning a share of the costs to the municipalities. Our federal government finances the hospital care of sick mariners from a special levy on ocean freight tonnage. Also many of our large industries have their own hospitals and their own surgeons and often the families are cared for as well as the workmen. I mention this background of converging data to emphasize one particular point, namely that our hospitals are vitally concerned with the development of health insurance.[17]

Agnew contributed to the development of group hospitalization in North America by serving as one of the two Canadian representatives on the Council on Community Relations and Administrative Practices of the American Hospital Association in 1933. This body proposed a series of recommendations to guide hospitals in the adoption of group plans for hospitalization.[18]

Agnew's involvement with the genesis of group hospitalization in the U.S. was another indication of his growing ties with the American hospital system in the 1930s. He worked closely with Dr. Malcolm T. MacEachern, a Canadian by birth who was director of the American College of Surgeons' division of hospital activities. Agnew and MacEachern promoted the adoption of standard procedures for medical staff in hospitals across the continent. Agnew was made a charter honourary fellow of the American College of Hospital Administrators founded by MacEachern in 1933 to establish professional criteria in hospital administration.[19] Recognition of his contribution to the American scene came with his election to the Presidency of the American Hospital Association in 1938.[20]

One of the innovations witnessed by Agnew in his American travels was the introduction of voluntary prepayment group hospital insurance known as the Blue Cross movement. It originated with a teachers' hospitalization plan at Baylor University in Texas in the early 1930s. The first Blue Cross scheme in Canada was in Edmonton.[21] The depression had demonstrated the economic disaster that any hospital stay might impose on middle-class Canadians. Of course, most Canadians could not afford any hospitalization and were at the mercy of treatment in public wards supported by municipalities. Yet, in 1934, there were about twenty-five prepayment plans in Canada operated on a small scale by hospitals, service clubs, and mutual benefit societies.[22] To overcome the problem of high costs for a much larger group of individuals who could not afford a reasonable rate, Agnew helped to organize the Ontario Blue Cross Plan as a subsidiary of the Ontario Hospital Association.[23] Two other examples of a prepaid medical insurance scheme in Ontario were Associated Medical Services, founded in 1937 by Dr. Jason Hannah, and Physicians' Services Incorporated, a non-profit body organized by the Ontario Medical Association in 1947.[24] By 1943, Agnew's preference was for this type of group hospital insurance. "Our whole basis of financing hospital care will probably be changed", Agnew stated in as late as 1953, "but based, I hope, upon the Blue Cross principle."[25] However, in the 1940s there remained the much more pressing question, recognized by Agnew, of how to deliver the benefits of hospitalization to the average Canadian who could not afford such services.[26]

When the Second World War opened up serious discussions in Canada about the postwar planning of health services, Harvey Agnew was a key participant. On April 9, 1943, he appeared as the Secretary of the Canadian Hospital Council before the House of Commons' Special Committee on Social Security. As in all of his previous presentations, he reviewed the status of hospitals in Canada. By 1941, there were 1,220 hospitals with a total of 119,000 beds and cribs with an additional 7,000 bassinets. The hospital system was "mainly of the voluntary non-profit type" operated by lay and religious groups. After discussing the general strengths of this system, Agnew summarized its weakness in four points:

1. The costs of hospitalization strained severely the finances of families with moderate incomes;
2. Many rural communities lacked basic hospital facilities;
3. The lack of planning produced gaps and duplication in health services;
4. There was an inadequate system for covering the hospitalization of indigents.[27]

To correct the essential problem of the inability of the average Canadian to pay, Agnew's submission approved of the general principle of health insurance and called for the preservation of "the best in our present system of hospital care . . . without too radical revisions in our basic system."[28]

The proposal of Agnew for health insurance concentrated on hospital care. It did not address every aspect of medical care insurance, just coverage for hospitalization. There were fourteen points in the plan put forth by Agnew:

1. Use of voluntary hospitals;
2. Introduction of hospital insurance only in "public" hospitals;
3. A comprehensive system of hospital benefits;
4. Hospitalization for all classes of patients;
5. Financing of care for patients unable to pay for services;
6. Inclusion of dependants of the insured;
7. Adequate financial compensation to pay for the costs incurred by hospitals;
8. Equitable payment for all health care services;
9. Control over staffing by hospitals;
10. Insured must retain the option to pay for more expensive accommodation in hospitals;
11. Health insurance to be administered on a provincial basis but coordinated federally;
12. Management of hospital insurance to be non-political;
13. Hospital representation on advisory council overseeing the insurance scheme;
14. Contributions from insured to form the basis of the plan.[29]

Agnew had presented a blueprint for Canada's postwar system of hospital insurance. As usual, it was to be a gradual process taking years to implement.

POSTWAR DEVELOPMENTS IN HOSPITALS

Following the war, Agnew kept up the pressure to win better financing for Canadian hospitals. In May of 1947, Harvey Agnew and Dr. A.J. Swanson, the President of the Canadian Hospital Council, appealed to the Dominion Council of Health, the advisory body to the Department of National Health and Welfare, for help in alleviating the serious shortage of hospital facilities. The increasing usage of hospitals was the result, they observed, of a number of social factors reflecting the changes in Canadian living conditions:

> [These trends included] the desire for better diagnosis and better treatment, the trend toward obstetrical care in hospital, increased traffic hazards, increased utilization of voluntary non-profit or commercial insurance providing hospital coverage, decreased home accommodation and the lack of domestic help. Since 1939, two additional factors have been evident — the crowding of people into cities and towns and the financial ability of a large section of the population to finance short hospital admissions.[30]

The brief pointed to the halt in the construction of hospitals due to wartime shortages of materials and tradesmen followed by the rising costs of building. As a result, patients were being crowded into rooms, corridors and other spaces; many hospitals were functioning at 100 per cent patient capacity or some even reached 130 or 140 per cent of normal numbers. This submission ended by urging federal and provincial governments to give financial assistance. Voluntary efforts no longer were able to keep up with the demands.[31] One of the clearest indications of the shift in the management of hospitals to a professional status was the establishment of the Department of Hospital Administration in the University of Toronto School of Hygiene shortly after the Second World War.

The emergence of hospital administration as a profession in North America marked the opening of a new era in the provision of general health services. Prior to 1945, public health objectives in Canada dominated a variety of municipally, provincially and to a much lesser extent federally funded health programs. The emphasis was on the control and the prevention of communicable diseases such as tuberculosis, smallpox, diphtheria, and typhoid fever, and the care of infants and children. The success of these public health measures, as well as the experiences in the Second World War with military medicine and the development of group hospitalization insurance, shifted the focus to the extension of curative medicine to larger numbers in the population. Later in Canada, the federal government's funding of the construction of hospitals, the purchase of modern medical technology and the training of various health professionals concentrated attention on the hospital in the community as the centre of health services.[32] By the end of the 1950s, the adoption of government hospital insurance across Canada intensified this trend.[33]

EMERGENCE OF HOSPITAL ADMINISTRATION

Back in October, 1946, a significant sign of the upcoming importance of hospital administrators was the recommendation of a conference of the Professors of Preventive Medicine in Ann Arbor, Michigan, sponsored by the Rockefeller Foundation, that schools of public health "should take cognizance of the growing needs for instruction in hospital administration, not only for those who may serve as hospital administrators but also for the medical officers of health and for the administrators of medical care programmes."[34] In Great Britain, the national health planning had prompted the initiation of a course in hospital administration in the London School of Hygiene and Tropical Medicine. Harvey Agnew of the Canadian Hospital Council pointed out the need for formal education in the management of hospitals:

> Hospital administration is now an exacting vocation—in many respects it is a profession. Hospitals are an essential part of our social system and it has become increasingly obvious that organized training for such a career has great advantages over the old "apprenticeship" or "learn-as-you-go" methods. When vacancies occur, the hospital trustees ask for trained hospital administrators to fill the posts. Positions now vacant or becoming vacant will likely have to be filled by hospital administrators now occupying positions in the United States. In proportion to population, Canada should have at least one university providing an adequate course. Hospital administrators (physicians) generally fill the posts in the largest hospitals in Canada, non-medical administrators probably will continue to be the hospital heads—particularly in hospitals of 100 to 150 beds. Some hospital boards express a definite preference for the non-medical administrator who may have his degree in commerce and finance prior to the course in hospital administration.[35]

While there was clearly a growing need for a course in Canada, it was once again an American foundation that made possible the establishment of postgraduate instruction in hospital administration in the University of Toronto School of Hygiene.

ESTABLISHMENT OF DIPLOMA IN HOSPITAL ADMINISTRATION

"In a very large measure the successful establishing of the Department [of Hospital Administration]", Defries wrote in 1951, "was due to the personal interest of Mr. Graham Davis."[36] The Director of the Division of Hospitals of the W.K. Kellogg Foundation [founded in 1930][37] of Battle Creek, Michigan, Davis had contacted Defries in late 1946 about the possibility of assisting the School of Hygiene in the inauguration of a course in hospital administration.[38]

Within four months of the original proposal, the University of Toronto received a cheque of $21,500 from the Kellogg Foundation to establish the first year of a "three-year programme in hospital administration for university graduates" which included $9,000 for a scholarship fund to assist students of the "first class" to enter the course.[39]

FIRST FACULTY AND STUDENTS

The 1947-1948 Calendar of the School of Hygiene presented the initial listing of the Department of Hospital Administration. There were two members in the new department, Harvey Agnew, professor of hospital administration (part-time) and L.O. Bradley, associate professor of hospital administration and the only full-time member.[40] Over the subsequent decades, the growth of the department was in sharp contrast to these simple beginnings.

Leonard O. Bradley was the first permanent member of the faculty of the Department of Hospital Administration. A medical graduate of the University of Alberta in 1938, Bradley received a Mead-Johnson Fellowship in Paediatrics for his studies in the Minneapolis General Hospital. With the advent of war, he enlisted in the R.C.A.F. and served until late 1945. Thereafter, Dr. Bradley returned to the Royal Alexandra Hospital where he had completed an internship as assistant superintendent. After taking a course in hospital administration at the University of Chicago, Defries recommended his appointment. Bradley's total salary was financed by a grant from the W.K. Kellogg Foundation.[41] In addition to teaching in hospital administration, Bradley lectured in the Department of Public Health Administration.[42]

Bradley's ties to extra-departmental activities resulted in his part-time leave of absence to work on the Ontario Health Survey Committee in September, 1948. In 1950, Bradley succeeded Harvey Agnew as the Executive Secretary of the Canadian Hospital Council.[43] He left the School in August of 1952.[44]

Within a few months, William B. Trimble was given the status of a fellow in hospital administration (part-time). He taught personnel management and human relations. A veteran of the Second World War, Trimble earned his B.A. in political science and economics in 1946 and a M.A. in political economics the next year from the University of Toronto. At the time of his appointment in December of 1947, he was registered in the School of Graduate Studies as a candidate for a Ph.D.[45]

In the initial years of the program in hospital administration, much of the instruction depended on faculty outside of the department and the School. Various lectures were given by instructors from the Schools of Law, Social Work, Architecture, Nursing, the Faculty of Medicine, the Departments of Mechanical and Electrical Engineering, Accounting and Economics.[46] There were also in later years lectures delivered by specialists from outside the university; in November, 1949, Everett W. Jones, the vice-president of an American hospital association from Chicago, Illinois, lectured to the students.[47]

The inaugural courses for the Diploma in Hospital Administration (Dip. H.A.) began on Monday, September 22, 1947.[48] The first class had four candidates including two physicians.[49] There were ten courses: hospital organization and management, departmental management,

First class for Diploma in Hospital Administration in 1947. ***Front:*** *Wm. Trimble, fellow in personal relations; Harvey Agnew, professor; Leonard Bradley, associate professor.* ***Rear:*** *Ben Rothman, George Peacock, Walter Birch, Bob Cathcart.*

Diploma in Hospital Administration Graduating Class of 1950, University of Toronto School of Hygiene.

public relations of the hospital administrator, hospital staff relations, including personnel management, legal aspects of hospital administration, accounting and budgetary control, financing of general and special hospitals, hospital planning and construction, public health (a lecture and conference course) and medical background (for non-medical candidates). This section of the Dip.H.A. was given in one academic session from September to May. The second requirement was the completion of an internship of twelve months in a selected hospital under faculty supervision.[50] Two years later, the Calendar announced the inclusion of the requirement for a thesis in order to qualify for the Diploma in Hospital Administration.[51]

The first class to receive the Diploma in Hospital Administration, the designation given officially in the School of Hygiene Calendar, graduated in 1949. They were W.J. Birch, H.R. Cathcart, G.W. Peacock and B.G. Rothman.[52] As part of their course, they prepared a thesis which became a standard for the Diploma. Birch and Rothman completed "A Survey of Women's College Hospital" and Cathcart and Peacock produced "A Study of Mount Sinai Hospital."[53]

The attractiveness of the Dip.H.A. program was very apparent by the fall of 1948. There were "approximately thirty applications."[54] Eleven candidates registered in September, 1948.[55] Included in this group were individuals who returned later to teach in the department. D.M. MacIntyre joined the staff in June, 1951.[56] Dr. F. Burns Roth assumed the position of first full-time professor and head of Hospital Administration in 1962.[57] The composition of the backgrounds of the students entering the Dip. H.A. course in September, 1948 revealed the mixture of medical and other disciplines such as political science, economics and public administration. Many years afterwards, Roth recalled his experiences in the courses as one of getting "a hands-on training" for the management of every aspect of the operation of a hospital.[58] Seven out of the original eleven students entering in September, 1948, completed the Dip. H.A. curriculum.[59]

EUGENIE STUART

The fall of 1948 was also the beginning of Eugenie Stuart's long involvement with Hospital Administration in the School of Hygiene. Her first appointment was a temporary one to supplement the part-time services of Dr. L.O. Bradley.[60] Stuart stayed until her retirement in the 1970s. In the words of Harvey Agnew, she became a "mother confessor to succeeding classes for more than twenty years."[61]

Born in Palmerston, Ontario on August 22, 1903, Eugenie Margaret Stuart moved to Toronto to finish her education. A graduate of the School of Nursing of Toronto General Hospital in the class of 1925, Stuart became a surgical supervisor in the same institution. After working for a few years, she went back to studies. In 1929, Stuart earned a Diploma in Hospital and School of Nursing Administration in the Department of Nursing, then an independent division in the School of Hygiene Building. She also continued her education by taking summer courses at Northwestern University in Chicago where she received a Bachelor of Science in Hospital Administration in 1947. Later in 1950, she finished a Master of Hospital Administration. Her M.H.A. thesis examined the role of audio-visual education in hospital administration. Following a year at McGill University, Stuart joined the School of Hygiene.[62]

Professor Eugenie Stuart

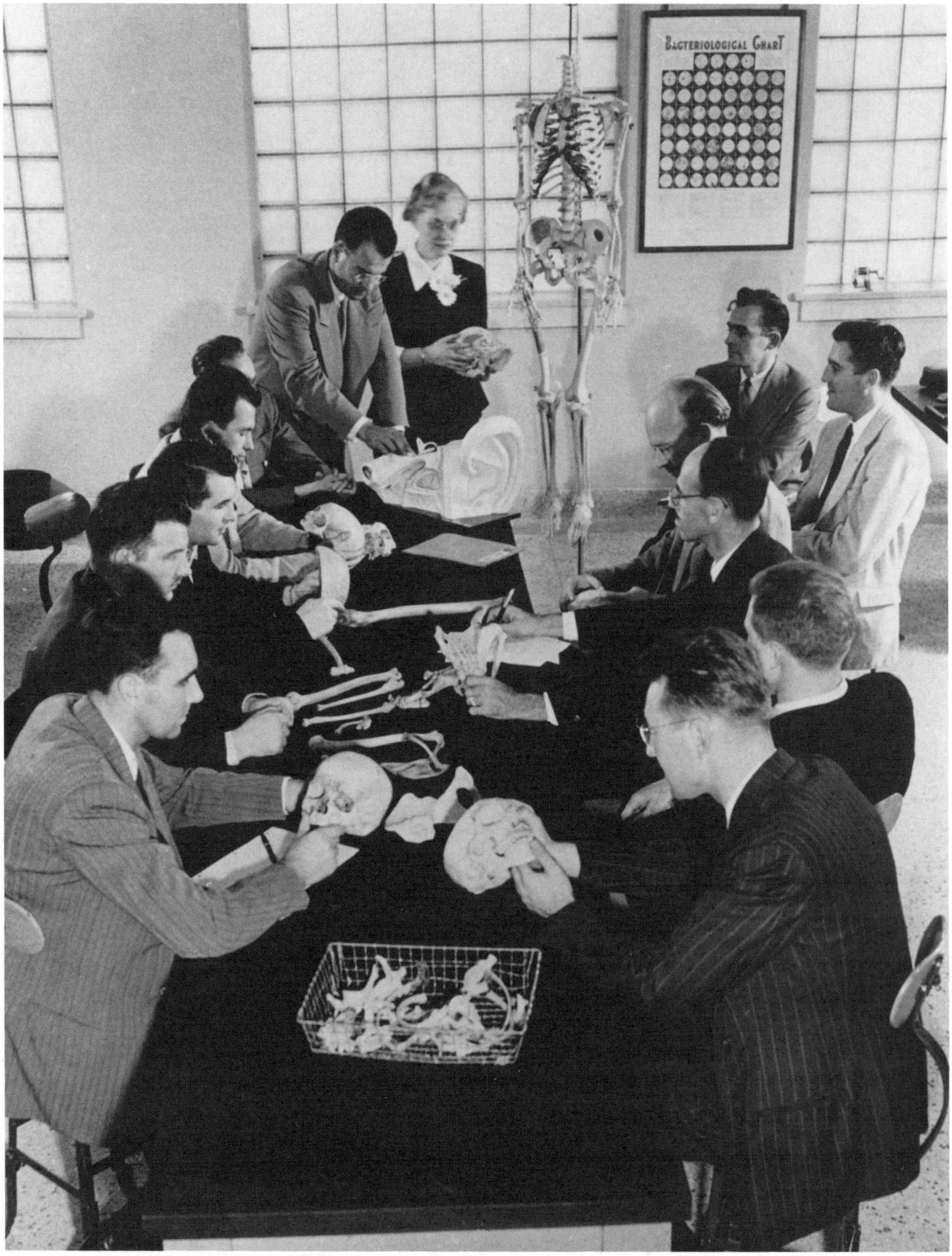

Stuart with students in hospital administration circa 1958.

Less than two years after her temporary appointment, Miss E.M. Stuart, as the Calendar of the School identified her,[63] was promoted to assistant professor.[64] She was the only full-time member in the department. Stuart developed the use of audio-visual aids in instruction as well as improving the educational role of hospitals in communities.[65]

Noting that most of her male students went on to higher paying jobs upon graduation, Harvey Agnew recommended Stuart's promotion to associate professor. He lauded her "magnificent job with the students" winning "their loyalty and affection" and credited Stuart with the development of Toronto's Dip.H.A. as "one of the best organized courses in the whole Association of University Programs in Hospital Administration." Agnew ended his request with what amounted to a social commentary on the status of women in the School during the 1950s: "There is no other woman in Canada with the necessary training in Hospital Administration and, if we have to replace her with a man with the necessary specialized training and executive ability, I am sure that we would need to pay him considerably more."[66] On July 1, 1954, the Board of Governors promoted Miss Stuart to associate professor.[67]

NEW DIRECTIONS AND NEW STAFF 1950 TO 1955

Another area in which the Department of Hospital Administration broke new ground was in its co-operation with the Canadian Hospital Council to provide an extension course in hospital management for administrators. At first, there was opposition to the idea from the heads of the departments in the School.[68] Even President Sidney Smith had reservations originally:

> In the meeting of the Council of the School of Hygiene, I expressed uneasiness about an offering by the University of a course in hospital administration leading to a diploma and, in addition, an extension type of course. The plan of co-operation outlined by Dr. Harvey Agnew and by Dr. Bradley in our conference with them does not contemplate that the University would give any certificate to those who have successfully completed the proposed course; recognition would be given by the Canadian Hospital Council . . .[69]

When it became apparent that the Canadian Hospital Council was going to offer the course without the help of the department, Smith, stating "We must consider the facts as of today", endorsed the proposal.[70] With funding from the W.K. Kellogg Foundation, the extension course with the assistance of the Department of Hospital Administration was established.[71] Donald M. MacIntyre, a Dip. H.A. graduate in 1950, was appointed an assistant professor to teach in the postgraduate program as well as to plan and to direct the Canadian Hospital Council extension course. Another Dip. H.A graduate, John Lee, joined the department on leave from the Health Services Planning Commission in Saskatchewan to help MacIntyre with the extension course.[72]

To replace L.O. Bradley who resigned in the summer of 1952, Dr. A.L. Swanson was appointed with the rank of assistant professor (part-time). A 1944 graduate of the medical school of McGill University, Swanson served for two years in the Royal Canadian Army Medical Corps. After joining the medical staff of the British Columbia Mental Health Services, he went on to complete a Master of Hospital Administration degree at Northwestern University in Chicago. He returned to B.C. in the position of a deputy medical superintendent of a Mental Hospital. Swanson succeeded Bradley as the Executive Secretary of the Canadian

Hospital Council (C.H.C.).[73] Swanson left after two years in 1954 to be replaced by W.D. Piercey, the Executive Director of the C.H.C.[74]

In the spring of 1955, the Kellogg Foundation granted almost $24,000 over two years to improve the postgraduate program in hospital administration. The funding was for the development of case teaching materials.[75] It was part of the department's determination to "keep in step with changing economic conditions, the progress of medical science and the effect of both on the hospital field." The model for this method of teaching was drawn from the School of Business at the University of Western Ontario and the Harvard Graduate School of Business.[76]

While business schools offered examples of pedagogical approaches, Harvey Agnew and professors from other university courses in hospital administration objected to turning their field into "the mere business of administration." Sidney Smith praised Agnew for that position and stated ". . . we might have to reconsider the offering of the course if it were to deal mainly with 'rules of thumb', techniques of office management, accounting, etc."[77] For Harvey Agnew and the other members of the department, the hospital in Canadian society represented not a business but "an essential participant in the community program for health care."[78]

"DIPLOMAS OR MASTER'S DEGREES"

Because of the prominent American influence in the emergence of the School's Diploma in Hospital Administration, it was only a matter of time before there were pressures from graduates to convert the Dip. H.A into a Master's degree in conformity with the system in the U.S. The practice of granting diplomas for postgraduate studies by professionals was a part of the British heritage continued by the University of Toronto Faculty of Medicine.[79] The similarity and, in many instances, the higher standards of the Toronto diploma in comparison with American Master's counterparts justified even further their demands for the establishment of a Master's in Hospital Administration degree in the School of Graduate Studies.[80]

The awarding of a diploma for professional postgraduate studies followed the model of British universities. However, the growing influence of the American educational model following the First World War was evident, especially in medicine. For example in the 1920s, the University of Toronto Faculty of Medicine adopted the award of the M.D. for the completion of an undergraduate medical course to replace the M.B. It may be noted also that the generous support of the Rockefeller Foundation for improvements in postgraduate public health instruction strengthened the North American character of medical education in Toronto.[81]

The distinction between postgraduate and graduate studies lay at the core of an increasingly strident discussion about Diplomas or Master's Degrees. Later, in the 1960s, this definition was the subject of much debate within the university, which led to changes in the 1970s.[82] One of the major participants in those deliberations was Dr. Andrew J. Rhodes, then the Director of the School of Hygiene and Head of the Graduate Department of Hygiene, who chaired a Senate Committee investigating the undergraduate and postgraduate diplomas granted by the University of Toronto.[83] In 1961, he explained lucidly the then perceived difference between the Diploma and the Master's Degree:

> In the University of Toronto the degrees of Master of Arts and Doctor of Philosophy are under the jurisdiction of the School of Graduate Studies. Work for these degrees is done in departments known as Graduate Departments approved by the School of Graduate Studies. A reasonably clear distinction exists between the admission requirements and curricula for Master's degrees, for example the Master of Arts, and for diplomas. Thus, in most departments, Master of Arts degrees are awarded on satisfactory completion of a program of advanced work based on research. The courses, seldom more than four or five in number, are chosen so as to afford background for the research project. Candidates for the degree must be well prepared at the undergraduate level, and have the equivalent of an honours course in the subject to be studied at the Master's level. Candidates not so well prepared are required to spend a qualifying year before admission to the formal program, which lasts for one or two years, depending on the tradition of the particular department sponsoring the candidate, and the nature of the research project undertaken.
>
> Toronto diploma courses, in contrast, are intensive, last for one academic year and many subjects are taught during the year. Although most of the constituent courses are at an advanced level, some are of an introductory nature, designed to present material not covered in the undergraduate course, e.g., courses in sociology and in accounting offered to some students in hospital administration, and anthropology offered to students in nutrition. Most of the working day, five days a week, is occupied with formal lectures, seminars, assignments, library periods, and laboratory exercises. Research does not form part of the course.
>
> A diploma course may be said to cover the field of study in width, whereas a Toronto Master's program focuses in depth on part of the field. Furthermore, a Master's program is of a general cultural character and is not a professional qualification. A diploma is generally regarded as a recognized professional qualification.[84]

One of the initial and ongoing challenges to this traditional view came from the rising number of Dip. H.A. graduates of the School of Hygiene.

Back in the 1950s, Harvey Agnew had raised forthrightly the issue of the need to change to a Master's Degree for satisfactory completion of the course in Hospital Administration. In a letter to R.D. Defries on January 8, 1954, Agnew wrote,

> I realize there are traditional attitudes towards graduate work in vocational fields, but it may not be realized to what extent we are working under a handicap by not being able to confer a Master's degree as is done by every other university providing a course in hospital administration. We know of a number of Canadians who have gone elsewhere because they realize that other universities would give them a Master's degree for the same work which would be recognized here by a diploma only. We are concerned that a Department of the Federal Government has permitted its employees to take a Master's course in hospital administration in the United States although it has been a recognized principle in Federal financing of education that it would not finance courses in the United States if comparable work could be obtained in Canada. . . .
>
> On the basis of qualification, I think we are well entitled to a Master's degree status. I know of no other diploma course in the university which is open only to university graduates of recognized standing which requires two years of study with a time-table definitely requiring a thesis on the completion of the course. It is really not fair to our graduate students to expect them to complete the heavy timetable (nearly 1,000 hours in

> the first year), plus numerous assignments and projects, to write a thesis of the quality demanded by us and to give them a diploma only for such work.[85]

In response to Agnew's letter passed on to him by Defries, President Sidney Smith emphasized the control of the School of Graduate Studies over the establishment of a new degree which had to be for a course of study "reaching into the frontiers of knowledge and not to be a mere presentation of more material designed to train a person for employment in a specific field."[86] This exchange was just the opening shot of a struggle that was to continue for over two decades and may not even yet be resolved.

DEPARTMENT IN 1955

When Defries retired, forty-two students had earned the Diploma in Hospital Administration from the School of Hygiene.[87] Another thirty-seven had completed the course requirements.[88] The large number of applicants for admission to the program demonstrated its growing popularity.[89] Within a few years, the adoption of hospital insurance in the provinces as a result of the federal Hospital Insurance and Diagnostic Services Act of 1957, augmented even more the demand for the education of professional hospital administration and health care planners by the School's most recently established Department.[90]

Convention of Association of University Programs in Hospital Administration in Iowa 1953. Note: Dr. Harvey Agnew, first row, fourth from right; Dr. Malcolm T. MacEachern, first row, third from right; Professor Eugenie Stuart, second row, first from right; and Dr. A.L. Swanson, second row, fourth from left.

The School's Class of 1953 included five students who completed the Dip. H.A.: L. Bennett-Alder; Dr. E.N. Boettcher; R.C. Cox; Sister Jeanne-Mance; and C.M. Mikail.

CHAPTER SIX

NUTRITION, PARASITOLOGY AND VIROLOGY, 1945-1955

Teaching must be illuminated by research.[1]

Dr. Andrew J. Rhodes, 1956

From the beginning, a distinctive feature of the University of Toronto School of Hygiene was the basic scientific research undertaken by the staff. In the post-1945 era, the "new sciences" of public health in the School, nutrition, parasitology, virology and microbiology, achieved a degree of maturity which laid the foundation for their emergence as major departments in the years following 1955. The joint appointments of most faculty to the School and the Connaught Medical Research Laboratories provided a fertile environment for researchers to exchange ideas, techniques and to acquire an appreciation of the practical problems in applying research. The general approach to medical sciences fostered by FitzGerald, Defries and Fraser brought into the Hygiene Building a wide range of scientists. Many were not physicians but they added an innovative and broader perspective to the causes of human diseases. Dr. Murray Fallis' research on blackflies, Dr. Earle McHenry's investigations of proteins and vitamins, and Dr. Raymond Parker's studies on tissue culture appeared to be esoteric and unrelated to larger public health problems. Yet each of these lines of inquiry shed light on the development of ways to prevent diseases and illnesses.

McHENRY AND PUBLIC HEALTH NUTRITION

"Not only have you and your colleagues produced a creditable amount of valuable research", Dr. Hugh H. Smith of the Rockefeller Foundation stated in commending Earle W. McHenry in the fall of 1950, "but you have succeeded in arousing an increased interest in nutrition in the public health workers throughout Canada."[2] The basis for such praise was McHenry's report on the research funded by grants of $36,700 from the International Health Division and $30,000 from the Division of Natural Sciences of the Rockefeller Foundation. That support had expanded the staff to thirteen including one professor, one lecturer, one associate, five research fellows, four technical assistants and a secretary in the Department of Public Health Nutrition. The significance of McHenry's work in the 1940s had resulted in the formation of a Sub-department in 1941 and its elevation to department status in 1946. From 1934 until 1950, there were ninety-four papers published on nutrition studies with twenty-eight of them directly the result of financing from the Rockefeller Foundation.[3]

McHenry's department caught the attention of the visiting Dr. C-E.A. Winslow of the American Public Health Association in February of 1947. Calling it "unusual" for the balance of research, teaching and practice, Winslow concluded that:

> In this field, the Harvard program is the only one of comparable vitality. The course (in Toronto) occupies 45 hours and covers the various nutritive factors (from a practical clinical standpoint and not as a theoretical course for the expert in physiological chemistry). The influences of industrial processes and cooking on food values, and the clinical and field methods of assessment of physiological status and practical administrative and educational methods for improving food habits [are covered.][4]

The impressive record of research built by McHenry and his associates established the School of Hygiene as an international leader in the field of nutrition.

The best summary of the nature of the research in McHenry's department was given in a general description in the records of the Rockefeller Foundation:

> Since July 1, 1944, when the current grant became effective, the Department of Public Health Nutrition has completed or undertaken the following investigations: (1) an investigation of ascorbic acid requirements, using a group of patients in the Toronto Mental Hospital; (2) a study of nutritional conditions in a group of 200 elementary school children; (3) a study of haemoglobin levels in children and in young women, (which will be extended to young men and adults), to obtain data regarding distribution of haemoglobin values in normal subjects; (4) collection of data regarding the incidence of underweight and obesity in the Canadian population; and (5) a long-term study to evaluate the effects of a general health program, including nutritional aspects, of a group of elementary school children in the East York Health Unit. Two additional studies in human nutrition will be commenced this fall, as follows: (a) an investigation of the metabolism of pyruvic acid in normal and obese persons to determine whether rapid conversion of carbohydrate to fat is a factor in causing obesity in some people, and (b) an attempt to evaluate an amino (acid) tolerance test to determine the effectiveness of protein catabolism in humans. These two studies are planned in cooperation with the Department of Medicine, University of Toronto.[5]

On the practical side, the document noted that the Directors of the Provincial Division of Nutrition in New Brunswick and of the Manitoba Division of Maternal and Child Hygiene received their education in nutrition in the Department of Public Health Nutrition of the School of Hygiene.[6]

By the 1950s, researchers in nutrition had forged links to clinical medicine. Dr. William McGanity of the Department of Obstetrics and Gynecology joined the department on a part-time basis to do some teaching and research. He was in charge of the clinical aspects of a joint study on nutritional abnormalities in pregnancy. A similar co-operative venture was established with the Departments of Radiology and of Surgery to investigate protein metabolism in cancer patients.[7] This type of clinical experience as well as work in the community influenced the development of courses in the department.

Professor Earle McHenry's experiences as an advisor to a variety of governmental committees during the war years and thereafter "had a direct effect upon teaching" in the Department of Public Health Nutrition.[8] By the fall of 1947, there were nine courses: a general course of thirty-three hours, nutrition education, nutrition in relation to dentistry, determination of nutritional status, industrial nutrition (all included ten hours of lectures and demonstrations), advanced nutrition which was a lecture course of forty-four hours, a laboratory course of sixty-six hours in research methods, food processing and preservation (twenty-two hours) and field work in community nutrition which consisted of sixty- six hours of practical experience in nutrition education in health departments and the nutritional problems of nurseries and school lunch rooms.[9] At the beginning of the 1950s, a reorganization of the courses resulted in a reduction of their number to five which were related directly to the requirements of the different students. A general course was given to those enrolled in the Diploma in Public Health, the Diploma in Dental Public Health, and the

Certificate in Public Health (Nutrition) which offered fifty hours of lectures and demonstrations in "human requirements, determination of nutritional status, and practical application of nutrition." The other general course was for candidates in the Diploma of Veterinary Public Health and graduates taking the M.A.Sc. in sanitary engineering; it was thirty hours of lectures on the human nutritional needs, food preparation and processing and preservation. Those registered in the Diploma in Hospital Administration received a program of eight hours of lectures. An advanced course in nutrition of reading and discussion was available as well as seminars for graduate students.[10]

Because there was no diploma course in public health nutrition until 1959, students from the Diploma in Public Health and the Certificate in Public Health courses were able to specialize in nutrition in order to assume positions in health departments. By 1950, three D.P.H. graduates had specialized in nutrition and four recipients of the Certificate in Public Health specializing in nutrition worked as nutritionists in health departments.[11] One example of an individual who earned the C.P.H. was Doris Loreen Noble. She graduated in 1949 and then went into a career as a nutritionist in British Columbia working for private industry, the provincial government and then as a consumer consultant with the Department of National Health and Welfare on the west coast.[12]

Despite the small staff in Public Health Nutrition, they supervised the largest number of graduate students in the School of Hygiene. From 1949 to 1954, fifteen graduate degrees were obtained by students in McHenry's department which represented almost half of the graduate degrees earned in the School.[13] In the decade following the Second World War, there were twenty-one theses completed on nutrition, fifteen being for the M.A. and six for the Ph.D.[14] The numbers of students overtaxed the limited accommodation within the department's laboratory in the Hygiene Building. In the 1951 to 1952 session, there were eight graduate candidates and a fellow supported by Colombo Plan occupying space meant for only five persons.[15]

Two brothers, J.R. Beaton and G.H. Beaton, were appointed to teach in the Department of Public Health Nutrition. In the fall of 1949, John Beaton was a research fellow.[16] The following year, he completed a M.A. thesis entitled, "Studies on glutamic acid" and in 1952 a Ph.D. thesis entitled "B vitamins and protein metabolism." By the fall of 1953, Beaton was promoted to the rank of assistant professor,[17] a position he held until his resignation in 1954 to work in Ottawa.[18] His brother, George Beaton, finished a M.A. in 1953 with a dissertation on vitamin B_6 compounds in animal and human tissue and then a Ph.D. in 1955 with a thesis on protein metabolism in pregnancy. He succeeded his brother as assistant professor.[19] Professor George Beaton became the head of the department following McHenry's death in 1961.[20]

McHENRY'S CONTRIBUTIONS

In the fall of 1953, the holding of an international symposium on protein metabolism, the first in Canada, at the School of Hygiene under the direction of the Department of Public Health Nutrition was a tribute to the international reputation that E.W. McHenry and his colleagues had established in the field of nutrition in less than twenty years.[21] McHenry was invited to many conferences in the United States. From 1954 to 1955, he gave addresses to the Gordon Research Conference on Vitamins in New London, New Hampshire and the Henry Ford

Senior staff of School in the 1960s whose association with the School extended back before 1955. Seated: Dr. F. Burns Roth (second from left), Dr. A.J. Rhodes (centre), and Dr. George Beaton (second from right).

Hospital Symposium in Detroit, Michigan.[22] Under his direction, papers were presented to the Federation of Biological Societies and the International Physiological Congress. McHenry was the Canadian correspondent for the British Nutrition Society and in 1956 became the first Canadian member of the Council of the American Institute of Nutrition.[23]

At home, McHenry turned nutrition into a respected scientific field through his numerous activities. Nationally, he was a major force in the Canadian Council on Nutrition. Provincially, he was the chairman of the Ontario Inter-departmental Nutrition Committee which promoted nutritional improvements through the circulation of bulletins and booklets. A popular spokesman, McHenry gave about fifty addresses to different meetings in 1950 to 1951 as well as writing a series of articles in the Toronto Telegram.[24]

Earle McHenry's career was another outstanding illustration of how the senior faculty of the School of Hygiene exerted pioneering leadership in the development of Canadian medical sciences and health care. Early in his academic life, McHenry displayed a willingness to open up and to foster new fields of scientific research. On August 19, 1935, a provisional committee composed of Professors J. Tait and J.S.L. Browne of McGill University, V.E. Henderson and E.W. McHenry of the University of Toronto, K. Ferguson of the University of Western Ontario and G.H. Ettinger of Queen's University met in McHenry's office in the Hygiene Building to establish the Canadian Physiological Society. Over two decades later in 1957, McHenry played an instrumental role in the organization of the Canadian Federation of Biological Societies. During the following year, McHenry was one of the leaders in the formation of the Nutrition Society of Canada. In addition, his work with the Ontario Departments of Health and Public Welfare demonstrated his commitment to putting into practice his knowledge of nutrition.

An individualist with strongly held opinions, McHenry exemplified the innovative thinking brought to the problems of health care by the teaching staff of the School of Hygiene. Like some of his fellow departmental heads, Earle McHenry could be irritatingly irreverent in his questioning of the established order. He challenged the system both within the School, much to the chagrin of the administration, and outside in the larger community. However, his probing criticism most always had as its focus the advancement of knowledge or the improvement of health conditions.

McHenry was an articulate spokesman for what became known in many circles as the philosophy of the School of Hygiene. Typical of his provocative approach was his paper in the late 1940s entitled "Confusion and Stupidity in Nutrition Education" in which he enunciated his three "lessons":

1. Those of us who are interested in nutrition education should get together and agree to tell the same story;
2. Those of us who guide nutrition education need to remember that information which is simple to us is complicated to those who lack familiarity with the subject;
3. The third lesson . . . is that of concentration. . . . Why waste our time and money by spreading our efforts very thinly over every possible endeavour? The lesson of the water drops is that the repetition of a simple process, concentrated on one spot, eventually gives results.

With this type of emphasis, McHenry was able to instill in his junior faculty members and students the tradition of combining research, teaching and public service, the hallmark of the School of Hygiene.[25]

PARASITOLOGY

For over a decade dating back to the late 1930s, medical parasitology, the study of how parasites invade and live in the human body, was taught in the School of Hygiene because of the generosity of the Ontario Research Foundation (O.R.F.). The Council permitted A.M. Fallis to give instruction to undergraduate, postgraduate and graduate students. However, soon after 1945, the suitability of this arrangement came into question. The result of the re-assessment of the Sub-department of Parasitology over a number of years was the decision to upgrade to the status of a full department.[26]

By the fall of 1948, the four-year-old Sub-department of Parasitology was still primarily a part-time operation. The head was Professor A.M. Fallis. To help with the teaching load, J.F.A. Sprent was appointed an assistant professor. Both Fallis and Sprent were full-time members of the Ontario Research Foundation. An associate in tropical medicine, Dr. R.G. Struthers worked principally in the laboratory of the Ontario Department of Health.[27] Although not given recognition in the Calendar, Dr. Fred A. Urquhart, an entomologist in the Royal Ontario Museum, gave instruction on medical and veterinary entomology to engineers and veterinarians in the School of Hygiene.[28] The only full-time person in the Department was Dr. Ella Kuitunen.[29]

A substantial growth in number of students, particularly graduate students, taking courses overtaxed the part-time faculty. In order to increase the staff, Fallis drew attention to the growing teaching load. In 1947, he wrote to Dr. Defries who reported the following to President Sidney Smith:

> An increasing number of graduate students enrolled in the Department of Zoology desired instruction in parasitology. At present there is no course in parasitology offered in that department. In establishing a course in parasitology in the School of Hygiene, instruction for the post-graduate students proceeding to the Diploma in Public Health was provided. Afterwards this was extended so as to include in the classes for instruction graduate students in engineering proceeding to the Master of Science degree and later, the veterinarians proceeding to the Diploma in Veterinary Public Health. For these several groups a basic course is given. This is now supplemented in respect of the engineers and veterinarians by some special instruction in which Professor Urquhart has assisted. The problem has become more involved through the request for instruction from graduate students in Zoology who desire to use parasitology as a minor subject or even to become parasitologists eventually. It is evident, therefore, that there has been a substantial increase in the amount of instruction.[30]

Meanwhile, the enlargement of the Ontario Research Foundation's research program in parasitology where Fallis worked full-time created for him a genuine concern about the ability of the part-time faculty to offer effective instruction in the School. Clearly, something had to be done.

What followed was a series of meetings and exchanges of memoranda over the next four and a half years. Fallis summarized the results as follows:

> Until 1948 the teaching at the University had been supplied *gratis* by the Foundation. With the demand for additional courses and graduate research it seemed logical to suggest that the university should obtain its own personnel. Fallis advised the university

> of his willingness to resign and let it select its own staff. He felt research at the Foundation was being neglected and the university budget carried the teaching responsibilities to a limited extent only. Announcement of these concerns led in 1952 to discussions of President Sidney Smith with Dr. Speakman,* Dr. Defries and Dr. J.R. Dymond, Head, Department of Zoology. In keeping with the co-operation that had prevailed over the years it was agreed that a resignation be discouraged and that the university would transfer annually to the Foundation an amount that would pay for an additional technician and a portion of the salaries of Fallis and Sprent. This payment was in addition to the small budget the university provided the [Sub-department] to support Dr. Kuitunen, a technician, and provided for limited equipment and supplies. Fallis and Sprent accepted the arrangement conscious of the co-operative spirit that had prevailed among their superiors over the years. Otherwise, the situation might have been most difficult as some in other departments of the university opposed the association and especially the arrangements for supervision of graduate students.[31]

The administration of the University of Toronto agreed to pay part of the salaries of Fallis and Sprent with the payment going directly to the Ontario Research Foundation and also the salary of a technician. Moreover, the university agreed to give adequate status to parasitology and to permit of the development of the work in this field as it relates to both research and teaching. The Sub-department was to be elevated to a Department in the School of Hygiene[32] which occurred in 1952.[33] (The Department of Parasitology was transferred entirely from the Ontario Research Foundation to the School of Hygiene in 1966.)[34]

At about the same time as these negotiations were in progress, Dr. Sprent resigned to accept an appointment at the University of Queensland in Australia. His replacement was R.S. Freeman from the University of Southern Illinois.[35]

The Department of Parasitology offered two courses. Medical parasitology was a lecture and laboratory course of fifty hours. It examined the "etiology, mode of transmission, life history, laboratory diagnosis, methods of prevention and control of parasitic diseases". The laboratory work involved the examination of parasites, the practice of diagnosis and the study of insects, ticks and mites. General parasitology consisted of thirty lectures and ninety hours of laboratory exercises and demonstrations. It focussed on the principles of parasitism, the classification of organisms and the study of their forms and structures, the life history of parasites, host-parasite relationships and the principles of immunity. The laboratory work familiarized the students with the form of parasites and the technique for doing autopsies on animals to recover and identify parasites.[36]

Throughout these years, a number of students completed graduate dissertations. In 1949, D. Davis was awarded a Ph.D. for his thesis on the ecology of blackflies. There were seven M.A. dissertations written.[37] An illustration of the type of research done by graduate students in parasitology was given in the Annual Report of the School in 1954:

> Mr. D.F. Bennett was awarded the degree of M.A.; his thesis concerned an arthropod parasite Cuterebra emasculator, in chipmunks and a discussion of the Genus Cephenemyia. Mr. Bennett is continuing the study and investigating this group of

*Dr. H.B. Speakman was, in 1952, the Director of the Ontario Research Foundation.

> parasites that live on nestling birds. Mr. R.C. Anderson continued his investigation of filarids in birds. He discovered a new parasite in ducks and published a description of it, together with descriptions of other microfilariae that occur in these birds. His work was supported by the National Research Council and the Ontario Research Foundation. Mr. E. Turnbull began a study of a trematode that is an external parasite on tropical and other fish and is apt to cause mortality.[38]

Such work attracted international recognition to the teaching of parasitology in Toronto. Outside of Canada, many believed, as Fallis has noted, that the Ontario Research Foundation which funded the operations of the Department was a part of the university.[39]

The application of parasitology to the solution of medical problems was part of the work of Dr. Ella Kuitunen. In the second half of the 1940s and into the 1950s, she undertook a series of studies on parasitic diseases among the inhabitants of the Canadian Arctic. Supported by the Defense Research Board and the Government of Canada Public Health Research Grants, Kuitunen with the aid of Mrs. Zoe Fleming investigated trichinosis in the animal and human population in the Canadian North; trichinosis is a disease due to infection with trichina, a small parasite, that is caused by eating undercooked meat containing *Trichinella spiralis.*[40] Her research included visits to the Arctic in the summer.[41] During 1951 and 1952, Kuitunen studied two outbreaks of trichinosis.[42] In 1953, she resigned to join the Division of Laboratories of the Ontario Department of Health from which she eventually retired after a successful career.[43]

Many of the accomplishments of teaching and research in parasitology in the School of Hygiene were due to the efforts of Murray Fallis. Conscious of the interdisciplinary nature of the School of Hygiene, Fallis found the School an hospitable environment for the development of parasitology, itself an interdisciplinary field. "It has been the consistent policy", Fallis wrote to the President of the University of Toronto in 1961, "to conduct fundamental research and present courses that would meet the needs of those with a medical background and others with a basic training in Biological Sciences."[44] For Fallis, parasitology in the School of Hygiene made valuable contributions to diagnostic and preventive medical services in the treatment and control of parasitic diseases such as pinworms in children. The work in Fallis's department shed light on the role of parasites in food and water, the influence of environmental factors on the prevalence and spread of parasitic diseases, and research in immunity. Like the other basic sciences of public health, nutrition and microbiology, fundamental research in parasitology, however remote from the study of human beings, had "important implications" for human health.[45] For example, Fallis, using the Wildlife Research Station of the Ontario Department of Lands and Forests in Algonquin Park in the 1950s, undertook during the summer months the study of how a certain species of blackfly transmitted parasites to ducks and grouse. This same type of blackfly, Simulium, in Central Africa, carried a worm called Onchocerca that was responsible for the disease, onchocerciasis, causing blindness in its victims. Fallis' research assisted in the development of a program by the World Health Organization and other agencies to control blackflies in parts of Africa.[46]

The Sub-department of Parasitology in the School of Hygiene was a unique entity. Because of the support from the Ontario Research Foundation, the University of Toronto was one of the few Canadian universities with postgraduate and graduate education in parasitology. In keeping with the tradition of the School of Hygiene, Professor Fallis and his colleagues used fundamental research on insects and parasites to help in understanding diseases in humans.[47]

VIROLOGY AND ELECTRON MICROSCOPY

Research on human viruses originated in the University of Toronto with the work of Dr. James Craigie and then Dr. Ronald Hare in the 1930s. The recognition of the important role of viruses in human diseases resulted in the initiation of the first formal courses in the School with the establishment of the Sub-department of Virus Studies in 1942; two years later, the name was changed to the Sub-department of Virus Infections. Craigie's contribution to the development of typhus vaccine and Hare's work on influenza virus and a vaccine in the war years saved thousands of lives. This fact underscored the importance of virological research. Conscious of its possibilities, Defries moved to strengthen the scientific staff and technical facilities for the study of viruses.[48]

Within the span of a decade, the diagnosis of virus infections evolved from "an academic exercise for research workers" to "a practical reality" in medical diagnostic services.[49] Technological advances in the 1930s, 1940s and 1950s played an essential role in making possible the ready isolation and identification of viruses. High-speed centrifuges, special filters, radioactive isotopes, the use of fertile eggs for virus cultivation and the development of *in vitro* cultivation of viruses in a chemically defined medium were essential to the study of viruses. Especially significant was the employment of the electron microscope to demonstrate viruses "under the microscope."[50]

Initially built in Germany in the early 1930s, the electron microscope was exhibited first in Canada at a seminar in the McLennan Physics Laboratory of the University of Toronto in April of 1934. With funding from the National Research Council, the Banting Foundation for Medical Research, the Columbia Carbon Company of New York and the Ontario Mining Association, research work in the late 1930s and the early 1940s led to the construction of prototypes and the assembly in 1944 of the University of Toronto Electron Microscope by Grantley Woodward.[51] The value of this microscope to medical research was recognized speedily:

> In the early stages of the application pictures were taken of disease agents, many of which are below the range of optical microscopes. Even in the case of those which are visible in ordinary microscopes many new details are made visible. It is not beyond the realm of probability that we may soon be able to make convincing studies of the life history of these minute individuals which serve such an important function in the human body, for good or ill.[52]

To illustrate this point, the authors of the book on the Toronto Electron Microscope employed micrographs "taken at Toronto" of the pneumococcus, the tubercle bacillus and the smallpox virus which revealed the internal structure of these organisms.[53] In the early 1940s, Dr. Craigie of the School of Hygiene, who was the first head of the new Sub-department of Virus Studies, co-operated with the team developing the electron microscope in the McLennan Laboratories in their efforts to apply their technology to the study of viruses.[54] The McLennan Laboratory was located only a short distance west of the Hygiene Building. Craigie's successor and others were drawn to Toronto partly because of the opportunities provided by the electron microscope and other appropriate facilities in the Connaught Laboratories.[55]

RESEARCH ON VIRUSES

The study of Virus Infections was part of the teaching arm of the Connaught Medical Research Laboratories program throughout the period. These virus studies used facilities in the College Division and Spadina Division of the Laboratories, but the centre of the work was the Dufferin Division where the original main laboratory building underwent remodelling and the installation of special equipment. Especially noteworthy was the acquisition of an electron microscope donated by the J.P. Bickell Foundation of Toronto after 1945. Grants from the Canadian Life Insurance Officers' Association, the Department of National Health and Welfare and the National Foundation for Infantile Paralysis Incorporated of New York funded much of this pioneering program.[56]

STAFF CHANGES

The first problem confronting the Sub-department of Virus Infections in the aftermath of the war was the replacement of the senior staff. At the end of April, 1946, James Craigie resigned to accept an appointment in the Imperial Cancer Research Fund Laboratories in London, England. Craigie had just received the United States of America Typhus Commission Medal for "advancing medical science and public health through research in typhus" and was President-Elect of the Society of American Bacteriologists. His research in Toronto had "developed a new tool in epidemiological practice through the use of bacteriophage in tracing outbreaks of typhoid fever."[57] Four months later, Ronald Hare left the School to assume the Professorship of Bacteriology at St. Thomas's Hospital Medical School of the University of London in England.[58] "I shall always look upon my stay at the University [of Toronto] as one of the happiest periods of my life", Hare wrote graciously, "and consider my present appointment to be largely due to the appointment given me in Canada."[59] Much later, Hare acknowledged his fondness for the experiences and the lessons learned in Toronto. His memoirs offer a rare insider's view of the major figures in the School and the Laboratories in the 1930s and 1940s.[60]

Another member of the team in virus research during the war years who left was Dr. Laurella McClelland. She had joined the Connaught Laboratories in 1941 after graduating in 1938 from the medical faculty of the University of Toronto.[61] McClelland oversaw the production of typhus vaccine. With Hare, she participated in the development of an influenza vaccine.[62] Hare and McClelland made an important discovery about influenza virus. As Dr. Andrew J. Rhodes noted, they uncovered the fact that "influenza virus agglutinates red blood cells thus rendering detection of the virus relatively simple. Furthermore, agglutination of red cells is prevented by influenza antibody. This procedure became a popular test for immunity to influenza."[63] Later she collaborated with van Rooyen in the study of chemical compounds with viricidal properties. McClelland left Toronto to accept an appointment in an American pharmaceutical company.[64]

Defries lost no time in finding a successor to Craigie and others. In less than a month, he appointed Clennel Evelyn van Rooyen (1907-1989) to be a professor of the School of Hygiene and a research associate in the Connaught Laboratories. Dr. van Rooyen formally joined the School in September, 1946.[65] This was the beginning of what one might call the "Edinburgh Connection" with the School's Sub-department of Virus Studies. In the next four years, three other graduates of the University of Edinburgh came to join van Rooyen in Toronto. Later in the middle of the 1950s, van Rooyen moved to Dalhousie University in Halifax.

Born in what is now Sri Lanka (Ceylon), van Rooyen received his medical degrees, M.B., Ch.B., M.D., and the D.Sc. from the University of Edinburgh. From 1931 to 1939, van Rooyen

Dr. C.E. van Rooyen (in uniform) and Dr. James Craigie with Mrs. Craigie and the Craigie children.

lectured there in bacteriology where he met a young Scottish physician.[66] Together, they authored a major medical textbook, *Virus Diseases of Man*, which was completed "largely during the troubled times between the months of September, 1938 and December, 1939."[67] That man's name was Andrew James Rhodes.

Both van Rooyen and Rhodes left Edinburgh for war service elsewhere. Responsible for "special investigations in epidemic jaundice, typhus fever and certain other diseases", van Rooyen was a major in the Royal Army Medical Corps in the Near East.[68] Rhodes worked as a pathologist and bacteriologist in the Emergency Medical Services, first in Edinburgh and later in Shrewsbury, Shropshire, England until 1945.[69]

Like van Rooyen, Rhodes, who was born in Inverness, Scotland in September, 1911, earned his university degrees in medicine, M.B., Ch.B. and later the M.D. from the University of Edinburgh. At the end of the war, he became a lecturer in the Department of Bacteriology and Immunology in the London School of Hygiene and Tropical Medicine. Then in June, 1947, Rhodes came to Toronto after accepting a challenging offer from the Director of the School of Hygiene and the Connaught Medical Research Laboratories in the University of Toronto.[70] That was the beginning of the Toronto career of the future Director of the School of Hygiene.

Five months after Rhodes joined the university in 1947, Defries secured the services of a third graduate of the University of Edinburgh, Dr. Angus F. Graham, who taught Virus Infections part-time in the School. Graham was a Canadian. A chemical engineer who graduated from the University of Toronto in 1938, he gained a M.A.Sc. there in 1939 and then went on to the University of Edinburgh to earn a Ph.D. in 1942. During the war, Graham did secret biochemical research on gas warfare. He also was a demonstrator and then a lecturer in the Department of Biochemistry, University of Edinburgh. He taught a special course on the physical chemistry of enzymes and proteins. "Dr. Graham was associated with Dr. van Rooyen in the study of virus diseases", Defries pointed out in a letter to President Sidney Smith, "relating his work to new developments in the field of nuclear physics."[71] Assisting van Rooyen in his investigation of cell-virus relationships, Graham headed a team of researchers that utilized "bacteriophage strains 'tagged' with radioactive isotopes, such as carbon-14 to examine the various reactions and development of new virus particles that take place when infections occur."[72] Graham left the School and the Laboratories after five years to work in the United States before returning to McGill University.[73]

The fourth graduate of the University of Edinburgh to come to the C.M.R.L. was Dr. George Dempster in July of 1950. After completing a medical degree in the University of Edinburgh, Dempster lectured in the Department of Bacteriology, joined the Royal Army Medical Corps for service in Africa and then returned to the university.[74] In Toronto, Dempster investigated the antigenic character of influenza strains in Ontario.[75] He later became head of the Department of Bacteriology in the medical school, University of Saskatchewan, Saskatoon.[76]

The School's Calendar for the session of 1952 to 1953 noted the addition of another scientist to Virus Infections. His name was J.F. Crawley.[77] For a number of years, Crawley had worked in the Connaught Laboratories. During the Second World War, Crawley was a member of the group developing typhus vaccine.[78] In 1950, he finished a Ph.D. program in the University of Toronto with a thesis on the virus of western equine encephalitis.[79] Two years later, Crawley took over from Dr. Everett G. Kerslake as director of the Laboratories' new section of veterinary medicine. This division developed a variety of vaccines for use by veterinarians. Earlier, the value of virus studies had been more widely recognized when van Rooyen and Rhodes were appointed to the staff in the Ontario Veterinary College, Guelph and lectured to veterinary students.[80]

In the 1950s, the Sub-department of Virus Infections was a training ground for scientists who went on to other fields of inquiry. Dr. Louis Siminovitch was an example of this pattern.[81] Siminovitch, who later developed a notable scientific career in medical genetics and immunology in the University of Toronto, was a member of van Rooyen's research unit. After working at L'Institut Pasteur in Paris, France, from 1947 to 1953, Siminovitch joined the Connaught Medical Research Laboratories where he stayed until 1956.[82] At the Connaught, Siminovitch and Graham employed a number of new techniques such as bacteriophage and radioactive isotopes to study changes brought about by infections. Siminovitch's studies on bacterial viruses demonstrated how the staff of the Connaught and the School of Hygiene integrated innovative approaches into research. In 1956, Graham and Siminovitch became members of the School's new Department of Microbiology. Afterwards, Siminovitch joined the division of biological research in the Ontario Cancer Institute and later was Professor of Medical Genetics in the University of Toronto.[83]

RAYMOND PARKER'S CONTRIBUTIONS

Dr. Raymond Parker's role in the Sub-department of Virus Infections illustrated the vital role of fundamental research in the School of Hygiene and the value of the close link between the School and the Connaught Medical Research Laboratories. Devoted to pure research, Parker nonetheless acknowledged the worth of the unique structure of the School and the Laboratories. "I like the idea of this dual institution", he confided to Defries in May, 1949, "as it was organized. I like the people here. I like the idea of working in and for my own country after seventeen years abroad. And though I was born a Maritimer, I am even beginning to like Toronto, which I know will surprise you."[84]

The organization of the first international course in tissue culture during July of 1948 in the School of Hygiene Building testified to the importance of Parker's studies on the subject. Supported by the Tissue Culture Association of the United States and also a grant from the National Cancer Institute of Washington, D.C., the course which was offered thereafter annually at different research facilities around the U.S. attracted many distinguished scientists.[85] The publication of the second edition of Parker's *Methods of Tissue Culture* in 1950 was more evidence of the influence and rising stature of the School's professor of experimental cytology.

VIRUS DISEASES OF MAN

The science of virology developed conspicuously in the 1940s, a fact reflected by the publications of the new members of the School's Department of Virus Infections. In 1948, the second edition of *Virus Diseases of Man* by van Rooyen and Rhodes chronicled the advances in virology since 1940 when the first edition was published. It was a pioneering work of reference. The revised book drew attention to how research had increased the scientific understanding of viruses. The authors noted these changes in the preface:

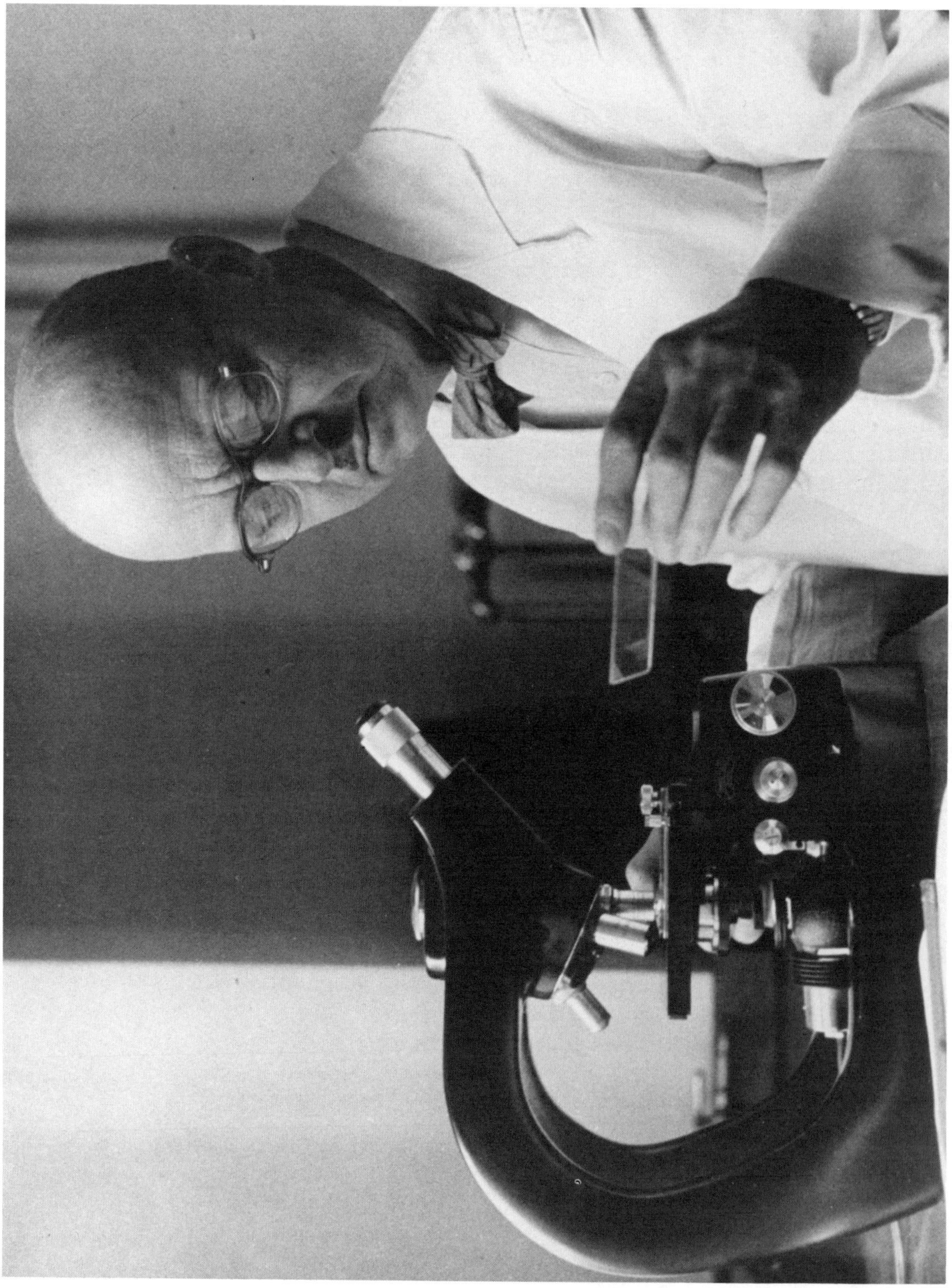

Dr. Raymond Parker circa 1958.

> Nearly ten years have passed since the first edition appeared, and in this time so many advances have taken place in the fundamental and applied aspects of virus research that a thorough revision of the text has become necessary. Thus the following chapters have been rewritten and expanded: The Electron Microscope; Use of the Fertile Egg for Virus Cultivation; Mumps; Yellow Fever; Influenza; Psittacosis; Epidemiology, Diagnosis and Prevention of Smallpox; Antirabies treatment; Poliomyelitis; St. Louis, Japanese, and North American Equine Encephalomyelitis. Among virus diseases described in this volume for the first time are: German measles; West Nile disease and related conditions; Colorado tick fever; Newcastle disease; epidemic keratoconjunctivitis; pneumonitis and atypical pneumonia; Venezuelan equine encephalomyelitis; Russian spring-summer encephalitis; infective hepatitis and serum jaundice. Altogether some twenty new virus infections have been added and reference is made to some others of lesser concern.[86]

Both van Rooyen and Rhodes acknowledged a variety of individuals for their help in specific areas: Airey (diseases of the skin); Burton (electron microscopy); Boswell (electron microscopy); Crawley (equine encephalomyelitis and statistical methods); Coutts (lymphogranuloma); Graham (physical chemistry); and McClelland (influenza).[87]

To assist medical students and practitioners as well as veterinarians, Rhodes and van Rooyen wrote the more modest *Textbook Of Virology For Students And Practitioners Of Medicine* published in 1949. The volume was the product of the lectures given by the two authors over a period of the previous fifteen years. Like their major work on virus diseases, the smaller textbook was revised and reprinted in five editions over the next twenty years.[88]

The potential worth of the research and teaching in the Sub-department of Virus Infections was recognized by one distinguished visitor to the School in December of 1949. C-E.A. Winslow, in the report of the third accreditation visit of the American Public Health Association's Committee on Professional Education, stated:

> While supported primarily by the Connaught Medical Research Laboratories rather than the School, the work of Drs. C.E. van Rooyen and A.J. Rhodes at the Dufferin Division of the Connaught Laboratories deserves special mention as part of the School background. These investigators have done pioneer work in the field of viruses. Their application of the electron microscope has been outstanding (and has led to an excellent procedure for smallpox diagnosis). Studies now being conducted by Dr. R.C. Parker on the effect of various stimuli on mammalian cells in tissue culture offer promise of important new light on the problems of malignancy.[89]

Parker's work on tissue culture and Rhodes' interest in polio virus were instrumental in the development of a vaccine against poliomyelitis.

POLIO VACCINE

Beyond the inner circle of those involved, the story of the development of polio vaccine by staff from the Connaught Medical Research Laboratories and the School of Hygiene is not known widely. Much of the reason for that was the direct result of the secrecy surrounding the research on poliomyelitis in Canada because of the wishes of the American body financing the studies. The National Foundation for Infantile Paralysis Incorporated of New York (N.F.I.P.), better known as "The March of Dimes", funded numerous research programs. In 1940, the N.F.I.P. provided a grant for physiological research by Dr. Donald Solandt of the

School's Department of Physiological Hygiene; it gave support to Solandt for nine years. During the summer of 1949, the Foundation showed interest in the work of Rhodes on poliomyelitis and asked him to undertake a special project. It provided a grant which was for the purchase and maintenance of large numbers of monkeys housed in the basement of the School of Hygiene Building for use by Rhodes in his investigations on polio. "As the (Directors of the) Foundation are embarassed by making grants for this work in the University of Toronto from the campaign funds of the March of Dimes in the United States", Defries reported to President Sidney Smith, "I understand that they would appreciate no public announcement of these grants."[90] Over the next five years, the N.F.I.P. gave hundreds of thousands of dollars for research on a polio vaccine in the Connaught Medical Research Laboratories.[91]

The development of a polio vaccine was the product of the efforts of many individual scientists joining together as a team to tackle a specific problem. Dr. Defries was conscious of the value of the team approach. In the words of Rhodes, Defries was "an amazingly competent, cool and collected research director."[92] Interestingly, the effort to produce an effective polio vaccine in Toronto resembled in some ways the earlier campaign of FitzGerald and Defries to prepare diphtheria toxoid in the 1920s and 1930s.

The Toronto program also demonstrated how fundamental research had practical applications far beyond the scope of the original objective. The research of Parker in experimental cytology was a dramatic example of this fact. For years dating back to the 1930s, Parker studied the growth of cells in an artificial medium. The Connaught's research laboratories in Rooms 219 to 223 of the Hygiene Building were the centre of Parker's studies in tissue culture.[93] With funding from the Ontario Cancer Treatment and Research Foundation and later the new National Cancer Institute of Canada, Parker focussed his research on cancer and the "development of a chemically defined medium for animal cells in tissue culture." Defries later pointed out Parker's convictions about the value of his research: "If cells could be cultivated in completely defined media, it should be possible not only to detect more readily any differences that might exist between normal and malignant cells but also to improve the tissue culture method for many other sorts of undertakings, including the propagation of viruses."[94] In 1947, Dr. Joseph F. Morgan joined Parker and, with Miss Helen J. Morton, prepared the first chemically defined synthetic culture medium which the three scientists described in a paper published in 1950 under the title of "Nutrition of Animal Cells in Tissue Culture. I. Initial Studies on a Synthetic Medium."[95] This was Medium 199; it contained sixty ingredients.[96] The work in Parker's laboratory in the School of Hygiene Building established the basis of the modern use of tissue culture technology.

Rhodes, then involved in the attempt to propagate poliomyelitis virus in cell culture in order to prepare an inactivated vaccine for polio, recognized the potential of Medium 199. Rhodes later noted that "it was in fact Mixture 199 that played a major role in the modern era of progress in the laboratory study of viruses in cell cultures."[97]

Using Medium 199, Rhodes and his colleagues in 1952 grew polio virus in monkey and human tissue. Because it possessed neither serum nor proteins, the Medium was ideal for the production of vaccine. The three main types of polio virus were identified in 1951; Rhodes and his associates working in the Virus Research Department of Toronto's Hospital For Sick Children grew them successfully in Medium 199.[98] Benefitting from these findings, Dr. Jonas

Salk of the University of Pittsburgh inoculated humans with a vaccine consisting of fluids obtained from tissue culture of monkey cells grown in Medium 199 and infected with polio virus. This vaccine was inactivated chemically. To prove the safety and effectiveness of the vaccine, the National Foundation for Infantile Paralysis of New York established a controlled trial of the vaccine in almost two million children in forty-four American states, Finland and three Canadian provinces. The Connaught Medical Research Laboratories was given the task of manufacturing large quantities of virus culture fluids for what now is known as the Francis trial.[99]

At the forty-third meeting of the Canadian Public Health Association in Edmonton, Alberta during September, 1955, an American representative of the campaign against polio acknowledged the role of the staff of the Connaught Medical Research Laboratories and the School of Hygiene. In an address to that convention, Dr. Hart E. Van Riper, the Medical Director of the National Foundation for Infantile Paralysis of New York, singled out four major contributions:

> One of the early Canadian contributions to vaccine development was the work of Morgan, Morton and Parker in discovering a satisfactory synthetic medium for the feeding of animal cells in tissue culture. . . .
>
> A second major contribution of Canadian research was the early demonstration of methods for quantity production of poliomyelitis viruses in culture of monkey kidney. This was accomplished in 1953 at the Connaught Laboratories of the University of Toronto by Rhodes, Farrell, Wood, Franklin, Shimada and Macmorine.
>
> A third Canadian contribution to vaccine development relates to an important safety factor in its manufacture. Occasionally normal and healthy monkeys harbour Virus B in their kidney. While the preparation of poliomyelitis virus fluids was going on at the Connaught, it was anticipated that these fluids produced from cultures of monkey kidney, might also contain Virus B. Wood and Shimada undertook to study this problem . . . . They isolated six strains of Virus B from pools of poliomyelitis virus fluids. This represented a contamination rate of about 1% (6 of 650 pools). They also showed that under the conditions at which the poliomyelitis virus was inactivated, for vaccine production, namely, in a solution of 1:4000 formalin at 37 degrees centigrade, the rate of inactivation of a strain of Virus B was such that no infectivity could be demonstrated after 22 hours. . . . This work adds confidence to the safety of vaccines prepared from tissue cultures of rhesus and cynomolgus monkeys and also confirms the need for regular testing of poliomyelitis virus pools for Virus B prior to inactivation.
>
> A fourth, and highly significant Canadian contribution to vaccine development was the actual production at Connaught of practically all the poliomyelitis virus fluids which were converted at two United States Laboratories into the vaccines used in the 1954 field trials . . . .
>
> A recent report by Farrell, Wood, Macmorine, Shimada and Graham describes the materials and technique used at Connaught for the production of 5,521 litres of tissue culture fluid . . .[100]

The man largely responsible for the expeditious manner in which the whole polio project was handled was Defries. Rather fittingly, the preparation of the polio vaccine was the climax of Defries' career just as he was about to retire.

Former American President Harry Truman congratulating Dr. Defries on receiving the Albert Lasker Award in 1955.

International recognition of Defries' contribution to the production of polio vaccine for general use came from the American Public Health Association. In 1955, Defries was the recipient of the distinguished Albert Lasker Award In Public Health Administration. The citation for this honour summarized succinctly Defries' accomplishment, not only in bringing about the control of polio, but also his career as a public health professional:

> Seldom is there combined in one man great scientific knowledge and judgment, together with the personality and organizing ability to carry through new technical advances in the control of disease. From his position as head, and to a considerable extent the creator of the Connaught Medical Research Laboratories and the School of Hygiene of the University of Toronto, Robert Defries has played a unique part in the development of preventive medicine and public health in Canada. . . .
>
> The public health professions in the United States and Canada are deeply in debt to the Connaught for developing a method of large-scale production and supplying nearly all the virus used in the successful field trials of the Salk poliomyelitis vaccine in both countries in 1954. The fruitful use in 1955 of this virus in Canada is also founded on the work at the Connaught Laboratories under Dr. Defries.[101]

CONCLUSION

When R.D. Defries finished medical school in 1911, thousands of Canadians died yearly from infectious diseases such as diphtheria, measles, poliomyelitis, scarlet fever, smallpox, typhoid fever and tuberculosis. When he retired at the end of June, 1955 (Defries died in 1975), epidemics of these diseases in Canada were beginning to decline in their size and severity.

Defries' career spanned the evolution of health services from the part-time and voluntary efforts of lay people to the permanent and professional work of specialists. With John G. FitzGerald, Defries built the Connaught Laboratories and then the School of Hygiene into major institutions. FitzGerald and Defries demonstrated how scientific research could be utilized to finance and to further the development of general health services through the education of public health experts. The intimate linkage between the Connaught Laboratories and the School of Hygiene made possible the establishment of a system of medical officers of health and other specialists long before the acceptance by the federal and provincial governments of financial responsibility for public health. Moreover, through the Canadian Public Health Association and its Journal which he edited for decades, Defries helped to formulate over a long period a growing political consensus about the role of government in the provision of health care.

The graduates of the University of Toronto School of Hygiene from 1927 to 1955 who entered health departments at every level of government in the country were a testament to the influence of Defries on the development of the public health system in Canada. Although small in numbers by the standards of the 1980s, these men and women constituted for the most part the leadership of the Canadian public health profession. Including the graduates from courses prior to 1927, 554 candidates received the Diploma in Public Health after completing requirements in the School; 70, the Master of Applied Science (Engineering); 63, the Diploma in Veterinary Public Health; 42, the Diploma in Hospital Administration; 26, the Diploma in Dental Public Health; 24, the Certificate in Public Health; and 7, the Diploma in Industrial Hygiene, for a total of 776 graduates. In addition, there were a significant number of M.A. and Ph.D. theses supervised by the staff of the School.[1] The variety of diplomas and degrees available in the School reflected Defries' own appreciation of the multifaceted nature of public health. His career was an illustration of this holistic view.

Defries was much more than a physician; he was an administrator, a teacher, an editor, a manufacturer of biological products, a planner and a lobbyist. The improvement of general health standards, and his career stand out as a model for this betterment, dependent on an understanding of the scientific, social, economic and political realities of our society. That interdisciplinary and general approach, the hallmark of the Connaught Laboratories and the School of Hygiene, continues to merit serious consideration by contemporary educators of health professionals.

SCHOOL OF HYGIENE'S UNIQUENESS

From 1927 to 1955, the University of Toronto School of Hygiene had a distinctive identity emanating from its relationship to the Connaught Laboratories. Dr. John G. FitzGerald's and then Dr. Robert D. Defries' policy of making joint appointments of staff to the School and the Connaught forged a vital link between scientific research in the laboratories and education of

Dr. R.D. Defries on his retirement

Dr. Defries' final report as Director of the School of Hygiene

public health professionals in the classrooms. In essence, the School was the academic arm of the Connaught Laboratories. These two institutions sharing human resources and facilities in the Hygiene Building embodied the principle of combining research, teaching and public service.

It was that unique blend of research, teaching and public service devised by FitzGerald in the Connaught Laboratories and the Department of Hygiene and Sanitary Science in the Faculty of Medicine of the University of Toronto which attracted the officers of the Rockefeller Foundation to Ontario's capital city. Obviously, they regarded the FitzGerald operation as a model for their international activities in public health because the Rockefeller Foundation provided financing for an endowment and the construction of a building to establish the School of Hygiene. Throughout the era from 1927 to 1955, the University of Toronto School of Hygiene was one of the Rockefeller Schools of Public Health. For most of this period, the major source of funding for the School came from the Foundation which also donated additional support to undertake research in nutrition, and to train medical officers of health and public health nurses.

Because of its status as a Rockefeller School of Public Health, the School of Hygiene had a global orientation. This characteristic was reinforced by the participation of staff members in the international public health community. Both Dr. John FitzGerald and Dr. Donald Fraser attended conferences at the League of Nations representing Canada. Moreover, FitzGerald, serving first on the Health Board and then as a scientific director to the International Health Division of the Rockefeller Foundation, toured numerous countries. The international stature of the School of Hygiene was obvious in the steady stream of visitors from other countries who came annually to observe and to study in the Hygiene Building. Without a doubt, these contributions by members of the School of Hygiene laid the foundation for the Canadian role in the World Health Organization following the Second World War.

Before 1955, the School of Hygiene was the national centre for teaching, research and planning in public health. The staff of the School, through the Canadian Public Health Association and the Canadian Journal of Public Health, lobbied federal and provincial governments for the adoption of basic health services across the country. They promoted water and sewage treatment, public health nursing, milk pasteurization, mass immunization programs and a variety of other reforms to better the health of average Canadians. In these campaigns, the staff of the School established a national public health constituency and most of all, the profession of health officers.

Above all else, the School of Hygiene was the staff college for Canadian health officers. The Diploma in Public Health, the primary course offered by the School, qualified physicians professionally to be medical officers of health. Open only to graduates of medical schools and taught jointly with the University of Toronto Faculty of Medicine's Department of Hygiene and Preventive Medicine, the D.P.H. produced the leaders of Canada's public health services at the municipal, provincial and federal levels. These graduates became the first generation of modern health administrators and planners in the country.

Applicability was the trademark of the course work for the D.P.H. From its inception until the 1920s, it was, in essence, an apprenticeship program. Later, the "hands on" experience of service in health departments and related facilities constituted a formal requirement for the completion of the diploma. In addition, the part-time teaching by officials from the Ontario Department of Health and municipal health officers created a close relationship between the School and the public service, the future employers of the School's graduates. Ironically, the practical emphasis of the D.P.H. that made the postgraduate program so effective in educating physicians to be health officers was later to become a point of criticism in the debate over whether "Master's Degrees or Diplomas" should be the basic qualification for the profession of medical officers of health. However, prior to the middle of the 1950s, the stress on practicality in the D.P.H. program was ideally suited to that stage in the evolution of public health services in Canada.

The School's curriculum for the D.P.H. mirrored the evolution of the public health system in Canada. Initially, there was an emphasis on sanitation in the course for the diploma taught by FitzGerald and Defries in the Department of Hygiene and Sanitary Science. By the 1920s and into the 1930s, reflecting the involvement of the Connaught Laboratories in the launching of general immunization programs against diphtheria, the subject of immunology became the focus not only of the teaching of medical postgraduates taking the D.P.H. but also of the instruction of undergraduate students. The war years of the 1940s witnessed the operation of much larger schemes of mass immunization using multiple vaccines in the Canadian military.

Following the Second World War, there began to be a gradual shift in the focus of the D.P.H., evident by the 1950s, to the study of principles of the administration and planning of health care. This move marked the fading of the distinction between curative and preventive medicine. It signalled the passing of the "old public health" with its emphasis on the control of infectious diseases. With the establishment of the School's Diploma in Hospital Administration and the emergence of medical care studies, the D.P.H. course began to change once again in order to make students aware of the increasing importance of integrating all medical services; this became a major concern in the 1960s.

Despite the predominance of the D.P.H. program in the School, FitzGerald, Defries and Fraser pioneered the formation of public health education programs for non-medical health workers. Prior to 1945, public health nurses, most of whom were not university graduates, constituted the second major category of students after medical undergraduates and postgraduates. For FitzGerald, these nurses represented key health workers capable of delivering a variety of health and social services to those in need. Another group of undergraduates taught in the School were students seeking courses in the emerging fields of microbiology and nutrition.

At the other end of the spectrum from those seeking a general background in the sciences of public health, there were university graduates coming to the School for education in the emerging specialties of public health. The proliferation in the 1940s of diplomas in Industrial Health, Dental Public Health, Veterinary Public Health and Hospital Administration, as well as the establishment of a Certificate in Public Health, demonstrated the faculty's commitment to the instruction of specialists in public health.

The growth of the postgraduate diplomas was a spin-off of the research and graduate teaching done by the staff of the School of Hygiene. During the FitzGerald and Defries regimes, a small but significant number of M.A. and Ph.D. theses completed in the School revealed the growth of research in the "new public health sciences": cytology, immunochemistry, microbiology, nutritional sciences, parasitology and virology. Both

FitzGerald and Defries exhibited a shrewd eye for the scientific talent able and willing to open up new areas of research. These sciences emerged within the School's multidisciplinary approach to public health problems.

The School of Hygiene's philosophy of health education and health care espoused a view of human health much broader than the medical model. Unlike the medical model that concentrated on the treatment of individual diseases, the public health model of the School encompassed a wider spectrum of factors responsible for health, not illness. It took into account the social context, not just the etiology of diseases, and raised the question of what constituted healthiness. Most importantly, that perspective addressed the role of the relationship between the individual and the societal structures in the promotion of healthiness.

Significantly, as FitzGerald and Defries had recognized early, more than just the education of medical doctors was necessary to develop an effective system of understanding and promoting human healthiness. For this reason, FitzGerald and Defries recruited an eclectic staff that included the sanitary engineer, the health educator, the social worker, the political scientist, the public health nurse, and in a limited but nonetheless valuable way, the historian.

Interestingly, R.D. Defries' concern with the historical background of public health services in Canada was evident in his work as the editor of the *Canadian Journal of Public Health* for over thirty years and as an instructor in his course on public health administration. For decades, the two books edited by Defries, *The Development of Public Health in Canada* (Toronto, 1940) and *The Federal and Provincial Health Services in Canada* (Toronto, 1959) were the only major works on the subject.

In fact, the School of Hygiene's philosophy of public health with an interdisciplinary and a multidisciplinary focus brought together many different types of experts in an era of increasing specialization, especially in medicine. That philosophy was a practical way of overcoming the fragmentation of knowledge from medical sciences and clinical experiences. The University of Toronto School of Hygiene's philosophy, one can argue strongly, was its greatest contribution to the development of Canadian health care in the 1940s and the 1950s.

Besides promoting a philosophy of public health, the staff of the School had to face the difficulty of providing instruction in preventive medicine to medical undergraduates whose orientation was very different. By the middle of the 1920s, FitzGerald had succeeded in making such a course mandatory for "med" students. He had hoped to reorient upcoming physicians from a purely curative and clinical viewpoint towards a preventive one. In comparison with American schools, FitzGerald's undergraduate course in preventive medicine was apparently more successful. Still, there were problems. Public health matters took a back seat to the more pressing demands and relevancy of undergraduates studying to be clinicians. After 1945, despite changes in the programs of preventive medicine which introduced the subject in all years, the indifference of the student body remained a concern for educators in the School of Hygiene.

No educational institution like the School of Hygiene, especially in light of its dismantling in 1975, was without its critics, especially within the medical profession. By the mid-1950s, the success of the School in developing appropriate strategies to control infectious diseases such as diphtheria, typhoid fever and then polio led to a re-examination of its changing role. With the impending retirement of Defries, senior faculty and administrators in the university began to rethink the organization and structure of the School separated from the Connaught Laboratories. Some questioned the continuation of "one-man" departments long after the resolution of the medical problems which had prompted their initial organization. There was a desire to bring the School into a closer relationship with the medical faculty.[2] Many felt uncomfortable with the School's independent status and the positions taken by its staff in public discussions about health services. At the centre of the debate was the issue of the relationship of the School to the Faculty of Medicine. The key point was, and is to this day, not only in Canada and North America but elsewhere in the world,[3] whether a School of Public Health can best fulfill its role of bettering the health of the entire population by being placed within a medical school or outside as an independent institution.[4] Clearly in 1956, the decision was to maintain and promote the School of Hygiene's independence, a story to be told in the second volume of the School's history. Less than twenty years later, the decision of the administration of the University of Toronto was that the goals of public health, renamed community health, were best pursued within the Faculty of Medicine. The debate continues to this day.

POSTSCRIPT

Over sixty years after the founding of the University of Toronto School of Hygiene, many of the same health problems remain in different forms. Millions of human beings, especially the young, still die or suffer from preventable diseases around the globe. According to the World Health Organization, an estimated 3.5 million children under five years of age succumbed every year during the 1980s to contagious diseases.[5] This fact is an enormous tragedy in light of the existence of the means to control many of these diseases. Even in North America, contagious diseases have not disappeared but pose a serious threat, as demonstrated by the AIDS crisis. As Dr. Andrew J. Rhodes, the Director of the University of Toronto School of Hygiene from 1956 to 1970, has stressed, vaccines or other types of products manufactured in laboratories (such as antibiotics) are of little value unless health workers can use them in the treatment of the general population.[6] Developing means to get basic health services including vaccines, sera and antibiotics to those who need them was the chief accomplishment of the University of Toronto School of Hygiene from 1927 to 1955.

ABBREVIATIONS

AO	Archives of Ontario, Toronto, Ontario
ARSH	Annual Report of the School of Hygiene
CA	Connaught Archives, Connaught Laboratories Limited, North York, Ontario
CDPNHR	Canada, Department of Pensions and National Health Report
CJPH	Canadian Journal of Public Health
FFY	R.D. Defries, *The First Forty Years 1914-1955: Connaught Medical Research Laboratories University of Toronto.* (Toronto: University of Toronto Press for Connaught Medical Research Laboratories, 1968)
NAC	National Archives of Canada, Ottawa, Ontario
ODH	Ontario Department of Health
ODHAR	Ontario Department of Health Annual Report
OPHAR	Ontario Provincial Board of Health Annual Report
PHJ	Public Health Journal (predecessor of Canadian Journal of Public Health)
RAC	Rockefeller Archive Center, North Tarrytown, New York
RDCL	Report of the Director Connaught Laboratories
RDSH	Report of the Director School of Hygiene
RDFMUT	Report of the Dean, Faculty of Medicine, University of Toronto
UTA	University of Toronto Archives
UTFMC	University of Toronto Faculty of Medicine Calendar
UTSHC	University of Toronto School of Hygiene Calendar
UTSHHP	University of Toronto School of Hygiene History Papers (Deposited in University of Toronto Archives)

CHAPTER ONE: NOTES

1. Charles J. Hastings, "Democracy and Public Health Administration", *PHJ* 10:111.
2. J. Callwood, "The Miracle Factory that began in a Stable", *Macleans*, October 1, 1955, 89.
3. R.D. Defries, "The Connaught Medical Research Laboratories 1914-1948", *CJPH* 39:331.
4. G. Rosen, *A History of Public Health* (New York: M.D. Publications, 1958), 314-35.
5. J.T. Phair, "The Ontario Department of Health", in *The Federal and Provincial Health Services in Canada: A Volume Commemorating the Fiftieth Year of the Canadian Public Health Association and of the Canadian Journal of Public Health, 1910-1959*, ed. by R.D. Defries (Toronto: Canadian Public Health Association, 1959), 79.
6. Mary A. Ross, "Typhoid Fever Mortality in Ontario, 1880-1931", *CJPH* 26:81.
7. R.L. Huckstep, *Typhoid Fever and Other Salmonella Infections* (Edinburgh and London: E.S. Livingstone Ltd., 1962) and William Burrows, *Textbook of Microbiology* Seventeenth Edition (Philadelphia and London: W.B. Saunders Company, 1957), 482-3.
8. Ross, "Typhoid Fever Mortality in Ontario . . .", 82.
9. J.G. FitzGerald et al., *An Introduction to the Practice of Preventive Medicine* (St. Louis, Missouri: C.V. Mosby Company, 1922), 156-7.
10. Ross, "Typhoid Fever Mortality in Ontario . . .", 82.
11. Jonathan M. Leibenau, "Public Health and the Production and Use of Diphtheria Antitoxin in Philadelphia", *Bulletin of the History of Medicine* 61:217.
12. *Ibid.*, 216.
13. Mary A. Ross, "The Mortality in Ontario of Four Communicable Diseases of Childhood", *CJPH* 23:332.
14. Mary A. Ross, "A Statistical Study of the Mortality from Diphtheria in Ontario for the years 1880 to 1925", M.A. Thesis, University of Toronto, 1928, 28.
15. Paul Adolphus Bator, "'Saving Lives on the Wholesale Plan': Public Health Reform in the City of Toronto, 1900 to 1930", Ph.D. Thesis, University of Toronto, 1979, 31-46.
16. R. Ramsay Wright, "The Germ Theory of Disease", in the Royal Canadian Institute, *Proceedings New Series* Volume I (Toronto: Copp Clark and Co., 1884), 348.
17. Bator, "'Saving Lives on the Wholesale Plan' . . .", 122-3.
18. J.W.S. McCullough, "1910-1920 A Review of Ten Years' Progress", in OPBH, 39th AR 1920, 23.
19. ODH, "The Development of Public Health in Ontario", *CJPH* 36:111.
20. "Doctor Peter H. Bryce", *CJPH* 23:88.
21. Peter H. Bryce, "A Winter in Paris Fifty Years Ago", *Canadian Lancet and Practitioner* (May, 1931), 135-9.
22. ODH, "The Development of Public Health in Ontario", 111.
23. McCullough, "1910-1920 A Review of Ten Years' Progress", 33-4.
24. Wright, "Mr. Hanna, An Appreciation", *PHJ* 10:271.
25. Bator, "'Saving Lives on the Wholesale Plan' . . .", 36-7.
26. See Heather MacDougall, "Health is Wealth: Development of Public Health Activity in Toronto 1834-1890", Ph.D. Thesis, University of Toronto, 1981.
27. W.S. Wallace, *A History of the University of Toronto* (Toronto: University of Toronto Press, 1927), 187.
28. Edward Horne Craigie, *A History of the Department of Zoology of the University of Toronto up to 1962* (Toronto: University of Toronto Press, 1966), 24.
29. *Ibid.*, 13-34.
30. UTFMC 1890, 11.
31. UTFMC 1919-1920, 30.
32. Craigie, *A History of the Department of Zoology*, 17-24.
33. Craigie, *A History of the Department of Zoology*, 125.
34. See Sandra McRae, "The Spirit of Science in Medicine at the University of Toronto", Ph.D. Thesis, University of Toronto, 1987.
35. UTA, A75-005, Senate Minutes, Volume 7, April 14, 1902, 558.
36. "R. Ramsay Wright — Formerly Vice-President of the University of Toronto and Professor of Biology", in *University of Toronto Monthly* 34:31.
37. H.B. Maitland, "Memorial to Professor John Joseph Mackenzie, B.A., M.B., Toronto", *Canadian Practitioner* 48:54-6.
38. ODH, "The Development of Public Health in Ontario", 116.
39. J.J. Mackenzie, cited in McCullough, "1910-1920 A Review of Ten Years' Progress", 27.
40. *Ibid.*
41. *Ibid.*, 29.
42. J.J. Mackenzie, "Chairman's Address", *PHJ* 10:265.
43. ODH, "The Development of Public Health in Ontario", 118.
44. McCullough, "1910-1920 A Review of Ten Years' Progress", 27.
45. *Ibid.*, 31.
46. UTA, A67-007, Box 1, Dr. John Amyot to Robert Falconer, July 18, 1907.
47. J.G. FitzGerald, "Undergraduate Instruction in Preventive Medicine", *Journal of the American Medical Association* 110:1322.
48. J.G. FitzGerald, "Gordon Bell Memorial Lecture: Some Aspects of Preventive Medicine", *CJPH* 20:62-3.
49. R.D. Defries, "The Development of the Teaching of Hygiene", UTSHHP, 1-3.
50. *Ibid.*
51. UTSHHP, Interview with Dr. F. Burns Roth, July 12, 1985, Interviewer P.A. Bator Ph.D.
52. FitzGerald, "Undergraduate Instruction in Preventive Medicine", 1322.
53. Bator, "'Saving Lives on the Wholesale Plan' . . .", 38-40 and 90-5.
54. UTFMC 1919-1920, 33.

55. Charles Sheard, "How to Prevent Outbreaks of Infectious Diseases Amongst School Children and the Best Methods to Adopt Tending to Limit and Suppress these Diseases", *Canadian Journal of Medicine and Surgery* 15:153-4, 157.
56. Charles Sheard, "City of Toronto Disposal of Sewage and Water Filtration", *Empire Club Speeches 1907-8* (Toronto: William Briggs, 1910), 66-80.
57. Bator, "'Saving Lives on the Wholesale Plan'. . .", 95.
58. "The Retirement of Lt. Col. John Andrew Amyot, C.M.G., M.B., Deputy Minister of Pensions and National Health, Canada", *Canadian Medical Association Journal* 38:544-5.
59. John Amyot cited in ODH, "The Development of Public Health in Ontario", 117.
60. George G. Nasmith, "A Health Pioneer", *Saturday Night*, August 6, 1933, 68.
61. Amyot cited in McCullough, "1910-1920 A Review of Ten Years' Progress", 31.
62. ODH, "The Development of Public Health in Ontario", 121.
63. John A. Amyot, "Water Conditions in Toronto — A Plea for Filtration", *Canadian Journal of Medicine and Surgery* 21:287-91.
64. John. A. Amyot, "The Advantages and Disadvantages of Pasteurized Milk", *Dominion Medical Monthly and Ontario Medical Journal* 33:51-60.
65. See Michael J. Piva, *The Condition of the Working Class in Toronto 1900-1921* (Ottawa: University of Ottawa Press, 1979), 140-1.
66. See Norman J. Howard, "The Progressive Fight against Typhoid Fever in Canada during the Past Twenty Years", *CJPH* 23:376-83.
67. Bator, "'Saving Lives on the Wholesale Plan'. . .", 74.
68. J.T. Phair, "George Dana Porter, M.B." *CJPH* 33:466.
69. N. McKinnon, "George Dana Porter, M.D., 1870-1963", *CJPH* 55:452.
70. Phair, "George Dana Porter, M.B."
71. G.D. Porter, J.W.S. McCullough and J.D. Page, "History of the Canadian Public Health Association", *CJPH* 37:346.
72. *Ibid.*
73. Bator, "'Saving Lives on the Wholesale Plan'. . .", 112-30 and 315-16.
74. McCullough, "1910-1920 A Review of Ten Years' Progress", 31.
75. FFY, 48.
76. Bator, "'Saving Lives on the Wholesale Plan'. . .", 122.
77. *Ibid.*, 168-75.
78. *Ibid.*, 140-56.
79. *Ibid.*, 334.
80. McCullough, "1910-1920 A Review of Ten Years' Progress", 33 and 35.
81. Ontario, *Statutes 1912* (Toronto: L.K. Cameron, 1912), chapter 58: "An Act respecting the Public Health", 590-639.
82. ODH, 9th AR 1933, 94.
83. UTA, A68-0012, Senate Minutes Volume 7, Meeting of March 8, 1901, 368.
84. UTA, A68-0012, Senate Minutes Volume 8, Meeting of May 20, 1904, 378-9.
85. UTFMC, 283-9.
86. UTA, A70-005, Senate Minutes Volume 11, 145-6.
87. UTA, A68-0012, Senate Minutes Volume 8, Meeting of May 20, 1904, 378-9.
88. NAC, R.G. 29 Volume 255, Department of National Health and Welfare, Dominon Council of Health, Seventh Meeting June 19, 1928, 24.
89. R.D. Defries, "Postgraduate Teaching in Public Health in the University of Toronto, 1913-1955", *CJPH* 48:286.
90. 29th ARSH, 15.
91. Defries, "Postgraduate Teaching in Public Health in the University of Toronto, 1913-1955", 285-7.
92. *Ibid.*
93. *Ibid.*
94. *Ibid.*
95. *Ibid.*
96. UTSHHP, "Doctors Who Have Received the Diploma in Public Health School of Hygiene University of Toronto."
97. "JOHN GERALD FITZGERALD", in *Torontonensis Nineteen Hundred and Three, Volume V* (Toronto: Graduating Classes in the Faculties of Arts, Medicine and Applied Science, 1903), 138.
98. UTA, A68-0006 Box 35, copy of a Minute adopted at a meeting of the Connaught Laboratories Committee, September 24, 1940.
98. "JOHN GERALD FITZGERALD", in *Torontonensis Nineteen Hundred and Three*, 138.
99. Callwood, "The Miracle Factory that began in a Stable", 89.
100. All of the extensive details on FitzGerald's early career are found in D.M. Greene (ed.), *Who's Who In Canada, 1928-29* (Toronto: International Press Limited, 1929), 994.
101. Ann Guthrie, *Don Valley Legacy A Pioneer History* (Erin, Ontario: The Boston Mills Press, 1986), 164-6 and 186.
102. *Perley's BJ Map Book Metropolitan Toronto and Vicinity*, 28th edition (Toronto: Perley's Maps, Ltd., 1986), see map 5, Map Area C6.
103. Guthrie, *Don Valley Legacy*, 165-6.
104. *The Canadian Who's Who, Vol. IV, 1948* (Toronto: Trans-Canada Press, 1948), 248.
105. "DEFRIES, ROBERT DAVIES", in *Torontonensis the Annual Year Book of the Students of the University of Toronto Vol. XIII, 1911*, (Toronto: Undergraduates Parliament, 1911), 162.
106. "Obituary Robert Davies Defries", *CJPH* 66:511.
107. Callwood, "The Miracle Factory that began in a Stable", 89.
108. CA, 83-001-14, FitzGerald Papers, "Miscellaneous Correspondence 1911-1940", Mazych P. Ravenal to J.G. FitzGerald, November 20, 1911, and John F. Anderson to J.G. FitzGerald, November 9, 1913.
109. FFY, 4.
110. *Ibid.*, 8.

111. *Ibid.*, 10.
112. *Ibid.*, 66.
113. CA, 83-001-14, FitzGerald Papers, "Miscellaneous Correspondence 1911-1940; see pamphlet "Every Culture Station of the Department of Health now has a Supply of Provincial Board of Health Diphtheria ANTITOXIN."
114. *Ibid.*
115. J.G. FitzGerald, "The Work of the Antitoxin Laboratory", *University of Toronto Monthly* 17:96.
116. J.W.S. McCullough, "An Appreciation", *CJPH* 31:395.
117. Andrew MacPhail, *Official History of the Canadian Forces in the Great War 1914-1919: The Medical Services* (Ottawa: F.A. Acland, Printer to the King's Most Excellent Majesty, 1925), 106-7.
118. FFY, 24.
119. "Ontario Vaccine Farm, Palmerston", in Ontario Ministry of Culture and Recreation, *Historical Sketches of Ontario 1976* (Toronto, 1976), 98.
120. FFY, 26.
121. *Ibid.*, 34.
122. Desmond Morton, "Military Medicine During and After the First World War—Precursor of Universal Public Health Care in Canada", *Canadian Defence Quarterly* 13:34-42.
123. UTA, A73-0026/007 (35), Department of Graduate Records, "Dr. Amyot Outlines Health Work in War".
124. *Ibid.*, "University of Toronto Roll of Service, Amyot, John A."
125. G.F. Amyot, "Some Historical Highlights of Public Health in Canada" *CJPH* 5:339-40.
126. UTA, A73-0026/007 (35), "Dr. Amyot Outlines Health Work in War".
127. UTA, A73-0026/103 (66).
128. NAC, R.G. 29, Volume 255, Department of National Health and Welfare, Dominion Council of Health, Meeting of May 18, 1919, 26.
129. Major J.G. FitzGerald and Major J.W.S. McCullough, "Sanitation in some Canadian Barracks and Camps", *American Journal of Public Health* 7:659.
130. *Ibid.*
131. *Ibid.*, 660.
132. *Ibid.*
133. Bator, "'Saving Lives on the Wholesale Plan' . . .", 251-5.
134. J.G. FitzGerald, "The Advisory Committee on Venereal Diseases for Military District No. 2", *PHJ* 9:49-52.
135. *Ibid.*
136. FitzGerald, "Gordon Bell Memorial Lecture: Some Aspects of Preventive Medicine", 68.
137. N.W. Rowell cited in Canada, House of Commons, *Hansard*, April 4, 1919, 1165-6.
138. *Ibid.*
139. *Ibid.*
140. Bator, "'Saving Lives on the Wholesale Plan' . . .", 285-6.
141. FFY, 49-50.
142. A.H.W. Caulfield and Captain Donald T. Fraser, "Certain Bacteriological and Serological Aspects of Epidemic Influenza", *Canadian Medical Association Journal* 10:436-7.
143. "The Federal Health Bill", *PHJ* 9:179-81.
144. FFY, 61-2.
145. J.J. Heagerty, "History and Activities of the National Health Division of the Department of Pensions and National Health", *CJPH* 35:528-39.
146. *Ibid.*, 540.
147. *Ibid.*
148. *Ibid.*
149. NAC, R.G. 29, Volume 255, Department of National Health and Welfare, Dominion Council of Health, Meeting of October 2, 1919, 1.
150. *Ibid.*, Meeting of May 19, 1920, 40.
151. *Ibid.*, Meeting of June 19, 1923, 1.
152. ODH, "The Development of Public Health in Ontario", 114-15.
153. *Ibid.*
154. *Ibid.*
155. A.J. Slack, "Public Health", in University of Western Ontario, *Golden Jubilee Endowment Campaign, 1923* (London, Ontario, 1928), 2-3.
156. Bator, "'Saving Lives on the Wholesale Plan' . . .", chapter VI.
157. Marion Royce, *Eunice Dyke Health Care Pioneer* (Toronto and Charlottetown: Dundurn Press, 1986), 105-18.
158. *Ibid.*
159. Helen M. Carpenter, *A Divine Discontent Edith Kathleen Russell: Reforming Educator* (Toronto: Faculty of Nursing, University of Toronto, 1982), 13-14.
160. FFY, 88.
161. J.G. FitzGerald et al., *An Introduction to the Practice of Preventive Medicine* (St. Louis, Missouri: C.V. Mosby Company, 1922), 198-9.
162. Paul Adolphus Bator, "The Health Reformer versus the Common Canadian: The Controversy Over Compulsory Vaccination Against Smallpox in Toronto and Ontario, 1900-1920", *Ontario History* 75:365.
163. Ronald Hare, *The Birth of Penicillin and the Disarming of Microbes* (London: George Allen and Unwin Ltd., n.d.), 203.
164. David Eisen, *Diary of a Medical Student* (Toronto: Canadian Jewish Congress, 1974), 53.
165. "Students in Residence Under Smallpox Quarantine", *Toronto Telegram*, Thursday, October 20, 1927, 25.
166. AO, R.G. 62, Series 1-A-1, Box 327, Ontario Provincial Board of Health Records, Dr. J.W.S. McCullough to Dr. Ruggles George, May 11, 1923.

167. AO, R.G. 62, Series 1-A-1 Box 339, Ontario Provincial Board of Health Records, Dr. J.G. FitzGerald to Dr. J.W.S. McCullough, August 20, 1923.
168. AO, R.G. 62, Series 1-A-1 Box 345, Ontario Provincial Board of Health Records, Dr. J.W.S. McCullough to Mayor W.W. Hiltz, April 4, 1924.
169. AO, R.G. 62, Series 1-A-1 Box 360, Ontario Provincial Board of Health Records, Dr. W.J. Bell to Dr. T.C. Routley, November 5, 1926.
170. UTA, A68-002, Senate Minutes, Statute Number 829, October 10, 1919.
171. See "Curriculum For the Diploma of Public Health", in UTFMC, 1921-1922, 407.
172. FFY, 61-2.
173. *Ibid.*
174. ODH, "The Development of Public Health in Ontario", 121-2.
175. Defries, "Postgraduate Teaching in Public Health in the University of Toronto, 1913-1955", 289.
176. FFY, 66.
177. RDSH 1930, 30.
178. FitzGerald et al., *An Introduction to the Practice of Preventive Medicine*, xi-xvi.
179. *Ibid.*, 2.
180. *Ibid.*, 4.
181. RAC, R.G. 1.1, Series 427, Box 10, Folder 79, "Historical Record University of Toronto — Medical Faculty 1919-1932, 1934, 1927", 2.
182. UTA, A67-0007, Box 77, Leon Bernard cited in Wycliffe Rose to Dr. J.G. FitzGerald, November 4, 1922.
183. RAC, R.G. 5, Series 427, Box 262, Folder 3328, Clifford W. Wells to Dr. Charles J. Hastings, April 29, 1926.
184. George E. Vincent, "The British Empire and World Health", in Empire Club of Canada, *Addresses Delivered to the Members During the Year 1929* (Toronto: T.H. Best Printing Co., Limited, 1930), 58.
185. FFY, 68-75.
186. See Canon Cody, "The University of Toronto as Public Servant", in Canadian Club of Toronto, *Addresses 1927-28* (Toronto: Warwick Brothers and Rutter Limited, 1928), 143.
187. Elizabeth Fee, *Disease and Discovery A History of the Johns Hopkins School of Hygiene and Public Health 1916-1939* (Baltimore: Johns Hopkins University Press, 1987).
188. Jean Curran, *Founders of the Harvard School of Public Health with Biographical Notes, 1909-1946* (New York: Josiah Macy Jr. Foundation, 1970).
189. RAC, R.G. 1.1, Series 427L, Box 24, Folder 227, F.F. Russell to Dr. J.G. FitzGerald, May 22, 1924.

CHAPTER TWO: NOTES

1. RDSH 1934, 36.
2. "Hygiene School Opened", *Toronto Telegram*, Friday, June 10, 1927, 23.
3. "The Opening of the New School of Hygiene University of Toronto", *PHJ* 18:318-21.
4. Canon Cody, "The University of Toronto as a Public Servant", in *Canadian Club of Toronto Address 1927-28*, (Toronto: Warwick Brothers and Rutter Limited, 1928), 143-4.
5. J.G. FitzGerald, "The New School of Hygiene Will House Several Important Departments", *University of Toronto Monthly* 26: 327-38.
6. RDCL 1924, 77.
7. FFY, 81 and 88.
8. E.W. Haldenby, "The Hygiene and Public Health Building", *University of Toronto Monthly* 266: 229-36.
9. *Ibid.*, 229.
10. UTA, Photo Inventory 25.61: Hygiene Bldg. — construction, 31.8.26.
11. CA, 83-011-01, "Building, School of Hygiene Extension Approximate Floor Areas in Existing Hygiene Building May 28th, 1931."
12. Frederick Edwards, "A Peacetime Munitions Plant", *MacLean's*, January 15, 1928, 54.
13. *Ibid.*
14. *Ibid.*
15. *Ibid.*
16. *Ibid.*
17. Helen M. Carpenter, *A Divine Discontent Edith Kathleen Russell: Reforming Educator*, (Toronto: Faculty of Nursing, University of Toronto, 1982), 14-22.
18. UTSHC 1931-1932, 10-13.
19. UTSHC 1928-1929, 10-13.
20. UTSHHP, "List of Faculty of School of Hygiene."
21. *Ibid.*
22. *Ibid.*
23. "Frank Wishart", *CJPH* 53:265.
24. FFY, 110.
25. UTSHC 1931-1932, 10.
26. FFY, 126-8.
27. UTSHC 1938-1939, 14.
28. Ronald Hare, *The Birth of Penicillin And The Disarming of Microbes* (London: George Allen and Unwin Ltd., 1970), 190-4.

29. UTSHC 1928-1929, 12.
30. FFY, 103.
31. UTSHC 1928-1929, 12.
32. UTA, A67-0007, Box 93, J.G. FitzGerald to President Falconer, January 25, 1926.
33. Mary A. Ross, "A Statistical Study of the Mortality from Diphtheria in Ontario For the Years 1880 to 1925", M.A. Thesis, University of Toronto, 1928.
34. Mary A. Ross, "A Survey of mortality of diphtheria, scarlet fever, influenza and other respiratory diseases and diabetes for fifty years in Ontario and an analysis of the results of the use of toxoid in the prevention of diphtheria in school children", Ph.D. Thesis, University of Toronto, 1934.
35. RDSH 1937, 40.
36. R.D. Defries and A.H. Sellars, "The Physician and the New Canadian Death Certificate", *CJPH* 26: 160-7.
37. RAC, R.G. 1.1, Series 427L, Box 24, Folder 234, "General Data relating to the School of Hygiene University of Toronto", see section on "Epidemiology."
38. UTSHC 1928-1929, 12.
39. R.D. Defries, "Postgraduate Teaching in Public Health in the University of Toronto, 1913-1955", *CJPH* 58: 290-1.
40. R.G. 1.1, Series 427L, Box 24, Folder 234, "General Data Relating to the School of Hygiene University of Toronto", 11.
41. RAC, R.G. 1.1, Series 200, Box 185, Folder 2222, Thomas Parran and Livingston Farrand, "Report To The Rockefeller Foundation On the Education of Public Health Personnel, October 28, 1939", 58-9.
42. D.A. Scott, "Earle Willard McHenry 1899-1961", in Royal Society of Canada, *Proceedings and Transactions Third Series — Volume LVI Meeting of June, 1962* (Ottawa: The Royal Society of Canada, 1962), 219-24.
43. RAC, R.G. 1.1., Series 427L, Box 24, Folder 234, "General Data Relating to the School of Hygiene University of Toronto", see section on Course in Industrial Hygiene.
44. UTA, R.D. Defries to Sidney Smith, January 17, 1946.
45. UTSHC 1935-1936, 17.
46. UTSHHP, "Graduate degrees awarded in the School of Hygiene."
47. F.O. Wishart, "The serology of vaccinia-variola virus", M.A. Thesis, University of Toronto, 1933.
48. E.G. Gavin, "The B vitamins and fat metabolism", Ph.D. Thesis, University of Toronto, 1939.
49. RAC, R.G. 1.1, Series 427L, Box 15, Folder 140, "List of Published Papers Arising from Studies Supported by Grants from the Rockefeller Foundation", 1.
50. RAC, R.G. 1.1, Series 200, Box 185, Folder 2222, Thomas Parran and Livingston Farrand, "Report To The Rockefeller Foundation On the Education of Public Health Personnel, October 28, 1939", 65.
51. FFY, 301.
52. NAC, R.G. 29, Volume 255, Department of National Health and Welfare, Dominon Council of Health, Meeting of June 19, 1928, 24.
53. *Ibid.*
54. RDSH 1931, 83.
55. FFY, 90.
56. *Ibid.*
57. Joan Hollobon, "Part of Canada's insulin history vanishes", *Globe and Mail*, October 22, 1981, 5.
58. RAC, R.G. 1.1., Series 427L, Box 24, Folder 233, "University of Toronto School of Hygiene 1930-1939", J.G. FitzGerald to Dr. F.F. Russell, November 5, 1936.
59. CA, 83-001-02, "School of Hygiene, Construction and Additions To", J.G. FitzGerald to President Falconer, December 2, 1930.
60. UTA, A68-0006, Box 21, File 03, J.G. FitzGerald to President Cody, January 13, 1936.
61. CA, 83-001-02, "School of Hygiene, Construction and Additions To", and "A Statement of the Reasons Which Necessitate Extension of the Hygiene Building" in J.G. FitzGerald to Rev. H.J. Cody, December 5, 1930.
62. *Ibid.*, J.G. FitzGerald to Dr. F.F. Russell, April 1, 1931.
63. FFY, 89 and RAC, R.G. 1.1., Series 427L, Box 24, Folder 233, "University of Toronto School of Hygiene 1930-1939", Norma S. Thompson to Sir Robert Falconer, April 16, 1931.
64. *Ibid.,* Norma S. Thompson to Sir Robert Falconer, September 29, 1932.
65. RDSH, 1932, 26.
66. FFY, 318.
67. *Ibid.*
68. RDSH 1933, 28.
69. FFY, 89.
70. *Ibid.*, 89-90.
71. RDCL 1930, 86.
72. FitzGerald, "The New School of Hygiene", 327.
73. RDCL 1936, 124.
74. Hare, *The Birth of Penicillin*, 197.
75. CA, 83-002-06, R.D. Defries Correspondence with E.W. McHenry, see memo of Defries to McHenry dated December 30, 1947 regarding tea in the afternoon.
76. Hare, *The Birth of Penicillin*, 198.
77. *Ibid.*, 197-8.
78. The FitzGerald Cup now resides in the Connaught Archives of the Balmer Neilly Library in the Connaught Laboratories Limited in the city of North York.
79. RAC, R.G. 1.1., Series 427, Box 10, Folder 81, "University of Toronto Psychiatry 1933-1937", Alan Gregg Diary, Monday, December 11, 1933.
80. FFY, 77.
81. UTA, A67-0007, Box 107a, G. Ramon to J.G. FitzGerald, November 3, 1927.

82. George Dana Porter, *Crusading Against Tuberculosis, The Memoirs of George Dana Porter* (Ottawa: The Canadian Tuberculosis Association, 1953), 27.
83. Claude E. Dolman, "The Donald T. Fraser Memorial Lecture 1973: Landmarks and Pioneers in Control of Diphtheria", *CJPH* 54: 319.
84. G.D.W. Cameron, "The First Donald Fraser Memorial Lecture", *CJPH* 51:348.
85. RAC, R.G. 1.1., Series 427L, Box 24, Folder 234, "General Data Relating to the School of Hygiene University of Toronto", 24.
86. UTA, A68-007, Box 003(09), R.D. Defries to President Sidney Smith, January 31, 1946.
87. UTA, A73-0026, Box 108(57), Department of Graduate Records, "Senate Resolution respecting the late Professor Fraser", in J.C. Evans to Mrs. D.T. Fraser, November 9, 1954.
88. Cameron, "The First Donald Fraser Memorial Lecture", 342.
89. D.A. Scott, "Donald Thomas Fraser 1888-1954", in The Royal Society of Canada, *Proceedings and Transactions Third Series — Volume XLIX Meeting of June, 1955* (Ottawa: The Royal Society of Canada), 93.
90. Madawaska Club, *1898-1973 Go Home Bay* Toronto. The Madawaska Club Limited, 1973, p. 109. Fraser joined the Madawaska Club in 1923.
91. UTSHC 1928-1929, 10.
92. Scott, "Donald Thomas Fraser 1888-1954", 93.
93. Cameron, "The First Donald Fraser Memorial Lecture", 343.
94. FFY, 46.
95. Cameron, "The First Donald Fraser Memorial Lecture", 344.
96. FFY, 108.
97. J.G. FitzGerald et al., *An Introduction to the Practice of Preventive Medicine* (St. Louis: C.V. Mosby Company, 1922), see acknowledgements.
98. CA, 83-011-01, Buildings, "School of Hygiene, extension 1931", D. Fraser to Bob Defries, August 27, 1931.
99. UTA, A67-0007, Box 26a, Sir Robert Falconer to J.G. FitzGerald, May 21, 1931.
100. Donald T. Fraser and George D. Porter, *Ontario Public School Health Book* (Toronto: The Copp Clark Company Limited, 1925).
101. D.T. Fraser, "Protection Against Disease", *PHJ* 16:562.
102. Cameron, "The First Donald Fraser Memorial Lecture", 346.
103. Paul Adolphus Bator, "The Health Reformer versus the Common Canadian: The Controversy Over Compulsory Vaccination Against Smallpox in Toronto and Ontario, 1900-1920", *Ontario History* 75:3.
104. H. Parrish, *A History of Immunization* (Edinburgh and London: E.& S. Livingstone Ltd., 1965), 151-2.
105. FFY, 115.
106. "Toronto Doctor Applies Theories to Own Children", *Toronto Star*, Friday, June 20, 1929, 12.
107. Cameron, "The First Donald Fraser Memorial Lecture", 346.
108. Tom Rivers, *Reflections and Life in Medicine and Science An Oral History Memoir* Prepared by Saul Benson (Cambridge, Massachussetts: The M.I.T. Press, 1967), 192.
109. Cameron, "The First Donald Fraser Memorial Lecture", 346.
110. *Ibid.*, 345-6.
111. *Ibid.*
112. Scott, "Donald Thomas Fraser, 1888-1954", 97.
113. UTSHC 1933-1934, 10.
114. FFY, 64-5.
115. UTA, A68-006, Box 32(01), D.T. Fraser to President Cody, April 4, 1937.
116. RAC, R.G. 1.1., Series 427, Box 24, Folder 234, "General Data relating to the School of Hygiene University of Toronto", 4-7.
117. UTSHC 1937-1938, 11-12.
118. UTA, A67-0007, Box 582, J.G. FitzGerald to President Falconer, September 29, 1919.
119. UTA, A68-007, Box 003 (09), Curriculum Vitae of Peter Moloney in R.D. Defries to President Sidney Smith, January 31, 1946.
120. "Peter J. Moloney O.B.E., M.A., Ph.D., F.R.S.C.", *CJPH* 53:259.
121. Peter J. Moloney, "On the purification of insulin", Ph.D. Thesis, University of Toronto, 1924.
122. H.J. Parrish, *A History of Immunization*, 150.
123. FFY, 76-9.
124. P.J. Moloney, "Diphtheria Toxoid in Canada", *CJPH* 46-87.
125. FFY, 78.
126. *Ibid.*, 79.
127. UTSHC 1933-1934, 15.
128. Sir Christopher Andrewes, "James Craigie 1899-1978, Elected F.R.S. 1947", *Biographical Memoirs of Fellows of the Royal Society 1979* Volume 25 (London: The Royal Society, 1979), 233-40.
129. *Ibid.*, 238.
130. *Ibid.*
131. C.H. Andrewes, "James Craigie", *Nature* 276: 427, November 23, 1978.
132. RAC, R.G. 1.1., series 427L, Box 24, Folder 234, "General Data relating to the School of Hygiene University of Toronto."
133. UTSHC 1938-1939, 14.
134. Andrewes, "James Craigie 1899-1978. . .", 233.
135. J.W.S. McCullough, "An Appreciation", *CJPH* 31: 396-7.
136. ODH 15th AR, 8.
137. UTSHC 1928-1929, 11.
138. "John Thomas Phair, M.B., D.P.H. 1888-1965", *CJPH* 56: 216-17.
139. UTSHC 1933-1934, 14.

140. R.D. Defries, "The Canadian Public Health Association, 1910-1956", *CJPH* 49:39.
141. John T. Phair, "Public Health Administration" in ODH, 15th AR, 11.
142. John R. Brown, "John Grant Cunningham, B.A., M.B., D.P.H., 1890-1965", *Canadian Medical Association Journal* 94:48.
143. J.G. Cunningham, "Industrial Hygiene", in J.G. FitzGerald et al., *An Introduction to the Practice of Preventive Medicine*, 167.
144. J.G. Cunningham, "Industrial Hygiene Division", ODH 15th AR, 180.
145. Mary A. Ross, "Typhoid Fever Mortality in Ontario 1880-1931", *CJPH* 26:73-83.
146. UTA, A73-0026, Box 28 (03).
147. "Albert E. Berry", *CJPH* 53:265.
148. See A.E. Berry, "Municipal Control of Garbage", M.A.Sc. Thesis, University of Toronto, 1921, and A.E. Berry, "Pathogenicity in butter", Ph.D. Thesis University of Toronto, 1926.
149. UTSHC 1928-1929, 12.
150. UTA, A76-004, Box 14, University of Toronto Faculty of Medicine Records, Dr. B. Bucove to J.D. Hamilton, October 3, 1971.
151. "Albert E. Berry", 265.
152. RDSH, 1939, 37.
153. See "Appendix A: Historical Developments Influencing Graduate Teaching and Research in Public Health", in UTSHC 1974-1975, 84.
154. FFY, 76.
155. J.G. FitzGerald, D.T. Fraser, N.E. McKinnon, and Mary A. Ross, "Diphtheria—A Preventable Disease", *The Lancet* (February 12, 1938), 391.
156. F.S. Burke, "The Administrative Control of the Diphtheria Toxoid Campaign in Toronto", *CJPH* 20:210.
157. *Ibid.*, 213.
158. FitzGerald, Fraser, McKinnon and Ross, "Diphtheria—A Preventable Disease", 395.
159. *Ibid.*
160. *Ibid.*
161. FFY, 79.
162. P.J. Moloney, "Diphtheria Toxoid in Canada", *CJPH* 46:87-8.
163. Jane Lewis, "The Prevention of Diphtheria In Canada and Britain 1914-1945", *Journal of Social History* 20:171.
164. FitzGerald, Fraser, McKinnon, and Ross, "Diphtheria — A Preventable Disease", 395.
165. UTFMC 1935-1936, 104.
166. RDFMUT 1935, 29.
167. *Ibid.*
168. RDFMUT 1933, 18.
169. RDFMUT 1935, 29.
170. RDFMUT 1936, 29.
171. UTSHHP, "Doctors Who Have Received the Diploma In Public Health From the School of Hygiene University of Toronto."
172. J.G. FitzGerald, "Undergraduate Instruction in Preventive Medicine", *Journal of American Medical Association* 110:1321.
173. Hare, *The Birth of Preventive Medicine*, 188-204.
174. FFY, 102.
175. UTSHHP, FitzGerald, "The Place of Preventive Medicine in the Medical Curriculum."
176. FitzGerald, "General Outline of the Problem of Training Health Workers", 631.
177. *Ibid.*, 632.
178. Donald T. Fraser, "Special or Post-Graduate Public Health Training", *British Medical Journal*, October 18, 1930, 635.
179. J.G. FitzGerald, "Undergraduate Instruction in Preventive Medicine", 1326.
180. *Ibid.*, 1322-3.
181. *Ibid.*, 1324.
182. *Ibid.*, 1325.
183. Hare, *The Birth of Penicillin. . .*, 191-3.
184. UTSHHP, Arthur J. Viseltear, "Social Forces Leading to the Establishment of Pioneering Public Health Education Programs in the United States", a paper presented to the Rockefeller Conference on the History of Education in Public Health, Bellagio, Italy, August 19, 1987.
185. UTA, A76-0044, Box 13, Faculty of Medicine Records re School of Hygiene, "American Public Health Association, Report of Accreditation Visit, Committee on Professional Education, University of Toronto School of Hygiene, Visit of C.-E.A. Winslow, Dr. P.H., December 5-7, 1949, 3.
186. Fraser, "Special or Post-Graduate Public Health Training", 636.
187. Defries, "Postgraduate Teaching in Public Health in the University of Toronto, 1913-1955", 292-3.
188. FitzGerald et al., *An Introduction to the Practice of Preventive Medicine.*
189. J.G. FitzGerald, "Gordon Bell Memorial Lecture Some Aspects of Preventive Medicine", *CJPH* 20:69.
190. *Ibid.*
191. FitzGerald cited in Canada House of Commons, Select Standing Committee on Industrial and International Relations, Report, *Proceedings and Evidence of the Select Standing Committee of Industrial and International Relations upon the question of Insurance against Unemployment, Sickness and Invalidity as ordered by the House on the 18th of February, 1929* (Ottawa: F.A. Acland, Printer to the King's Most Excellent Majesty, 1929), 32-3.
192. *Ibid.*, 34.
193. *Ibid.*, 35.
194. *Ibid.*
195. J.G. FitzGerald, "The Municipal Physician System in Operation of the Provinces of Manitoba and Saskatchewan", *University of Toronto Monthly* (March 1933), 194.

196. "The Retirement of Lt. Col. John Andrew Amyot, C.M.B., Deputy Minister of Pensions and National Health, Canada" *Canadian Medical Association Journal* 38:544-55.
197. J.T. Phair, "The Canadian Public Health Association: An Appreciation", *CJPH* 41-307.
198. R.D. Defries, "The Canadian Public Health Association 1910-1956" *CJPH* 48:39-42.
199. J.T. Phair, "Dr. R.D. Defries Retires as Editor", *CJPH* 55:124.
200. Phair, "The Canadian Public Health Association. . ."
201. "Report of the Editorial Board 1935-1936" *CJPH* 36:297.
202. See Index to *CJPH* 36:IV-VII.
203. See *CJPH* 38, No. 6.
204. RAC, R.G. 1.1., Series 427L, Box 24, Folder 234, "General Data relating to the School of Hygiene University of Toronto."
205. *Ibid.*
206. *Ibid.*, see Table I, 16.
207. UTSHHP, "Doctors Who Have Received the Diploma in Public Health from the School of Hygiene University of Toronto."
208. RDSH 1939, 38.
209. 22nd ARSH, 9.
210. RAC, R.G. 1.1., Series 200, Box 185, Folder 2222, Thomas Parran and Livingston Farrand, "Report To The Rockefeller Foundation On the Education of Public Health Personnel, October 28, 1939", 65.

CHAPTER THREE: NOTES

1. "A Public Health Charter For Canada", *CJPH* 33:344.
2. RDSH 1943, 38.
3. RDFMUT 1941, 28.
4. UTA, A68-0006, Box 049(05), R.D. Defries to President H.J. Cody, February 20, 1942.
5. FFY, 151-96.
6. G.D.W. Cameron, "The First Donald Fraser Memorial Lecture", *CJPH* 51:347.
7. FFY, 138-9, 146-7, 311 & 318.
8. RAC, R.G. 1.1, Series 427L, Box 24, Folder 236, "University of Toronto School of Hygiene Faculty Salaries 1940-1943", and Developments in the School of Hygiene University of Toronto During 1941 and 1942. Memorandum — March 3, 1942" in R.D. Defries to Dr. John Ferrell, March 4, 1942.
9. RDSH 1944, 40.
10. 17th ARSH, 10.
11. CA, 83-002-12, Robert Davies Defries Papers, "Correspondence re blood serum", Memorandum from C.H. Best to Dr. Defries, May 3, 1941, and "Precis On Development of Canadian Project For The Preparation of Dried Human Blood Serum."
12. R.D. Defries, "The Connaught Medical Research Laboratories" in W.R. Feasby, (ed.), *Official History Of The Canadian Medical Services 1939-1945 Volume Two Clinical Subjects* (Ottawa: Edmond Cloutier Queen's Printer, 1953), 377-8.
13. *Ibid.*, 379-80.
14. *Ibid.*, 379.
15. FFY, 169-72.
16. Defries, "The Connaught Medical Research Laboratories", 380.
17. FFY, 172.
18. *Ibid.*, 173.
19. Defries, "The Connaught Medical Research Laboratories", 375-6.
20. FFY, 177-8.
21. Ronald Hare, John Hamilton and W.R. Feasby, "Influenza and Similar Respiratory Infections in a Military Camp over a Period of Three Years", *CJPH* 43:453-64.
22. Ronald Hare, Jean Morgan, Jocelyn Jackson and Dorothy M. Stamatis, "Immunization Against Influenza A", *CJPH* 44:353-9.
23. FFY, 194-6.
24. Defries, "The Connaught Medical Research Laboratories", 383.
25. FFY, 181-94.
26. *Ibid.*, 330-1.
27. *Ibid.*, 261-2.
28. Neil E. McKinnon, "War Time Problems In Communicable Disease Control", in *Collected Studies of the Connaught Laboratories and School of Hygiene University of Toronto Vol. XVI, 1944*, deposited in University of Toronto Science and Medicine Library.
29. "Milton H. Brown, O.B.E., M.D., B.Sc.Med., D.P.H., F.C.C.P., C.R.C.P.(C.)", in Canadian Public Health Association, Annual Report *CJPH* 1970; 62:10.
30. See Chapter 9, "Preventive Medicine and Hygiene" in W.R. Feasby, (ed.), *Official History Of the Medical Services 1939-1945 Volume Two Clinical Subjects*, 133-46.
31. UTA, A68-0007, Box 003(09), see Curriculum Vitae of Donald MacLean in R.D. Defries to President Sidney Smith, January 17, 1946.
32. UTA, A68-0006, Box 059(05), R.D. Defries to President Cody, January 19, 1944. See also "Neil E. McKinnon, M.B." *CJPH* 53:258 and death notice of "McKinnon, Neil E. . . ." *Toronto Star*, Wednesday, September 11, 1985.

33. "Donald Young Solandt, M.A., M.D., Ph.D., D.P.H., F.R.S.C." in 30th ARSH, 27.
34. R.D. Defries, "Postgraduate Teaching in Public Health in the University of Toronto, 1913-1955", *CJPH* 48:292.
35. *Ibid.*
36. FFY, 153-4.
37. UTA, A68-0006, Box 049 (05), R.D. Defries to President H.J. Cody, May 23, 1942.
38. *Ibid.*, Box 054 (06), R.D. Defries to President H.J. Cody, July 28, 1942.
39. *Ibid.*, R.D. Defries to President H.J. Cody, August 28, 1942.
40. UTSHC 1942-1943, 10 and 21.
41. FFY, 199.
42. RAC, R.G. 1.1, Series 427 L, Box 24, Folder 235, "University of Toronto School of Hygiene, Impact of Second World War On School", R.D. Defries to Dr. John A. Ferrell, January 25, 1941.
43. RAC, R.G. 1.1, Series 427 L, Box 24, Folder 239, "University of Toronto School of Hygiene East York Health Unit", R.D. Defries to Dr. W.A. McIntosh, April 22, 1943.
44. *Ibid.*, R.D. Defries to Dr. W.A. McIntosh, September 22, 1943.
45. FFY, 109 and 177.
46. UTA, A68-0007 Box 003(09), R.D. Defries to President S. Smith, January 17, 1946.
47. "Alfred Hardisty Sellers", *CJPH* 66:151.
48. See Feasby, (ed.), *Official History of the Canadian Medical Services 1939-1945: Volume One Organization And Campaigns*, 462-4.
40. A.H. Sellers, "The Immunization Program in the Royal Canadian Air Force", *CJPH* 33:575-87.
50. J.W. Tice, A.H. Sellers, R.M. Anderson and W. Nichols, "Some Observations On Venereal Disease Control in the Royal Canadian Air Force", *CJPH* 37:43-56.
51. For a report on the impressive record of the medical statistics of the R.C.A.F., consult Feasby, *Official History of the Canadian Medical Services: Volume Two Clinical Subjects*, Chapter 35, "R.C.A.F. Medical Statistics", 452-531.
52. UTA, A68-0006, Box 049(05), R.D. Defries to President H.J. Cody, October 27, 1941.
53. UTSHC 1942-1943, 16.
54. FFY, 155, and telephone interview with Dr. R.J. Wilson, Monday, September 12, 1988, Interviewer P.A. Bator, Ph.D.
55. For a general account of the enlarged role of Canadian females in society during the Second World War, consult Ruth Roach Pierson, *"They're Still Women After All": The Second World War and Canadian Womanhood* (Toronto: McClelland and Stewart, 1986).
56. UTSHC 1942-1943, 10, 15, 16, 17, 19, 21, and 23.
57. RAC, R.G. 1.1, Series 427 L, Box 24, Folder 236, "University of Toronto School of Hygiene Faculty Salaries 1940-1943", see list of faculty salaries and duties in memorandum attached to R.D. Defries to Dr. John A. Ferrell, August 12, 1942.
58. UTSHC 1928-1929, 10, 11 and 12.
59. Cameron, "The First Donald Fraser Memorial Lecture", 342.
60. UTA, A73-0026, Box 108 (67), File on Frieda Fraser.
61. UTSHC 1942-1943, 10.
62. FFY, 114.
63. UTA, A68-0006, Box 049(05), R.D. Defries to President H.J. Cody, February 20, 1942.
64. RDSH 1943, 41.
65. Edith M. Taylor, "The Action of Acids on Yeast", Ph.D. Thesis, University of Toronto, 1924.
66. UTSHC 1933-1934, 13.
67. Philip C. Enros, (comp.), *Bibliography of Publishing Scientists In Ontario Between 1914 and 1939*, Research Tools in the History of Canadian Science and Technology — 2 (Thornhill & Ottawa: HSTC Publications, 1985), 421.
68. FFY, 178-9.
69. Enros, (comp.), *Bibliography of Publishing Scientists in Ontario Between 1914 and 1939*, 357.
70. FFY, 163.
71. Enros, (comp.), *Bibliography of Publishing Scientists in Ontario Between 1914 and 1939*, 372.
72. FFY, 163.
73. UTA, A68-0007, Box 101(10), R.D. Defries to President Sydney Smith, October 27, 1952.
74. Enros, (comp.), *Bibliography of Publishing Scientists in Ontario Between 1914 and 1939*, 351.
75. *Ibid.*, 159.
76. UTA, A73-0026, Box 115(03), File on E.G. Gavin.
77. UTSHC 1940-1941, 10.
78. UTA, A73-0026, Box 253(42).
79. FFY, 155 and 173.
80. UTA, A68-0006, Box 054 (04), R.D. Defries to President H.J. Cody, December 1, 1943.
81. *Ibid.*, Box 059(05), R.D. Defries to President H.J. Cody, August 19, 1943.
82. *Ibid.*, R.D. Defries to President H.J. Cody, February 21, 1940.
83. UTSHHP, "Doctors Who Have Received the Diploma in Public Health School of Hygiene, University of Toronto", 1, 2, 3, 4, 7, 10, 13, 15, and 17.
84. The total number of nurses comes from the annual reports of the Director of the School of Hygiene from 1940 to 1945.
85. UTSHC 1938-1939, 15.
86. UTA, A68-0006, Box 041(05), Harold J. Kirby to Dr. J.G. FitzGerald, May 29, 1939.
87. See John T. Phair cited in ODH 15th AR, 10.
88. UTA, A68-0006, Box 041(05), R.D. Defries to Hon. Harold J. Kirby, June 22, 1939.
89. ODH 15th AR, 47.
90. ODH 16th AR, 10.
91. *Ibid.*
92. FFY, 301.
93. ODH, 10th AR, 33.

94. RAC, R.G. 1.1, Series 427, Box 24, Folder 239, "University of Toronto School of Hygiene East York Health Unit", Dr. John A. Ferrell to Dr. R.D. Defries, April 12, 1939.
95. *Ibid.*, "24 Mar 39 University of Toronto — School of Hygiene — Field Training Facilities—Designation"
96. *Ibid.*, R.D. Defries to Mr. John Warren Reeve, Township of East York, November 18, 1940.
97. *Ibid.*, W. Mosley to R.D. Defries, March 28, 1941.
98. *Ibid.*, "31 Oct 47 Estimates 1948—Schools and Institutes of Hygiene and Public Health — University of Toronto — School of Hygiene — Field Training Facilities."
99. *Ibid.*, "13 Nov 41 University of Toronto — School of Hygiene — Field Training Facilities."
100. *Ibid.*, C.E. Higginbottom to Dr. W.A. McIntosh, 11 December, 1943.
101. RAC, R.G. 1.1, Series 427L, Box 24, Folder 238, "University of Toronto School of Hygiene Faculty Salaries 1949-1951", "12 8 49 University of Toronto — Faculty Salaries, A Report."
102. RDSH 1941, 45.
103. "William Mosley, M.D.C.M., D.P.H., C.R.C.P.(C.)", Canadian Public Health Association, *Annual Report 1971-1972* (Toronto, 1972), 12.
104. UTSHC 1941-1942, 18-19.
105. RDSH 1943, 41.
106. Cunningham cited in ODH 15th AR, 180.
107. CDPNHR 1941, 89.
108. Feasby (ed.), *Official History of the Canadian Medical Services 1939-1945: Volume One*, 517-20.
109. W.R. Cruickshank, "Present Problems in Industrial Health", *CJPH* 35:144-7.
110. Cunningham cited in ODH 21st AR 1945, 36.
111. William A. Wrecher, "Industrial Health in Wartime", *CJPH* 34:267-71.
112. Harold M. Harrison, "Dr. J. Grant Cunningham An Appreciation", *Canadian Medical Association Journal* 94:49.
113. J. Grant Cunningham cited in Canada, House of Commons Special Committee on Social Security, *Minutes of Proceedings And Evidence No. 9 Tuesday, May 11, 1943* (Ottawa: Edmond Cloutier, Printer to the King's Most Excellent Majesty, 1943) 262.
114. RAC, R.G. 1.1, Series 427L, Box 24, Folder 236, "University of Toronto School of Hygiene Faculty Salaries 1940-1943", "Memorandum — March 3, 1942 Developments in the School of Hygiene University of Toronto During 1941 and 1942", 3.
115. D.Y. Solandt, "Postgraduate Education in Industrial Health and Hygiene", *Canadian Medical Association Journal* 50:63-5.
116. Feasby (ed.), *Official History of the Canadian Medical Services 1939- 1945 Volume One Organization and Campaigns*, 456.
117. J.G. Cunningham cited in ODH 16th AR, 156.
118. Cunningham cited in ODH 17th AR, 113.
119. RDCL 1941, 63.
120. UTA, A70-0005, Box 020, Senate Minutes, Meeting of February 12, 1943, 77, Senate Statute 1579.
121. D.Y. Solandt, "Postgraduate Education in Industrial Hygiene", 63-5.
122. UTA A68-0006, Box 45 (05), R.D. Defries to President H.J. Cody, May 21, 1941.
123. UTSHC 1944-1945, 32.
124. Solandt, "Postgraduate Education in Industrial Hygiene", 65.
125. UTSHC 1945-1946, 49.
126. UTSHHP, "Doctors Who Have Received the Diploma in Public Health School of Hygiene University of Toronto", 15.
127. RDSH 1941, 45.
128. RAC, R.G. 1.1, Series 427L, Box 24, Folder 236, "Memorandum — March 3, 1942, Developments in the School of Hygiene University of Toronto During 1941 and 1942", 1.
129. UTSHC 1941-1942, 23.
130. NAC, R.G. 29, Volume 980 File 388-8-60 Part 1, Department of National Health and Welfare, Division of Nutrition Service, see leaflet in L.B. Pett to M.P. Murphy, Amalgamated Electric Corp. Ltd. Toronto, January 19, 1943.
131. D.A. Scott, "Earle Willard McHenry 1899-1961" in Royal Society of Canada, *Proceedings and Transactions Volume LVI* (Ottawa: Royal Society of Canada, 1961), 219-22.
132. UTA, A68-0007, Box 003(09), see Curriculum Vitae of McHenry in R.D. Defries to President Sidney Smith, January 17, 1946.
133. E.W. McHenry, "The Nutritional Aspects of Relief Work", *CJPH* 24:206.
134. E.W. McHenry, "Some Causes of Malnutrition", *CJPH* 28:547.
135. AO, Ontario Department of Public Welfare, E.W. McHenry, *Report on Food Allowances for Relief Recipients in the Province of Ontario* (Toronto, 1945).
136. E.W. McHenry, "Nutrition and Child Health", *CJPH* 33:152.
137. CDPNHR 1942, 102.
138. CDPNHR 1943, 57.
139. See "The Formation and Activities of the Canadian Council on Nutrition", in CDPNHR 1938, 147.
140. See E.H. Bensley, "Nutrition", in Feasby (ed.), *Official History of the Canadian Medical Services 1939-1945 Volume Two Clinical Subjects*, 153.
141. L.B. Pett, "Food Makes A Difference", *CJPH* 33:568.
142. Canada, Dominion Bureau of Statistics, *The Canada Year Book 1943-44* (Ottawa: Edmond Cloutier, Printer to the King's Most Excellent Majesty, 1944), 521-6.
143. UTA, A73-0026, Box 272 (28), File on E.W. McHenry, "Prof. E.W. McHenry Did Research", *Globe & Mail*, December 22, 1961.
144. "The Canadian Nutrition Program", *CJPH* 34:39.
145. 17th ARSH, 18.
146. 18th ARSH, 18.
147. RAC, R.G. 1.1, Series 427D, Box 15, Folder 137, "University of Toronto — Nutrition", E.W. McHenry to Dr. John A. Ferrell, July 5, 1943.

148. 19th ARSH, 18.
149. RAC, R.G. 1.1, Series 427D, Box 15, Folder 137, "University of Toronto — Nutrition", see "Annual Report for Year Ending March 31, 1944, Sub-Department of Nutrition, School of Hygiene" in E.W. McHenry to Dr. John A. Ferrell, June 22, 1944.
150. *Ibid.*, Folder 135 R.D. Defries to Dr. John A. Ferrell, May 27, 1941.
151. RDSH 1942, 41.
152. RAC, R.G. 1.1, Series 427D, Box 15, Folder , Defries to Dr. John A. Ferrell, May 27, 1941.
153. RDSH 1942, 41.
154. RAC, R.G. 1.1, Series 427D, Box 15, Folder 136, E.W. McHenry to Dr. W.A. McIntosh, June 29, 1942.
155. E. Riggs, H. Perry, J.M. Patterson, J. Leeson, W. Mosley and E.W. McHenry, "A Nutrition Survey in East York Township. I. Descriptions of Survey and General Statements of Results", *CJPH* 35:66.
156. H.P. Ferguson and E.W. McHenry, "A Nutrition Survey in East York Township.III. Repetition of Dietary Studies After Two Years", *CJPH* 35:265.
157. 19th ARSH, 18-19.
158. RAC, R.G. 1.1, Series 427D, Box 15, Folder 137, "Annual Report For Year Ending March 31, 1944. Sub-Department of Nutrition, School of Hygiene", in E.W. McHenry to Dr. John A. Ferrell, June 22, 1944.
159. For a medical definition of metabolism, see *Dorland's Illustrated Medical Dictionary Twenty-Sixth Edition* (Philadelphia: W.B. Saunders Company, 1985), 803.
160. RAC, R.G. 1.1, Series 427D, Box 15, Folder 138, "University of Toronto — Nutrition Resolved RF 441117."
161. UTA, A68-0006, Box 063 (05), R.D. Defries to President H.J. Cody, December 22, 1944.
162. RDSH 1942, 40.
163. UTA, A68-006, Box 049(05), R.D. Defries to President H.J. Cody, February 20, 1942.
164. UTSHC, 1942-1943, 16.
165. Sir Christopher Andrewes, "James Craigie 1899-1978, Elected F.R.S. 1947", *Biographical Memoirs of the Royal Society, 1979* Volume 25 (London: The Royal Society, 1979), 233-40.
166. 18th ARSH, 13-14.
167. FFY, 303.
168. 18th ARSH, 14.
169. 29th ARSH, 15.
170. F.E. J. Fry, "Edmund Murton Walker 1877-1969", *Proceedings of the Royal Society*, Series IV, Volume VIII (Ottawa: The Royal Society of Canada, 1970), 150-2.
171. A.M. Fallis, "Parasitology At Toronto With Special Reference To The University of Toronto", 2. The author thanks Dr. Fallis for providing a copy of his privately printed history.
172. UTFMC 1922-1923, 373.
173. Fallis, "Parasitology At Toronto With Special Reference To The University of Toronto", 3.
174. UTSHC 1929-1930, 10.
175. Fallis, "Parasitology At Toronto With Special Reference To The University of Toronto", 3.
176. *Ibid.*, 4.
177. *Ibid.*, 3-4.
178. 17th ARSH, 13.
179. UTSHC 1944-1945, 20.
180. UTSHC 1944-1945, 20.
181. UTA, A68-0006, Box 049 (05), R.D. Defries to President H.J. Cody, July 8, 1941.
182. UTSHHP, "Doctors Who Have Received The Diploma In Public Health School of Hygiene University of Toronto", 4-11.
183. UTA A68-0006, Box 054 (04), R.D. Defries to President H.J. Cody, October 9, 1942.
184. *Ibid.*, President H.J. Cody to R.D. Defries, October 10, 1942.
185. UTA, A70-0005, Box 020, Senate Minutes Volume 20, Meeting of April 14, 1944, 323, Senate Statute 1646.
186. *Ibid.*, Senate Statute 1647.
187. UTSHC 1945-1946, 35.
188. *Ibid.*
189. UTA, A70-0005, Box 020, Volume 20, Senate Minutes, Meeting of June 21, 1943, 184, Senate Statute 1596.
190. UTA, A68-0006, Box 059 (05), President H.J. Cody to R.D. Defries, February 24, 1944.
191. UTA, A70-0005, Box 020, Volume 20, 184-5 and 326.
192. UTA, A68-0006, Box 059 (05), Defries to President H.J. Cody, May 5, 1944.
193. "The Canadian Public Health Association 1942-1943", *CJPH* 34:515.
194. *Ibid.*, 513.
195. "The Association's Work During 1941-42 (Part IV) Report of the Editorial Board", *CJPH* 33:476.
196. R.D. Defries cited in "Report of the Editorial Board", *CJPH* 34:518.
197. "The Association's Work During 1941-42 (Part IV) Report to the Editorial Board", *CJPH* 33:505-6.
198. *Ibid.*
199. "Report To The Editorial Board", *CJPH* 36:442.
200. R.D. Defries (ed.), *The Development of Public Health In Canada: A review of the history and organization of public health in the provinces of Canada with an outline of the National Health Section of the Department of Pensions and National Health, Canada* (Toronto: Canadian Public Health Association, 1940).
201. R.D. Defries, Mary A. Ross, Eric L. Davey and Walter Moore, "Full-Time Health Services In Canada In 1938", *CJPH* 33:407.
202. "Report of the Committee On Full-Time Local Health Services", *CJPH* 33:405.
203. Defries, Ross, Davey and Moore, "Full-Time Health Services In Canada In 1938", 407.
204. "A Public Health Charter For Canada", 344-5.
205. Canada, House of Commons, Special Committee On Social Security, *Minutes of Proceedings and Evidence No. 12, Friday, May 21, 1943* (Ottawa: Edmond Cloutier, Printer to the King's Most Excellent Majesty, 1943), 356-7.
206. UTSHHP, Interview with Dr. A.J. Rhodes, July 16, 1985, Interviewer P.A. Bator, Ph.D.
207. "A Public Health Charter for Canada", 344.

CHAPTER FOUR: NOTES

1. "The Connaught Medical Research Laboratories and the School of Hygiene University of Toronto", *University of Toronto Monthly* (February, 1953) 54:73-6.
2. CA 83-012-01, R.D. Defries Papers, R.D. Defries "The Connaught Medical Research Laboratories — A Survey of their history and accomplishments during the past forty years and some observations on their future."
3. Jules Gilbert, "The School of Hygiene of the University of Montreal: Its Program, Present and Future." *CJPH* 42:500-2.
4. See Malcolm G. Taylor, *Health Insurance and Canadian Public Policy* (Montreal: McGill-Queen's University Press, 1978), Chapters I and II.
5. RDSH 1946, 53.
6. UTA A68-0007, Box 003 (09), American Public Health Association "Report of Accreditation Visit, Committee on Professional Education University of Toronto School of Hygiene Visit of C-E.A. Winslow Dr. P.H., December 5-7, 1949.
7. UTSHC 1953-1954, 3.
8. UTA, A68-0007, Box 003 (09), American Public Health Association, "1945 Accreditation Report on the University of Toronto School of Hygiene", 1.
9. UTA, A71-0011, Box 004, American Public Health Association Committee on Professional Education, Wilson G. Smillie "Summary Report on Accredited Schools of Public Health 1955-1956", 6, in A.J. Rhodes to Dr. Sidney Smith, August 13, 1956.
10. UTA, A68-0067, Box 017 (06), R.D. Defries to President Sidney Smith, October 3, 1946.
11. UTA, A68-0007, Box 003 (09) American Public Health Association, "1945 Accreditation Report on the University of Toronto School of Hygiene", 1.
12. UTA, A71-0011, Box 004, American Public Health Association Committee on Professional Education, Wilson G. Smillie "Summary Report on Accredited Schools of Public Health 1955-1956", 6, in A.J. Rhodes to Dr. Sidney Smith, August 13, 1956.
13. UTA, A68-0007, Box 035 (04), American Public Health Association Report of Accreditation Visit, Committee on Professional Education, University of Toronto School of Hygiene Visit of C-E.A. Winslow, Dr. P.H. February 6-8, 1946.
14. UTA, A71-0011, Box 004, American Public Health Association, Committee on Professional Education Wilson G. Smillie, "Summary Report on Accredited Schools of Public Health 1955-1956", 6.
15. RAC, R.G. 1.1, Series 427L, Folder A53-1955 "University of Toronto Medical Care" John B. Grant, Inter-Office Correspondence Re Toronto Visit, April 15, 1953.
16. *Ibid.*, Box 24, Folder 238, R.D. Defries to Dr. W.A. McIntosh; March 1, 1949.
17. *Ibid.*, Folder 237, R.D. Defries to Dr. Hugh H. Smith, July 5, 1948.
18. FFY, 301.
19. UTSHHP, Interview with Dr. A.J. Rhodes, Monday February 16, 1987, Interviewer P.A. Bator, Ph.D.
20. UTA, A68-0067, Box 019 (06), R.D. Defries to President Sidney Smith, October 3, 1946.
21. *Ibid.*, President Sidney Smith to R.D. Defries, October 4, 1946.
22. *Ibid.*, Box 050 (09), R.D. Defries to President Sidney Smith, December 29, 1948.
23. *Ibid.*, Box 077 (04) Raymond C. Parker to President Sidney Smith, June 14, 1950 and President Sidney Smith to Dr. R.C. Parker, May 18, 1951.
24. *Ibid.*, Box 133, Stewart Murray to Dr. S. Smith, February 14, 1956.
25. *Ibid.*, President Sidney Smith to Dr. Stewart Murray, February 17, 1956.
26. For a discussion of the impact of veterans on the University, see Mary Halloran, "Post-War Invasion: How U of T battled for those who returned", *Graduate The University of Toronto Alumni Magazine* 13:6-10.
27. RDSH 1946, 52.
28. UTA, A68-0007 Box 035 (04), American Public Health Association "1947 Accreditation Report on the University of Toronto School of Hygiene", 3-6.
29. *Ibid.*, 6.
30. *Ibid.*, 7.
31. UTA, A68-0007, Box 064 (06), American Public Health Association, "1949 Accreditation Report on the University of Toronto School of Hygiene", 6.
32. *Ibid.*, 3.
33. For the number of students entering the Class of 1949 in the D.P.H. program of the School of Hygiene see UTA, A68-0007, Box 050 (09), "Diploma in Public Health" and the names of those who finished the courses, see UTSHHP, "Doctors Who Have Received The Diploma In Public Health School of Hygiene University of Toronto", 22-3.
34. UTA, A68-0007, Box 050 (09), "Students Registered In Diploma in Public Health 1948-1949."
35. UTSHHP, "Doctors Who Have Received The Diploma in Public Health, School of Hygiene University of Toronto", 22.
36. *Ibid.*, 23.
37. 26th ARSH, 31.
38. UTSHC 1968-69, 7.
39. See City of Toronto, Department of Public Health, *1975 Annual Statement* (Toronto: The Corporation of the City of Toronto, 1975).
40. UTA, A68-0007, Box 050 (09), see list of students in Diploma in Hospital Administration, Diploma in Dental Public Health, Diploma in Veterinary Public Health, Master of Applied Science and Certificate in Public Health for 1948-1949.
41. See list of students in School of Hygiene Calendars from 1950-1951 to 1953-1955.
42. UTSHC 1953-1955, 35-6.
43. UTSHC 1950-1951, 44.
44. "The Rockefeller Foundation in Canada", *CJPH* 36:74.
45. FFY, 130.
46. J. Henry Horowicz, "The Development of Health Services in Canada During the Last Twenty Years", *CJPH* 57:123-4.
47. 27th ARSH, 9.

48. See list of students in School of Hygiene Calendar for 1947-1948, 1948-1949, 1952-1953 and 1953-1955.
49. R.D. Defries, "Postgraduate Teaching in the University of Toronto 1913-1955", *CJPH* 48:294.
50. UTSHHP, "Graduate degrees awarded in the School of Hygiene."
51. See list of students in School of Hygiene Calendars from 1945 to 1955.
52. *Canada Year Book 1962* (Ottawa: Roger Douhamel, Queen's Printer, 1962), 142-3.
53. 22nd ARSH, 9.
54. FFY, 213.
55. *Ibid.*, 207.
56. UTA, A68-0007, Box 019 (09), "Report of The Director of the Connaught Medical Research Laboratories 1946-1947", 5.
57. *Ibid.*, Box 050 (09), "Report of the Director of The Connaught Medical Research Laboratories 1947-1948", 1.
58. FFY, 207-11.
59. UTA, A68-0007, Box 019 (09), "Report of the Director of The Connaught Medical Research Laboratories 1946-1947", 4.
60. CA, uncatalogued, "Grants made by Connaught Medical Research Laboratories 1929 - 30th June, 1972." in A.M. Fisher, Executive Secretary Insulin Committee, to Dr. J.K. Ferguson, Director Connaught Medical Research Laboratories, 18 November 1971.
61. UTA, A68-0007, Box 019 (09), "Report of the Director of The Connaught Medical Research Laboratories 1946-1947", 1.
62. CA 83-002-01, R.D. Defries Papers, Correspondence with Allen, K.E., "Memorandum re: distribution of charges between School of Hygiene and College Division, Connaught Medical Research Laboratories [undated but circa 1948]".
63. FFY, 247.
64. Joan Hollobon, "Part of Canada's insulin history vanishes", *Globe and Mail*, October 22, 1981, 5.
65. UTA, A68-0007, Box 019 (06), "Report of the Director of The Connaught Medical Research Laboratories 1946-1947", 1.
66. FFY, 246 and 282-3.
67. Callwood, "The Miracle Factory that began in a stable" *Maclean's*, October 1, 1955, 90.
68. RDSH 1957, 89.
69. UTSHC 1953-1955, 24-7.
70. 29th ARSH, 9.
71. 22nd ARSH, 11.
72. 23rd ARSH, 10-11.
73. A. Rapport, "Summer Internship in a Health Unit", *CJPH* 40:87-9.
74. 29th ARSH, 13-14.
75. RAC, R.G. 1.1, Series 427, Folder 1948-1954, "University of Toronto School of Hygiene Medical Care", Elizabeth M.R. Clarkson "Report of the Year's Activities in the Elective Course in the Social Service Aspects of Medicine Given to the Third Medical Year University of Toronto."
76. For a discussion of the problem, consult Henry R. Beecher and Mark D. Altschuk, *Medicine at Harvard The First Three Hundred Years* (Hanover, New Hampshire: The University Press of New England, 1977), 3560-9.
77. UTSHHP, Interview with Dr. F. Burns Roth, July 12, 1985, Interviewer P.A. Bator, Ph.D.
78. CA, 83-002-03, R.D. Defries Papers, Correspondence with C.E. Dolman, C.E. Dolman to R.D. Defries, 1946.
79. FFY, 215 and 236.
80. 24th ARSH, 12.
81. UTSHHP, "Graduate Degrees Awarded In the School of Hygiene."
82. UTSHC 1956-1957, 27 and 32.
83. 30th ARSH, 14-15.
84. UTA, A68-007, Box 059 (05) R.D. Defries to President H.J. Cody, January 19, 1944.
85. *Torontonensis Volume XXIII, 1921.* (Toronto: Students' Administrative Council, 1921) 134.
86. N.E. McKinnon, "Mortality Reductions in Ontario, 1900-1942", *CJPH* 35:481.
87. *Ibid.*, 489.
88. N.E. McKinnon, "Mortality Reductions in Ontario, 1900-1942", *CJPH* 35:481.
89. N.E. McKinnon, "Mortality Reductions in Ontario, 1900-1942 IV (Tuberculosis)", *CJPH* 36:426.
90. 30th ARSH, 17.
91. N.E. McKinnon, "Cancer Mortality Trends Under Different Control Programs," *CJPH* 41:13-14.
92. N.E. McKinnon, "Cancer Mortality Trends In Different Countries", *CJPH* 41:240.
93. 30th ARSH, 17.
94. 39th ARSH, 12.
95. UTA, A71-0011, Box 004 (14), N.E. McKinnon to A.J. Rhodes, November 14, 1956.
96. UTA, A68-0007, Box 003 (04), R.D. Defries to President Sidney Smith, May 29, 1946.
97. 29th ARSH, 15.
98. UTA, A71-0011, Box 003 (04), N.E. McKinnon to A.J. Rhodes November 14, 1956.
99. FFY, 235.
100. UTA, A68-0007, Box 019 (06), R.D. Defries to President Sidney Smith, November 2, 1946.
101. FFY, 224, 279 and 314.
102. UTSHC 1953-1955, 20.
103. UTSHC 1946-1947, 27-8.
104. RAC, R.G. 1.1, Series 427L, Box 24, Folder 236, "University of Toronto School of Hygiene Faculty Salaries", R.D. Defries to Dr. John A. Ferrell, February 22, 1942.
105. UTA, A68-0007, Box 003 (09) R.D. Defries to President Sidney Smith, January 31, 1946.
106. 26th ARSH, 18-20.
107. UTA, A68-0007, Box 064 (06), American Public Health Association, "1949 Accreditation Report on University of Toronto School of Hygiene", 10.
108. 30th ARSH, 11.
109. *Ibid.*, 31.
110. "Dr. Peter Vaughan, 69, aviation medicine expert", *Toronto Star* Monday January 20, 1986, A 16.

111. RAC, R.G. 1.1, Series 427L, Box 24, Folder 238 "University of Toronto School of Hygiene Faculty Salaries", and "Teaching and Research Activities of the Department of Physiological Hygiene, School of Hygiene."
112. UTA, A68-0007, Box 035 (04), American Public Health Association, "1947 Accreditation Report on the University of Toronto School of Hygiene", 5.
113. 29th ARSH, 15.
114. 26th ARSH, 18.
115. 27th ARSH, 17.
116. 29th ARSH, 17-18.
117. UTA, A68-006, Box 036 (04), R.D. Defries to Miss Patterson, June 13, 1939.
118. UTA, A68-0007, Box 019 (06), H.M. Barrett to C.E. Higginbottom July 16, 1946.
119. H.M. Barrett, "Atmospheric Pollution in Toronto Canada", *CJPH* 29: 1-11.
120. UTA, A68-0007, Box 122 (04), W.G. Angus to A.G. Rankin, September 17, 1954.
121. 30th ARSH, 21.
122. 29th ARSH, 17.
123. *Ibid.*
124. UTA, A68-0007, Box 064 (06), R.D. Defries to President Sidney Smith, January 21, 1950.
125. FFY, 110-11, 120-1, 157, 165 and 215.
126. UTA, A68-0007, Box 122 (04), R.D. Defries to President Sidney Smith, June 13, 1955.
127. *Ibid.*
128. UTSHC 1945-1946, 19.
129. UTA, A68-0007, Box 003 (09), Defries to Smith, June 13, 1955.
130. UTSHC 1970-1971, 8.
131. UTA, A68-0007, Box 122 (04), R.D. Defries to President Sidney Smith, December 4, 1945.
132. UTSHC 1945-1945, 19.
133. FFY, 235-8.
134. UTA, A68-0007, Box 035 (04), American Public Health Association, "1947 Accreditation Report on the University of Toronto School of Hygiene", 6.
135. UTSHC 1949-1950, 29.
136. UTA, A68-0007, Box 050 (09), R.D. Defries to President Sidney Smith, January 19, 1949.
137. "Biochemist Anthony Tosoni helped spearhead penicillin breakthrough", *Toronto Star*, Friday September 6, 1985, A20.
138. FFY, 157,193,238,264 and 270.
139. UTA, A68-0007, Box 077 (04), R.D. Defries to President Sidney Smith, February 14, 1951.
140. 30th ARSH, 16-17.
141. For an insightful discussion of the threat to Ontario's water from inadequate sewage systems, see John Robarts "Problems Of Megalopolis", in Mason Wade (ed.), *The International Megalopolis; Eighth Annual University of Windsor Seminar On Canadian-American Relations* (Toronto: University of Toronto Press for the University of Windsor, 1969), 122-4.
142. UTSHC 1952-1953, 36.
143. Defries, "Postgraduate Teaching in Public Health in the University of Toronto 1913-1955", 294.
144. NAC, R.C. 29, vol. 255, Department of National Health and Welfare, Minutes to The Dominion Council of Health, Sixty-Fourth Annual Meeting October 5-7, 1953, A.E. Berry, "Provincial And Interprovincial Factors in Water Pollution."
145. NAC, M.G. 55 Number 208, Transcript of Interview with Dr. Albert E. Berry in 1983, Interviewer Norman Ball, 20-4.
146. UTA, A13-0026, Box 28 (03).
147. R.D. Defries, "Report of the Editorial Board", *CJPH* 36:442.
148. NAC, R.G. 29, Vol. 255, Department of National Health and Welfare, Dominion Council of Health, "Minutes of the 54th Meeting, June 7-8, 1948", 1.
149. UTSHC 1953-1955, 32.
150. UTA, A68-0007, Box 089 (09), R.D. Defries to President Sidney Smith, May 15, 1952.
151. "John Thomas Phair M.B., D.P.H., 1888-1965", *CJPH* 56:216.
152. UTSHC 1953-1955, 13 and 32.
153. 30th ARSH, 32.
154. Defries, "Postgraduate Teaching in Public Health in the University of Toronto 1913-1955", 294.
155. 26th ARSH, 26.
156. UTA, A68-0007, Box 064 (06), American Public Health Association, "1949 Accreditation Report on the University of Toronto School of Hygiene", 8.
157. UTSHC 1950-1951, 26.
158. 26th ARSH, 26.
159. RAC, R.G. 1.1, Series 427L, "University of Toronto School of Hygiene East York Health Unit", "31 Oct 47 Estimates 1948 University of Toronto School of Hygiene — Field Training Facilities."
160. *Ibid.*
161. 30th ARSH, 22-3.
162. RAC, R.G. 1.1, Series 427L, "University of Toronto School of Hygiene Medical Care Teaching and Research", R.D. Defries to Dr. W.A. McIntosh, July 23, 1948.
163. FFY, 223.
164. RAC, R.G. 1.1, Series 427L, Folder 1948-52, "University of Toronto School of Hygiene Medical Care Teaching and Research, 25 Oct 48".
165. UTA, A68-0007, Box 019 (06), R.D. Defries to President Sidney Smith, May 14, 1947.
166. 30th ARSH, 23.
167. UTA, A68-0007, Box 064 (06), R.D. Defries to President Sidney Smith, June 9, 1950.
168. *Ibid.*, R.D. Defries to President Sidney Smith, January 17, 1950.
169. M.G. Taylor, *The Administration of Health Insurance in Canada* (Toronto: Oxford University Press, 1956).
170. M.G. Taylor, *Health Insurance and Canadian Public Policy* (Montreal: McGill-Queen's University Press, 1978).

171. RAC, R.G. 1.1, Series 427, Folder 1948-1952, "University of Toronto School of Hygiene Medical Care Teaching and Research", R.D. Defries to Dr. D. Bruce Wilson, August 14, 1950.
172. *Ibid.*, D. Bruce Wilson to Dr. Hugh H. Smith, 7 December 1951.
173. *Ibid.*
174. G.M. Hatcher, "Trends in Medical Care Organization I. Their Relation To Public Health Practice", *CJPH* 93: 363-9; and G.M. Hatcher, "Trends in Medical Care Organization II. Government Hospitalization Insurance In Canada", *CJPH* 46:105-14.
175. RAC, R.G. 1.1, Series 427L, Folder 1948-1952 "University of Toronto School of Hygiene Medical Care Teaching and Practice" J.B. Grant Inter-Office correspondence April 20, 1953 Re: Toronto Visit April 15, 1953.
176. *Ibid.*, "File 54239 University of Toronto Medical Care Teaching and Research".
177. 30th ARSH, 23.
178. UTSHC 1953-1955, 32-4.

CHAPTER FIVE: NOTES

1. G. Harvey Agnew, "After Twenty-Five Years . . .", *Canadian Hospital* 30:74.
2. F.B. Roth, "The Health Officer and Hospital Regionalization", *CJPH* 42:467.
3. UTSHHP, Curriculum Vitae of Dr. F. Burns Roth.
4. Roth, "The Health Officer and Hospital Regionalization", 467-8.
5. *Ibid.*, 473.
6. UTA, A70-0005, Senate Minutes, Volume 21, May 1947.
7. *Torontonensis Volume XX, 1918*, (Toronto: Students' Administrative Council, 1918), 89.
8. "George Harvey Agnew M.D., L.L.D., F.A.C.P., F.A.C.H.A., (1895-1971)", *Hospital Administration in Canada*, 13:21.
9. G. Harvey Agnew, "After Twenty-five Years. . . ", *Canadian Hospital*, 30:45.
10. G. Harvey Agnew, *Canadian Hospitals 1920 to 1970 A Dramatic Half Century* (Toronto: University of Toronto Press, 1974), 65.
11. Agnew, "After Twenty-five Years. . . ", 45.
12. Harvey Agnew, "The Medical Survey of Canada", *Canadian Medical Association Journal* 14:123-9.
13. *Ibid.*
14. Agnew, *Canadian Hospitals 1920 to 1970*, 67-8 and 71.
15. "George Harvey Agnew M.D., L.L.D., F.A.C.P., F.A.C.H.A., (1895-1971)", 21.
16. Agnew, "After Twenty-five Years. . .", 74.
17. G. Harvey Agnew, "The Possible Effect Of Health Insurance Upon Hospitals", *Canadian Medical Association Journal* 27:182.
18. Harvey Agnew, "Periodic Payment Plans For the Purchase of Hospital Care (Group Hospitalization)", *Canadian Medical Association Journal* 28:658.
19. Agnew, *Canadian Hospitals 1920 to 1970*, 33-7, 131 and Appendix H.
20. "George Harvey Agnew M.D., L.L.D., F.A.C.P., F.A.C.H.A., (1895-1971)", 21.
21. Agnew, *Canadian Hospitals 1920 to 1970*, 155-7.
22. *Ibid.*, 155-6.
23. *Ibid.*, 162.
24. Frederick Bell, "Medical Economics Group Hospitalization, A Complement To Public Health Services", *CJPH* 34:524.
25. *Ibid.*
26. Agnew, "After Twenty-five Years. . .", 74.
27. Harvey Agnew cited in Canada, House of Commons, Special Committee on Social Security, *Minutes of Proceedings and Evidence No. 6 Friday April 9, 1943* (Ottawa: Edmond Cloutier Printer to the King's Most Excellent Majesty, 1943), 174-6.
28. *Ibid.*
29. *Ibid.*, 176-9.
30. NAC, R.G. 29, Volume 255, Department of National Health and Welfare Dominion Council of Health, Minutes of Fifty-First Meeting May 14-16, 1947. "Serious Lack Of Hospital Facilities".
31. *Ibid.*
32. *Canada Year Book 1954* (Ottawa: Edmond Cloutier Queen's Printer, 1954), 218 & 221-2.
33. Agnew, *Canadian Hospitals 1920 to 1970*, 168-70.
34. UTA, A68-0007, Box 019 (06), "Council Meeting School of Hygiene February 25, 1947, Memorandum (on proposed Department of Hospital Administration)", 1-2.
35. *Ibid.*, 3.
36. 26th ARSH, 10.
37. "Vital Contributions In The Training Of Public Health Personnel In Canada", *CJPH* 33:464.
38. UTA, A68-0007, Box 019 (06), Graham L. Davis to Dr. R.D. Defries, January 6, 1947.
39. *Ibid.*, President Sidney Smith to Emory W. Morris, April 29, 1947.
40. UTSHC 1947-1948, 30.
41. UTA, A68-0007, Box 019 (06), R.D. Defries to President Sidney Smith, June 11, 1947.
42. UTSHC 1947-1948, 26.
43. UTA, A68-0007, Box 089 (06), R.D. Defries to President Sidney Smith, June 21, 1950.
44. UTA, A68-0007, Box 101 (10), R.D. Defries to President Sidney Smith, August 1, 1952.
45. UTA, A68-0007, Box 035 (04), Dr. R.D. Defries to President Sidney Smith, December 24, 1947.
46. 23rd ARSH, 25.

47. UTA, A68-0007, Box 064 (60), Dr. R.D. Defries to President Sidney Smith, November 24, 1949.
48. UTSHC 1947-1948, 10.
49. 23rd ARSH, 25.
50. UTSHC 1947-1948, 36-7.
51. UTSHC 1949-1950, 36.
52. 24th ARSH, 32.
53. UTA, A76-0044, Box 16, Faculty of Medicine Records, Series Acting Director School of Hygiene "(Graduate Degree Students) School of Hygiene, Department of Hospital Administration" in George H. Beaton to Professor Brian S. Merilees, February 6, 1974.
54. UTA, A68-0007, Box 064 (06), Dr. R.D. Defries to President Sidney Smith, September 8, 1948.
55. *Ibid.*, Box 050 (09), "Diploma in Hospital Administration 1948-1949."
56. *Ibid.*, Box 007 (04), Dr. R.D. Defries to President Sidney Smith, June 6, 1951.
57. UTSHC 1967-1968, 83.
58. UTSHHP, Interview with Dr. F. Burns Roth, July 12, 1985.
59. 26th ARSH, 32.
60. UTA, A68-0007, Box 050 (09) Dr. R.D. Defries to President Sidney Smith, September 8, 1948.
61. Agnew, *Canadian Hospitals 1920 to 1970*, 133.
62. UTA, A68-0007, Box 050 (09), see "Outline Of Career Of Miss Eugenie Stuart" in Dr. R.D. Defries to President Sidney Smith, September 8, 1948. Additional details on Stuart's career were provided by Professor Ron McQueen, Department of Health Administration, Division of Community Health, Faculty of Medicine, University of Toronto.
63. UTSHC 1950-1951, 29.
64. UTA, A68-0007, Box 077 (04), Dr. R.D. Defries to President Sidney Smith, July 7, 1954.
65. 27th ARSH, 21-2.
66. UTA, A68-0007, Box 077 (04), Harvey Agnew to R.D. Defries, July 7, 1954.
67. *Ibid.*, President Sidney Smith to Professor E.M. Stuart, June 25, 1954.
68. UTA, A68-0007, Box 077 (04), Dr. R.D. Defries to President Sidney Smith, December 28, 1950.
69. *Ibid.*
70. *Ibid.*, President Sidney Smith to R.D. Defries, December 29, 1950.
71. *Ibid.*, Dr. R.D. Defries to President Sidney Smith, May 9, 1951.
72. 27th ARSH, 136-7.
73. UTA, A68-0007, Box 101 (10) Dr. R.D. Defries to President Sidney Smith, August 1, 1952.
74. 30th ARSH, 18.
75. UTA, A68-0007, Box 122 (04), Andrew Pattullo to Dr. G. Harvey Agnew, April 13, 1955.
76. *Ibid.*, "Practical Studies in Education for Health Administration", 3-5.
77. UTA, A68-0007, Box 111 (03), President Sidney Smith to Dr. G. Harvey Agnew, June 20, 1954.
78. *Ibid.*, G. Harvey Agnew to Dr. Sidney Smith, June 7, 1954.
79. UTSHHP, Interview with Dr. A.J. Rhodes, Friday, July 26, 1985, Interviewer P.A. Bator, Ph.D.
80. A.J. Rhodes, "Diplomas or Master's Degrees: Patterns of Postgraduate Education in Public Health", *CJPH* 52: 142-4.
81. UTA, A68-0007, Box 101 (03), Harvey Agnew to Dr. R.D. Defries, January 8, 1954.
82. UTSHHP, Interview with Dr. A.J. Rhodes, Friday July 26, 1985, Interviewer P.A. Bator, Ph.D.
83. UTA, University of Toronto Senate, Committee on Control of Certificate and Diploma Courses, *Report on Graduate Certificate and Diploma Courses April 25, 1966* (Professor A.J. Rhodes, Chairman).
84. Rhodes, "Diplomas or Master's Degrees. . . ", 143.
85. UTA, A68-0007, Box 101 (03), Harvey Agnew to Dr. R.D. Defries, January 8, 1954.
86. *Ibid.*, President Sidney Smith to R.D. Defries, January 14, 1954.
87. Defries, "Postgraduate Teaching in Public Health in the University of Toronto, 1913-1955", *CJPH* 48:294.
88. 30th ARSH, 17.
89. *Ibid.*, 18.
90. *Canada Year Book 1962*, 224-5.

CHAPTER SIX: NOTES

1. NAC, R.G. 29, Volume 255, Department of National Health and Welfare, Dominion Council of Health, Minutes, Seventh Meeting, November 7-9, 1956, 10.
2. RAC, Series 427D, Box 15, Folder 140, Hugh H. Smith to Dr. McHenry, October 17, 1950.
3. *Ibid.*, E.W. McHenry, "The Relation of Grants from the International Health Division and from the Division of Natural Sciences of the Rockefeller Foundation to the Development of Public Health Nutrition in the School of Hygiene University of Toronto", in E.W. McHenry to Dr. D. Bruce Wilson, September 19, 1950.
4. UTA, A68-0007, Box 035 (04), American Public Health Association, "1947 Accreditation Report on the University of Toronto School of Hygiene", 5.
5. RAC, R.G. 1.1, Series 427D, "University of Toronto Nutrition", "1 Nov 46, 46204. . ."
6. *Ibid.*
7. 26th ARSH, 21-4.
8. RAC, R.G. 1.1, Series 427D, Box 15, Folder 140, E.W. McHenry, "The Relation of Grants. . ."
9. UTSHC 1950-1951, 28.
10. UTSHC 1947-1948, 29-30.
11. RAC, R.G. 1.1, Series 427D, Box 15, Folder 140, E.W. McHenry, "The Relation of Grants. . ."

12. UTA, A73-0026, Box 348 (61), "File on Doris Loreen Noble"
13. *Ibid.*, A71-0011, Box 004, E.W. McHenry to Dr. R.F. Farquharson, January 13, 1956.
14. UTSHHP, "Graduate degrees awarded in the School of Hygiene."
15. 27th ARSH, 18.
16. UTSHC 1949-1950, 29.
17. UTSHC 1953-1954, 32.
18. 30th ARSH, 15.
19. *Ibid.*
20. RDSH 1963, 113.
21. RDSH 1954, 21.
22. 29th ARSH, 21.
23. 30th ARSH, 24.
24. UTA, A71-0011, Box 004, E.W. McHenry to Dr. R.F. Farquharson, January 13, 1956.
25. Dr. George Beaton to P.A. Bator, January 3, 1989 and E.W. McHenry, "Confusion and Stupidity in Nutrition Education" *CJPH* 40: 270-4.
26. For a description of the development of the teaching of Parasitology in the University of Toronto, consult A.M. Fallis, "Parasitology At Toronto With Special Reference To the University of Toronto", privately printed and circulated by Dr. Fallis. The author is grateful to Dr. Fallis for this paper.
27. UTSHC 1948-1949, 19.
28. UTA, A68-0007, Box 019 (06), R.D. Defries to President Sidney Smith, May 14, 1947.
29. *Ibid.*, Box 035 (04), R.D. Defries to President Sidney Smith, May 21, 1948.
30. *Ibid.*, Box 089 (09), R.D. Defries to President Sidney Smith, April 27, 1948.
31. Fallis, "Parasitology At Toronto. . .", 8.
32. UTA, A68-0007, Box 089 (09), R.D. Defries to Dr. Sidney Smith, February 27, 1952.
33. RDSH, 1952, 83.
34. Fallis, "Parasitology At Toronto. . .", 11.
35. *Ibid.*, 9.
36. UTSHC 1953-1954, 29.
37. UTSHHP, "Graduate degrees awarded in the School of Hygiene."
38. 29th ARSH, 16.
39. Fallis, "Parasitology At Toronto. . .", 9.
40. *Dorland's Illustrated Medical Dictionary*, Twenty-Sixth Edition (Philadelphia: W.B. Saunders Company, 1985), 1393.
41. 26th ARSH, 16.
42. 27th ARSH, 14.
43. 29th ARSH, 16 and Fallis, "Parasitology At Toronto . . .", 7.
44. UTA, A71-0011, Box 043 (06), A.M. Fallis to Dr. C.E. Bissell, April 19, 1961.
45. *Ibid.*
46. Hannah Institute For The History Of Medicine, Associated Medical Services Oral History, Interviews University of Toronto Faculty of Medicine, Interview with Dr. Albert Murray Fallis, January 12, 1981, Interviewer Valerie Schatzker, see transcript of interviews, 41-45.
47. UTA, A71-0011, Box 043 (06), A.M. Fallis to Dr. C.E. Bissell, April 19, 1961.
48. FFY, 172-7 and 194-6 and 242.
49. A.J. Rhodes and C.E. van Rooyen, *Textbook of Virology for Students and Practitioners of Medicine*, Third Edition (Baltimore: The Williams & Wilkins Company, 1958), in preface.
50. For a description of these technological advances, see C.E. van Rooyen and A.J. Rhodes, *Virus Diseases Of Man*, Second Edition (New York: Thomas Nelson & Sons, 1948), "Section 1. Technique", 1-144.
51. E.F. Burton and W.H. Kohl, *The Electron Microscope: An Introduction To Its Fundamental Principles And Applications* Second Edition (New York: Reinhold Publishing Corporation, 1946), 5-6 & 10, & 221-8.
52. *Ibid.*, 271.
53. *Ibid.*, 275 and 279.
54. *Ibid.*, 6.
55. UTSHHP, Interview with Dr. A.J. Rhodes, July 16, 1985, Interviewer P.A. Bator, Ph.D.
56. FFY, 272 and 245.
57. UTA, A68-0007, Box 003 (09), President Sidney Smith to Dr. J. Craigie, May 9, 1946.
58. *Ibid.*, R.D. Defries to President Sidney Smith, August 28, 1946.
59. *Ibid.*, R. Hare to President Sidney Smith, October 10, 1946.
60. Ronald Hare, *The Birth of Penicillin And The Disarming of Microbes* (London: George Allen and Unwin Ltd., 1970), 188-215.
61. UTA, A73-0026, Box 253 (42).
62. FFY, 173 and 196.
63. UTSHHP, Interview with Dr. A.J. Rhodes, June 8, 1987, Interviewer P.A. Bator, Ph.D.
64. FFY, 242 and 244.
65. UTA, A68-0007, Box 003 (09), R.D. Defries to President Sidney Smith, May 8, 1946 and R.D. Defries to President Sidney Smith, May 30, 1946, and President Sidney Smith to C.E. van Rooyen, July 8, 1946.
66. H.E. Barnett and H. Fraser, (eds.), *Who's Who In Canada 1969-70* (Toronto: International Press Limited, 1969), 827.
67. C.E. van Rooyen and A.J. Rhodes, *Virus Diseases of Man* Second Edition, see preface, VI.
68. UTA, A68-0007, Box 003 (09), R.D. Defries to President Sidney Smith, May 30, 1946.
69. UTSHHP, "Curriculum Vitae of Andrew J. Rhodes."
70. UTA, A68-0007, Box 019 (06), R.D. Defries to President Sidney Smith, September 30, 1946.
71. *Ibid.*, R.D. Defries to President Sidney Smith, February 17, 1947.
72. FFY, 242, 244 and 245.

73. UTSHHP Interview with Dr. A.J. Rhodes, June 8, 1987.
74. UTA, A68-0007, Box 064 (06), R.D. Defries to President Sidney Smith, November 8, 1949.
75. FFY, 244.
76. UTSHHP, Interview with Dr. A.J. Rhodes, June 8, 1987.
77. UTSHC, 1952-1953, 27.
78. FFY, 176.
79. J.F. Crawley, "Studies on the virus of Western equine encephalitis", Ph.D. Thesis, University of Toronto, 1950.
80. FFY, 228 and 231-2.
81. UTSHHP, Interview with Dr. A.J. Rhodes, June 15, 1987, Interviewer P.A. Bator, Ph.D.
82. Kieran Simpson, (ed.), *Canadian Who's Who 1986 Volume XXI* (Toronto: University of Toronto Press, 1986), 1204-5.
83. UTSHHP, Interview with Dr. A.J. Rhodes, June 15, 1987.
84. UTA, A68-0007, Box 064 (06), Raymond C. Parker to Dr. R.D. Defries, May 20, 1949.
85. FFY, 241.
86. C.E. van Rooyen and A.J. Rhodes, *Virus Diseases Of Man* Second Edition, see preface, VII.
87. *Ibid.*
88. UTSHHP, Curriculum Vitae of Andrew J. Rhodes.
89. UTA, A68-0007, Box 064 (06), American Public Health Association, "1947 Accreditation Report on the University of Toronto School of Hygiene", 9.
90. UTA, A68-0007, R.D. Defries to President Sidney Smith, December 17, 1949.
91. *Ibid.*, Box 101 (10), Basil O'Connor to Dr. Andrew J. Rhodes, October 31, 1952 and Box 111 (03) Basil O'Connor to Dr. Robert D. Defries, June 21, 1954.
92. UTSHHP, Interview with Dr. A.J. Rhodes, Tuesday July 16, 1985, Interviewer P.A. Bator, Ph.D.
93. *Ibid.*, Interview with Dr. A.J. Rhodes on tour of Hygiene Building Wednesday, August 20, 1986, Interviewer P.A. Bator, Ph.D.
94. FFY, 239.
95. Blythe Eagles, "Joseph Francis Morgan 1918-1976" in Royal Society of Canada, *Proceedings and Transactions Series W*, Volume XIV, 1976 (Ottawa: The Royal Society of Canada), 87-8.
96. FFY, 239.
97. A.J. Rhodes cited in Blythe Eagles, "Joseph Francis Morgan 1918-1976", 88.
98. FFY, 272.
99. *Ibid.*
100. Hart E. Van Riper, "Progress in the Control of Paralytic Poliomyelitis through Vaccination", *CJPH* 46:427-8.
101. "The Albert Lasker Award for 1955", *American Journal of Public Health* 45:1606.

CONCLUSION: NOTES

1. R.D. Defries, "Postgraduate Teaching in Public Health in the University of Toronto, 1913-1955", *CJPH* 48:294.
2. UTA, A71-0011, Box 004, Confidential Notes of Dean MacFarlane in Cleary L. Cassidy to President Sidney E. Smith, January 27, 1956.
3. UTSHHP, Paul Adolphus Bator, "The Rockefeller Foundation 633rd Conference, Bellagio, Italy, August 17-21, 1987, The Origins and Development of Public Health Education in the United Kingdom and the United States, A Summary."
4. UTSHHP, "Task Force To Review Community Health Final Report, February 1988", Appendix 5 and 6.
5. "World health body arms to stamp out children's diseases", *Toronto Star*, Saturday, June 28, 1986, section L2.
6. UTSHHP, Interview with Dr. A.J. Rhodes, September 10, 1986, Interviewer P.A. Bator, Ph.D.

APPENDIX A

GRADUATES OF THE SCHOOL OF HYGIENE

Explanatory Note: Dr. R.D. Defries completed this list of students. Some of the dates of the graduation of individuals may differ from the records of the University of Toronto. In addition, the names of the D.P.H. graduates include those who finished the Diploma in the Department of Hygiene and Preventive Medicine, and its predecessor, in the Faculty of Medicine, University of Toronto, prior to the first courses in the School of Hygiene that opened in 1927. To verify the information in this list, it is necessary to consult the records in the University of Toronto Archives.

GRADUATES OF THE SCHOOL OF HYGIENE
1911—1955

The following candidates received the Diploma in Public Health in the year indicated:

Abidh, S. P., 1941
Acker, M. S., 1946
Adams, F., 1914 (ob. 1943)
Aeberli, E. W., 1946
Aldis, R. M., 1949
Allanach, J. R., 1949
Allary, J. B., 1941
Allen, D. R., 1950
Allin, A. E., 1935
Amyot, G. F., 1930
Anderson, G. L., 1946
Anderson, J. L. M., 1938
Anderson, J. R., 1954
Anderson, W. G., 1955
Ansley, H. A., 1934
Appleford, R. D., 1946
Arthur, W. S., 1934
Asselin, N., 1943
Auger, D. L., 1943
Auger, P., 1939
Avison, D. B., 1927 (ob. 1952)

Baillie, J. H., 1941
Baker, H. G., 1939
Baker, R. H., 1943
Baldry, G. S., 1942
Balkany, A. F., 1953
Barron, R. D., 1949
Beattie, A. N., 1946
Beaudet, C. A., 1945
Beaudet, J. C., 1929
Beaudet, J. P., 1938
Beaulieu, D., 1941
Beauvilliers, J., 1943
Beauvilliers, R., 1943
Beckwith, C. J. W., 1937
Bédard, J. U., 1932
Bélanger, A., 1932
Belanger, P. A., 1946
Bell, J. S., 1946
Bent, W. I., 1940
Bergeron, M., 1942
Best, E. W. R., 1947
Bews, D. C., 1945
Binnington, V. I., 1944
Bissett, E. D. R., 1935
Black, D. M., 1954
Blain, R., 1946
Blais, J. A., 1942
Blais, N., 1945
Blake, D. J., 1950
Blumenfeld, E. A., 1946
Bolton, E. S., 1934
Bonner, A. A., 1948
Bossinotte, A., 1931
Bouchard, P. P., 1942
Bourassa, J. H. R., 1943
Bourgault, R., 1944
Bow, M. R., 1920
Bowman, M., 1935
Boyd, A. R. J., 1936
Brandon, K. F., 1934
Breithaupt, D. J., 1946
Breuls, A. M., 1950
Bright, H. J., 1946
Brockington, C. W. M., 1947
Broster, C. N., 1950
Brown, C. P., 1915
Brown, H. M., 1952
Brown, M. H., 1939
Brown, R. F., 1945
Brown, W. G., 1942
Bruneau, R. F., 1941
Bucove, B., 1946
Bull, A. F., 1952
Bulmer, H. R., 1940
Bustin, H. B., 1935
Butcher, J. J., 1947
Byrne, U. P., 1938

Cadham, R. G., 1940
Caldbick, G. D., 1946
Cameron, G. D. W., 1928
Cameron, J. R., 1955
Cantin, A., 1931
Caple, H. H., 1926
Card, J. R. J., 1942
Carswell, J. A., 1939
Cartier, P. E., 1940
Caswell, C. B., 1946
Caswell, J. W., 1933
Caux, A., 1932
Cawson, H. A., 1953
Cesare, J. C., 1953
Chabot, E., 1941
Chabot, J. A., 1940
Chabot, J. O. A., 1939
Chaisson, A. F., 1950
Chan, D. O., 1949
Chan, T. K., 1950
Chang, C-A., 1951
Chang, H. C., 1950
Charest, G., 1945
Chenel, J. L., 1943
Chepesiuk, M. W., 1949
Cheung, O. T., 1949
Chiang, T. H., 1949
Choquette, J. G., 1930
Chow, H. D., 1948
Chown, F. R., 1944 (ob. 1953)
Christie, R. G., 1949
Clark, L. M., 1946
Clarke, A. McM., 1935
Clarke, L. A., 1939
Claveau, P., 1940
Cleghorn, I. M., 1931
Cockroft, W. H., 1947
Coles, B. C., 1946
Collins, H. A., 1952
Collins, J. J., 1944
Conran, H. W., 1946
Cook, J. B., 1945
Cowle, J. E., 1953
Cram, E. J., 1946
Creighton, R. M., 1944
Cruikshank, W. H., 1941
Cruikshank, H. C., 1921 (ob. 1944)
Cull, J. S., 1935
Cunningham, J. G., 1920
Currey, D. V., 1941
Currie, E. V., 1952
Curtin, A. A., 1924
Curtis, O. H., 1950

Dalcourt, A. A., 1938
Dantow, M., 1946
Davey, E. L., 1938
Davey, L. M., 1946
Defries, R. D., 1914
Dehnel, M., 1951
DeKoven, M. J., 1941
de Lautour, G. A., 1947
Denne, A. J., 1945
Derome, F., 1940

Deschênes, R., 1930
Deshaye, J. V., 1954
Dewar, L. G., 1946
Doane, A. R., 1944
Dobbin, G. M., 1946
Donaldson, M. B., 1940
Donovan, C. R., 1932
Doucet, J. L. C., 1941
Dow, R. P., 1934
Doyle, H. S., 1945
Dumas, A., 1938
Dunlop, T. C., 1946
Dupont, J. A., 1955

Eagles, E. L., 1940
Eagles, G. H., 1925
Earle, W. P., 1946
Eaton, R. D. P., 1955
Elkerton, L. E., 1948
Elliot, G. R. F., 1940
Elliott, M. R., 1935
Evis, F. A., 1951

Falkland, S., 1953
Fang, J. J., 1949
Farah, G., 1948
Feindel, J. R., 1954
Felton, R., 1928
Ferguson, C. G., 1946
Ferriera, S. E. L., 1937
Filiatrault, J. M., 1947
Fitch, M., 1950
Flahiff, E. W., 1930
(ob. 1954)
Fleming, A. G., 1914
(ob. 1943)
Fleming, D. S., 1941
Fogo, E. M., 1944
Foley, D. E., 1917
(ob. 1938)
Fortin, J. B., 1943
Fowler, W., 1946
Fraser, D. T., 1921
(ob. 1954)
Fraser, G. M., 1946
Fraser, J. J., 1931
(ob. 1939)
Fraser, R. H., 1936
Fraser, R. H., 1944
Frenette, E., 1932
Frost, W. H., 1947
Fryer, D. H., 1937
Fryer, R. E., 1954

Gadeock, J. R., 1947
Gagnon, A., 1936
Garner, F. O. R., 1941
Gauthier, C. A., 1934
Gauthier, J., 1939
Gayton, J. L., 1939
Gendron, V. L., 1955
Genest, B., 1941
George, R. K., 1923
George, W. E., 1925
(ob. 1949)
Germain, J. E., 1931
(ob. 1939)
Gibbons, R. J., 1935
Gignac, A. B., 1946
Gilbert, J., 1939
Gilchrist, W. S., 1946
Gilhuly, I. K., 1937
Gill, D. G., 1924
Glen-Campbell, E. A. D., 1942
Glynn, J. J., 1955
Gonty, J. J., 1954
Gordon, N. S., 1949
Goulding, A., 1940
Goyette, R. B., 1955
Graham, A. H., 1925
(ob. 1954)
Graham, W. A., 1922
(ob. 1931)
Grant, M., 1950
Greenhill, S. E., 1947
Grenon, R. G., 1946
Guimont, F., 1944

Hamelin, P. E., 1946
Hames, C. F. W., 1931
Hardie, M. J., 1954
Hardman, R. P., 1929
Harper, W. S., 1950
Hastings, J. E. F., 1954
Hatcher, G. H. M., 1947
Hawkes, V. S., 1950
Hawkesley-Hill, W., 1932
Hazelwood, J. G., 1922
(ob. 1942)
Hazen, F. C., 1951
Heathcote, A. G. S., 1954
Henderson, D. L., 1949
Henry, W. E., 1930
Hershey, J. M., 1935
Hill, D. A., 1951
Hill, H. W., 1911
(ob. 1947)
Hiltz, J. E., 1947
Hoffman, C. M., 1950
Hoggarth, W. B., 1954
Hookings, C. E., 1946
Horner, C. M., 1942
Howatt, B. D., 1954
Howie, J., 1937
Huang, T. M., 1942
Huot, M., 1942
Hutchison, D. A., 1955
Hutton, G. H., 1932

Irwin, A. C., 1954

Jackson, F. W., 1929
Jackson, G. P., 1922
(ob. 1951)
Jackson, J. R., 1953
Jacques, E., 1941
Jeannotte, A., 1931
Jeffs, J. I., 1948
Jenkins, R. B., 1929
Johnston, H. W., 1930
Johnston, J. L., 1944
Jones, G. R., 1950

Kao, H., 1951
Keeping, B. C., 1931
(ob. 1951)
Kelly, R. A., 1941
Kendrick, T. D., 1932
Kennedy, H. K., 1950
Kennedy, R. A., 1945
Kennedy, W. D. B., 1923
(ob. 1928)
King, R. M., 1946
Kitching, J. S., 1934
Knipe, R. G., 1943
Kozakiewicz, M., 1953

Laberge, A., 1943
Labrecque, F., 1930
Lacoursière, A., 1944
Laferrière, U., 1942
LaHaye, B., 1931 (ob. 1954)
Lalande, E., 1932
Lambert, H. J., 1954
Lamberti, A. J. D., 1947
Landry, R. D., 1947
Lane, R. M., 1946
Langis, A., 1937
Lansdown, L. P., 1948
Laperrière, A., 1945
Lapierre, J. A., 1933
(ob. 1953)
Lapp, A. D., 1936
Large, G. E., 1946
Larose, J. R., 1930
Larsen, A. A., 1952
LaSaine, T. A., 1938
Laxton, J. E., 1931
Lavers, H. D., 1947
Leclerc, F., 1937
Leclerc, O., 1941
(ob. 1953)

Leeder, F. S., 1929
Leeson, H. J., 1946
Leger, G. C., 1937
Leroux, J. A., 1940
Létienne, G. J. E., 1946
Letts, F. L., 1922
L'Heureux, P. P., 1941
Little, G. M., 1933
Little, J. L., 1930
(ob. 1953)
Lochead, D. C., 1915
(ob. 1946)
Logan, H. L., 1936
Losier, P. J., 1937
Lougheed, M. S., 1937
Lowe, H. T., 1953
Lunan, M. B., 1946
Lynch, E. L., 1940

MacCharles, C. W., 1944
MacDonald, D. G. H., 1946
Macdonald, M. R., 1943
Macdonald, R. J., 1939
MacDonald, W. A., 1941
MacHattie, F. G. W., 1950
Mackay, A. F., 1946
MacKay, E. N., 1948
Mackey, L. R., 1942
MacKinnon, N. D. C., 1945
MacLean, D. L., 1935
MacLean, L. A., 1940
MacLeod, D. R. E., 1946
MacMillan, C. W., 1933
Macneill, N. F., 1950
Maddison, G. E., 1939
Mader, E. W., 1929
Mahabir, K. G., 1919
(ob. 1941)
Mahaffy, A. F., 1935
Maher, T. F., 1950
Mahoney, J. A., 1941
Manacki, J. A., 1954
Manly, C. C., 1946
Mao, S. F., 1955
Martel, E., 1933
(ob. 1952)
Martin, G. K., 1950
Mastromatteo, E., 1950
Mather, C. E., 1942
Mather, J. M., 1939
Matthews, V. L., 1947
May, E. S., 1949
McCallum, B. J. M., 1950
McCallum, M. G., 1942
McCammon, J. G., 1933
McCannel, J. S., 1946
McClenahan, D. A., 1920
(ob. 1933)

McClenahan, R. R.,
1921 (ob. 1935)
McClure, W. B., 1929
McCormack, C. W.,
1946
McCullough, J. W. S.,
1914 (ob. 1941)
McCurdy, D. G., 1945
McDougall, R., 1947
McGarry, J. M., 1945
McGavin, M. F., 1940
McGugan, A. C., 1940
McIntosh, J. W., 1919
(ob. 1939)
McKay, A. L., 1926
McQuaig, K. D., 1952
Melançon, D., 1944
Melanson, J. A., 1934
Menzies, A. M., 1931
Michell, W. A. R., 1924
Middleton, F. C., 1925
Miller, G. W., 1936
Miller, J. B., 1952
(ob. 1952)
Milot, J. L., 1945
Miner, T. S., 1947
Moffat, A. B., 1923
(ob. 1953)
Moffat, G. B., 1931
(ob. 1945)
Monahan, R., 1937
Mondor, E., 1932
Moodie, G. E., 1943
Mooney, W. C., 1940
(ob. 1946)
Moore, P. E., 1938
Morin, J. M., 1942
Morris, C. W. J., 1951
Mosley, W., 1937
Moss, G. W. O., 1949
Murray, R. B., 1953
Murray, S. S., 1934

Nadeau, R., 1942
Naismith, A. G., 1922
Nasmith, G. G., 1918
Ndukwe, O. D., 1948
Nelson, D. G. M., 1948
Neville-Smith, C., 1953
Nicholson, C. C., 1943
Nicolai, R., 1952
Northover, R. J., 1950

Oake, C. M., 1944
O'Keefe, J. M., 1951
O'Neil, A. J. E., 1954
O'Regan, K. R., 1954
Orr, H., 1920
(ob. 1952)
Ostry, E. I., 1942
O'Shaughnessy, J. K.,
1955

Paquet, J. N. E. B., 1939
Paquin, F., 1924
Paquin, J., 1936
Parker, J. M., 1946
Patenaude, J. A., 1932
Patterson, T. H., 1947
Paulin, J. E., 1934
Peachy, A. B., 1949
Pearson, C. L., 1941
Peart, A. F. W., 1943
Peat, R. S., 1938
Pelletier, J. A., 1942
(ob. 1949)
Pelletier, J. A. L., 1932
(ob. 1945)
Peloquin, L. P., 1945
Pequegnat, L. A., 1924
Peters, E. S., 1949
Phair, J. T., 1921
Pion, P. P., 1938
Poisson, E., 1941
Poliquin, P., 1937
Pomerleau, C., 1934
Porth, F. J., 1953
Potvin, E., 1931
Powers, O. C., 1942
Preston, J. H., 1946
Prowse, W. A., 1950
Puffer, D. S., 1942
Pugh, D. S., 1948

Ranta, L. E., 1939
Ratnasingham, P. K., 1949
Rawson, N. R., 1932
Read, J. H., 1952
Reed, W. A., 1953
Rerrie, J. I., 1936
Richard, J. B. L., 1947
Richards, L. A., 1946
Riddell, A. R., 1925
Rideout, V. K., 1955
Riggs, A. E. C., 1941
Rioux, E., 1952
Robb, W. M., 1930
Roberts, L. N., 1946
Robertson, J. S., 1938
Robertson, J., 1946
Robinson, C. E. A., 1949
Robinson, D. R., 1948
Rogers, J. W., 1945
Rolland, P. E., 1944

Roy, A., 1933
Roy, B., 1943
Roy, J. O., 1937 (ob. 1954)
Rutledge, E. J., 1936

Saunders, W. G., 1933
Savoie, L. P., 1930 (ob. 1940)
Scatliff, J. N. R., 1951
Schwenger, C. W., 1954
Scott, P. A., 1946
Searle, A., 1946
Sellers, A. H., 1933
Seymour, M. M., 1917 (ob. 1929)
Shaver, E. M., 1947
Shaw, J. H., 1939
Siang, T. C., 1948
Siemens, H., 1941
Simms, G. G., 1940
Sinclair-Loutit, K. W. C., 1949
Sirois, J. S., 1936
Slack, W. R. I., 1948
Smillie, R. A., 1946
Smith, C. E., 1934
Smith, D. C., 1949
Smith, G. M., 1947
Smith, H. G., 1937
Sneath, P. A. T., 1927
Solandt, D. Y., 1944 (ob. 1955)
Somerville, A., 1932
Sparks, F. P., 1937
Sparks, G. L., 1929
Stanton, J. J., 1950
Stephen, H. M., 1951
Stephenson, F., 1945
Stewart, D., 1954
Stiver, W. B., 1938
Story, C. F. R., 1947
Struthers, E. B., 1938
Struthers, R. G., 1943
Stuart, L. M., 1950
Stubbing, S., 1947
Stubbings, R. S., 1953
Sturgeon, L. W. C., 1945
Sung, C., 1941
Sutherland, G. Q., 1948
Sutherland, R. B., 1946
Sutton, N. H., 1925
Swan, A. M., 1938
Sylvestre, J. E., 1930

Tan, S.-k., 1951
Taylor, J. A., 1938
Templeton, D., 1949
Templin, M. I., 1945
Tennant, V. L., 1946
Thiboutot, L. P., 1930 (ob. 1938)
Thoms, A. E., 1946
Thomson, M. G., 1931
Todd, R. R., 1915 (ob. 1928)
Tourangeau, F. J., 1933
Trask, C. R., 1947
Tremblay, J. M., 1941
Tse, Y. T., 1947
Turcotte, L. A., 1944
Turpel, W. N., 1939
Valentine, E. J., 1943
Vaughan, P., 1946
Vézina, L. R., 1928

Walker, A. M., 1927
Walmsley, J. F. S., 1949
Walton, G. R., 1934
Walton, R. A., 1938 (ob. 1946)
Warren, C. A., 1926 (ob. 1954)
Warren, D. R., 1946
Watkinson, E. A., 1945
Watson, J. H., 1954
Watts, W. G., 1951
Webb, J. F., 1945
Wells, J. P., 1949
Wenger, P., 1951
Westman, E. R., 1946
White, J. C., 1953
White, J. H., 1928 (ob. 1950)
Whittal, J. K., 1948
Whyte, M. B., 1917 (ob. 1939)
Wilkey, J. R., 1940
Williams, J. C., 1954
Willis, J. S., 1950
Willits, R. E., 1940
Wilson, C. H., 1942
Wilson, D. B., 1928
Wilson, F. H., 1945 (ob. 1952)
Wilson, G. E. D., 1946
Wilson, R. J., 1946
Wior, H., 1946
Wishart, F. B., 1938
Wishart, F. O., 1942
Wodehouse, R. E., 1922
Wood, W. J., 1937
Woodhouse, C. F., 1922
Wride, G. E., 1946
Wyke, D. A., 1942
Wylde, E. W., 1953

Yen, C. H., 1938
Young, A. E., 1946
Young, E. J., 1946
Yue, K. T., 1951

Zeman, H. B. L., 1947

DIPLOMA IN INDUSTRIAL HYGIENE

The following candidates received the Diploma in Industrial Hygiene in the years indicated:

Byrne, U. P., 1948
Caswell, C. B., 1955
Collins, J. J., 1945
Huckvale, W. S., 1955
Oake, C. M., 1946
Sinclair-Loutit, K. W. C., 1950
Vaughan, P., 1947

DIPLOMA IN DENTAL PUBLIC HEALTH

The following candidates received the Diploma in Dental Public Health in the years indicated:

Brown, H. K., 1946

Chegwin, A. E., 1950
Clarke, G. K., 1947
Coburn, C. I., 1951
Compton, F. H., 1953
Connor, R. A., 1949

Dawson, W. G., 1951
Duncan, J. A., 1955

Feasby, R. E., 1954

Grainger, R. M., 1950

Honey, S. L., 1945
Hunt, A. M., 1955

Jarrett, M. E., 1953

Kapusta, M., 1948
Kohli, F. A., 1945

Langstroth, R. S., 1949
Lawrence, J. W., 1950

McCombie, F., 1950
McDonagh, W. A., 1950
McKenna, H. E., 1949
McLaren, H. R., 1946
Marsh, T. L., 1952
Mitton, G. T., 1948

O'Meara, B. J., 1949

Sutherland, A. B., 1948

Windrim, H. L., 1948

DIPLOMA IN VETERINARY PUBLIC HEALTH

The following candidates received the Diploma in Veterinary Public Health in the years indicated:

Abelseth, M. K., 1950
Allman, E. C. H., 1952
Allman, T. H., 1952

Bannister, G. L., 1948
Barnum, D. A., 1949
Bigland, C. H., 1945
Black, J. G., 1948
Blacklock, J. F., 1950
Bryson, H. L., 1946

Ceballo, H., 1954
Chamberlayne, E. C., 1945
Colgate, R. F., 1945

Damude, D. F., 1949
Dorland, R., 1950

Edge, G. A., 1945

Fish, N. A., 1945
Fleming, G. C., 1953

Gandier, J. C. C., 1945
Garrick, D., 1947
Glenroy, J. McL., 1951

Hall, A. V., 1948
Harden, F. J., 1950
Herlihey, G. J., 1948

Keefe, W. J., 1950
Khan, C. K. A., 1948
Kidd, A., 1947
Langford, E. V., 1950
Loos, P. W. J., 1948

MacDonald, D. R., 1946
Mader, C. K., 1949
Matthews, L. J., 1951
McDermid, K. A., 1952
McEwen, K. A., 1952
McGregor, J. K., 1950
Meads, E. B., 1952
Melady, T. R. I., 1952
Mitchell, W. R., 1950
Moynan, J. D., 1949
Murray, J. A., 1945

Olivares, J. W., 1953

Padilla, M., 1954
Pandurang, G., 1953
Penrose-FitzGerald, C. P., 1954

Ramirez, V. M., 1955
Raymond, O. C. G., 1948
Rousseau, B. J., 1954
Rowsell, H. C., 1950
Rumney, W. J., 1954
Rushton, F., 1946

Sanderson, N. V. C., 1951
Smith, O. G., 1948
Spence, T. H., 1950
Stewart, C. C., 1950
Studic, D. S., 1954

Tailyour, J. McC., 1951
Turnbull, W. J., 1951

Villa, L. J., 1955

Walker, F. W., 1954
Walker, V. C. R., 1948
Ward, S. N., 1953
Watt, J. E., 1950
Wilson, R. L., 1955
Worton, H., 1949

CERTIFICATE IN PUBLIC HEALTH

The following candidates received the Certificate in Public Health in the years indicated:

Davidson, S. J., 1952
Doyle, M. T., 1953

Geekie, D. A., 1955
Goodacre, R. H., 1952

Holowaty, R., 1955
Hughson, A. A., 1951

Iralu, C., 1953

Johnson, D. S., 1949

Love, E. M. Y., 1947

MacPherson, R. M., 1950
Ma, Y. C., 1949
Miller, C. E., 1954

Neil, J. H., 1952
Nichols, W., 1952
Noble, D. L., 1949

Paul, J. B., 1954
Penrice, M. V., 1950
Petursson, O. B., 1953

Ray, E. N., 1951
Richardson, T. B., 1951

Shimizu, A. G. S., 1955
Swan, F. B., 1945

Travis, R. B., 1949

Watt, E. G., 1948

DIPLOMA IN HOSPITAL ADMINISTRATION

The following candidates received the Diploma in Hospital Administration in the years indicated:

Armitage, D. T., 1951

Barr, N. K., 1954
Bennet-Alder, L., 1954
Birch, W. J., 1949
Boettcher, E. N., 1954

Cathcart, H. R., 1949
Clusiau, O. H., 1953
Cox, R. C., 1954

Daeschel, W. F. O., 1952
Dillon, H. G., 1952
Doney, J. J. Jr., 1954

Ferguson, R. B., 1950
Fleetwood, R. A., 1951

Graham, G. W., 1950

Hewig, A. H., 1950
Hornstein, J., 1951

Johnson, S., 1953
Johnston, J. C., 1950

LaSalle, G., 1951
Lee, J., 1951

MacIntyre, D. M., 1950
Mackay, J., 1952
McNabb, D. M., 1953
McNab, J. A., 1953
McTaggart, A. K., 1950
Mance, Sister Jeanne, 1954
Mikail, C. M., 1954
Palin, G. K., 1955

Peacock, G. W., 1949
Pearce, R., 1951
Peart, D. R., 1951

Radey, H. M., 1952
Renton, J. S., 1953
Roeder, E. W., 1953
Ross, H. F., 1952
Rothman, B. G., 1949

Stewart, G. C., 1951
Sutton, I., 1950

Temple, C. K., 1953
Thompson, J. A. D., 1953

Wahn, E. V., 1951
Wetzel, H. E., 1951

July, 1955

APPENDIX B

GRADUATE DEGREES AWARDED IN THE SCHOOL OF HYGIENE 1927-1955*

DEPARTMENT OF HYGIENE AND PREVENTIVE MEDICINE

Doctor of Philosophy		**Thesis**
1930	D.C.B. Duff	The bacterial spoilage of salmon, with reference to the sources of the organism responsible for putrefaction. Detection of indol in bacterial cultures. An improved pipette manipulator. Modification of Orskov single-cell technic. Physiological study of certain parasitic Saprolegniaceae. A possibly diphtheroid organism from a case of cerebro-spinal meningitis.
1932	Mrs. M.M. Johnston	Intestinal infections in infants.
1934	Miss H.C. Plummer	I. Determination of the accuracy of a skin test for streptococcal toxin and for streptococcal antitoxin in chinchilla type rabbits. II. Investigation of some factors concerned in the growth and toxin production of the Dochez (N.Y.5) strain of haemolytic streptococcus.
1934	Miss M.D. Smith	The detoxifying action of ox bile on diphtheria toxin.
1945	Miss M.E. Malcomson	Studies on the serology of typhus fever.
1950	J.F. Crawley	Studies on the virus of Western equine encephalitis.
1955	J.E.L. Fahey	Studies on chronic respiratory disease of chickens and turkeys: I. Studies on chronic respiratory disease of chickens. II. Studies on chronic respiratory disease of turkeys.
1955	S.M. Lesley	Relationship between virus and cell host.

Master of Arts		
1928	Miss E.H.C. Robertson	A study of the effect of various agents, chiefly sunlight, upon the susceptibility of rachitic rats to infection.
1928	Miss M.A. Ross	A statistical study of the mortality from diphtheria in Ontario for the years 1880-1925.
1933	Miss E. Anderson	The presence of specific types of pneumococcus in the throats of groups of normal individuals and the study of certain immunity reactions in the blood of these individuals.
1933	R.J. Gibbons	A study of some properties of single cell isolates of smooth and rough variants of *B. dysenteriae sonne*.
1933	F.O. Wishart	The serology of vaccinia-variola virus.

*The titles of these theses are taken from the records of the University of Toronto School of Hygiene and may differ from their final form. To verify these titles, it is necessary to consult the records in the University of Toronto Archives.

1941	J.W. Fisher	An application of the O resistance test to the study of the nutritional requirements of *B. typhosus*.
1942	Miss E.M. Clark	The inhibition of wound sepsis.
1943	W.J.A. Percy	The intracutaneous virulence test for *Corynebacterium diphtheriae*.
1943	Miss H.M.G. Macmorine	Factors influencing the production of staphylococcal alpha-haemolysin.
1946	Miss M.E. Curl	Absorption of influenza virus.
1948	Miss M.G. Langley	A study of streptococcus bacteriophage.
1948	G. Shaw	A study of the growth of the tubercle bacillus in Dubos' medium.
1948	Miss Z.W. Christie	A study of gametocytes in *Plasmodium gallinaceum* infections.
1950	Miss S. Toshach	A study of *C. diphtheriae* bacteriophage.
1950	Miss E.J. Whittaker	Studies on bacteriophage for the acid-fast micro-organisms.
1950	S.M. Lesley	Studies on radioactive coliphage.
1950	K.A. McKay	The normal and diarrheal bacteria flora of newborn animals.
1951	J.E.L. Fahey	Further studies on bacteriophages for *C. diphtheriae*.
1951	S.I. Hnatko	Studies in bacteriophages for mycobacteria.
1951	R.B.L. Gwatkin	Antibiotics from actinomycetes: I. History, recent discoveries and technical methods II. Studies on antibiotics from actinomycetes isolated from northern soils.
1953	J.D. Wilson	Proteinuria in the male albino rat.
1954	Miss B.K. Buchner	Epidemic influenza in Canada: a study of the preparation and trial of an experimental vaccine.
1954	J.N.J. Reichert	A study of the resistance of *Streptococcus lactis* to penicillin.
1954	P.M. Tracy	Studies of bacteriophage active against the Mycobacteria.
1954	Miss N.M. Howard	The immunological response to B.C.G. infection.

DEPARTMENT OF PHYSIOLOGICAL HYGIENE

Doctor of Philosophy

1932	Mrs. R.C. Partridge	Sensory nerve impulses.
1938	E.J. Reedman	Vitamin C. The nature, occurrence, and physiology of vitamin C and associated factors in nutrition.
1939	Miss E.G. Gavin	The B vitamins and fat metabolism.
1939	Miss J.H. Ridout	Certain factors controlling the disposition of liver fat.
1944	D. Murray Young	Observations on the assay of insulin.
1944	H.D. Bett	A study of the preparation and purification of the antipernicious anaemia substance of beef liver.
1944	Miss J.M. Patterson	Dietary production and prevention of kidney damage.
1949	H.M. MacFarland	The use of BAL in heavy metal poisoning.

Master of Arts

1929	Mrs. R.C. Partridge	The dynamics of muscular action.
1930	Miss E.G. Gavin	The diazo reaction.
1934	M.L. Graham	Studies on Vitamin C.
1940	D.G.H. MacDonald	Nutritional factors in the production of rat bradycardia.
1940	Miss H.M. Perry	Observations of the relation of vitamin C to scurvy.
1945	Miss E.C. Armstrong	The microbiological estimation of pyridoxine.
1945	Mrs. E.M. Semmons	Errors in the estimation of calcium in foods.
1945	Miss H.R. Virtue	Sources of error in dietary surveys.
1946	Miss K.E. Armbrust	The effect of liver extracts on explants of guinea pig bone marrow.
1949	Miss N.G. Hornstein	The effect of chronic exposure to alumina and other fumes on experimental animals.
1950	J.B. Gallagher	Changes in auditory thresholds following exposure to noise.
1954	K.K. Soga	Peripheral neuro-muscular effects of lead poisoning.
1954	A. Ma	An investigation and study in exact quantitative olfactometry.
1955	Miss M.K. Jamieson	Studies on insulin.

Master of Science in Agriculture

1943	Miss C.M. Young	Some sources of error in nutritional surveys: Differences between calculated and analytically determined values for ascorbic acid.

DEPARTMENT OF EPIDEMIOLOGY AND BIOMETRICS

Doctor of Philosophy

1934	Miss M.A. Ross	A survey of mortality of diphtheria, scarlet fever, influenza and other respiratory diseases and diabetes for fifty years in Ontario and an analysis of the results of the use of toxoids in the prevention of diphtheria in Toronto school children.

Master of Arts

1949	J.H. Doughty	A study of mortality changes in British Columbia between 1921 and 1946.

DEPARTMENT OF CHEMISTRY IN RELATION TO HYGIENE

Doctor of Philosophy

1948	A.L. Tosoni	The purification of penicillin and derivatives of penicillin which prolong the action of penicillin.
1949	S.S. Rao	I. Investigation concerning scarlet fever toxins and antitoxins. II. Study of specific absorption by diphtheria toxoid-antitoxin floccules.
1955	L. Goldsmith	Chemical and immunological studies on insulins.

1955	Miss H.M.G. Macmorine	Factors influencing the production of various biosynthetic penicillins, with special reference to hydrophilic types.

Master of Arts

1949	Mrs. S.S. Rao	I. A study of the action of crystalline trypsin and chymotrypsin on toxins and toxoids of diphtheria, tetanus and scarlet fever. II. A study of the action of crystalline trypsin and chymotrypsin on toxin-antitoxin and toxoid-antitoxoid floccules of diphtheria, tetanus, and scarlet fever.
1954	M.L. Coval	Studies of sensitization with ACTH and growth hormone and on antigenicity of insulin.

DEPARTMENT OF NUTRITION

Doctor of Philosophy

1948	Mrs. M.L.C. MacFarland	Studies on the lipotropic action of choline and inositol.
1951	W.W. Hawkins	Studies on Vitamin B_6.
1952	J.R. Beaton	B vitamins and intermediary metabolism.
1953	E.F. Caldwell	B vitamins and protein metabolism.
1955	Mrs. J.W. Maur	Studies on glutamic acid metabolism.
1955	G.H. Beaton	Protein metabolism in pregnancy.

Master of Arts

1949	Rhoda M. Ballantyne	Protein metabolism in cancer tissue. A study of pyridoxine and biotin in human cancer tissue.
1950	J.R. Beaton	Studies on glutamic acid.
1951	Marion J.H. Cavan	Observations on 4-pyridoxic acid.
1951	James Barsky	The relation of pyridoxine to protein metabolism.
1951	Janet R.M. Jackson	The relation of the B vitamins to the synthesis of lipids.
1952	Joyce L. Beare	Interrelation of hormones and B vitamins in protein metabolism.
1952	Jane M. White	Studies on plasma glutamic acid.
1952	Margery Jane McArthur	The estimation of 4-pyridoxic acid in tissues.
1952	Edith F. Hubbard	The relation of B vitamins to cholesterol synthesis.
1952	Helen B. Rush	The relation of B vitamins to fat synthesis.
1953	G.H. Beaton	Studies on vitamin B_6 compounds in animal and human tissue.

1953	Grace Ozawa	Metabolic defects in vitamin B_6 deficiency.
1954	Margaret E. Goodwin	Vitamin B_6 and intermediary metabolism.
1955	Mi Heh Ryu	Protein metabolism in pregnancy.

DEPARTMENT OF PARASITOLOGY*

Doctor of Philosophy

1949	D. Davies	Ecology of blackflies.

Master of Arts

1949	J. Wheeler	Study of life history of *Ascaridia* in ruffed grouse.
1951	J. Pearson	Studies on cercarial dermatitis.
1952	R.C. Anderson	Studies on microfilaria in birds.
1952	G. Sweatman	Studies on hydatid disease.
1954	G.F. Bennett	Study of rodent bot *Cuterebra emasculator*.
1955	Miss E. Turnbull	Life history and development of the monogenetic trematoda.

*Offered in conjunction with the Department of Zoology

APPENDIX C

Staff of School of Hygiene University of Toronto, 1928-1955[1]

List of Staff, with Department and Academic Sessions of Appointment*

Adams, Miss I.C.	Chemistry in Relation to Hygiene	1944-1946**
Agnew, Harvey	Hospital Administration	1947-1955
Allan, Miss D.	Physiological Hygiene	1944-1946
Anderson, Miss E.	Hygiene and Preventive Medicine	1933-1937
Armstrong, Miss C.	Nutrition	1945-1946
Armstrong, Miss E.M.	Physiological Hygiene	1947-1949
Armstrong, Miss J.	Public Health Nutrition	1951-1953
Arnoldi, Miss M.G.	Chemistry in Relation to Hygiene	1933-1936
Baillie, J.H.	Epidemiology and Biometrics	1941-1942
Baker, Mrs. J.	Chemistry in Relation to Hygiene and Sanitation	1953-1955
Ballantyne, Miss M.	Public Health Nutrition	1948-1950
Barber, Miss L.	Physiological Hygiene	1940-1943
———	Nutrition	1941-1948
Barr, Miss E.M.F.	Hygiene and Preventive Medicine	1931-1942
		1942-1946***
		1946-1951
Barrett, H.M.	Physiological Hygiene	1933-1942
		1942-1946***
		1946-1947
Barsky, J.	Public Health Nutrition	1948-1951
Barton, E.L.	Public Health Administration	1949-1951
Beare, Miss J.L.	Public Health Nutrition	1951-1955
Beaton, G.H.	Public Health Nutrition	1953-1955
Beaton, J.R.	Public Health Nutrition	1949-1955
Beattie, Miss L.	Epidemiology and Biometrics	1941-1943
Bell, Miss H.	Physiological Hygiene	1940-1942
Berry, A.E.	Epidemiology and Biometrics	1928-1943
———	Public Health Administration	1941-1951
———	Chemistry in Relation to Hygiene and Sanitation	1951-1955
Best, C.H.	Physiological Hygiene	1928-1941
Binnington, Miss V.I.	Public Health Administration	1944-1946
Bishop, A.J.	Hygiene and Preventive Medicine	1939-1949
———	Virus Studies [Virus Infections, 1944]	1942-1949
Blain, Miss P.	Public Health Nutrition	1946-1949
Blake, Mrs. F.E.	Hygiene and Preventive Medicine	1943-1945
Bourne, Miss E.	Public Health Nutrition	1950-1951

* Note Academic year runs from July 1 through June 30.

** Indicates appointments, for example, between July 1, 1944, and June 30, 1946. A similar format will be used throughout.

***Indicates "On leave of absence for duration of war".

1. Compiled by Dr. A.J. Rhodes and based largely on the annual calendars of the University of Toronto School of Hygiene including staff of the Connaught Laboratories.

Boyd, A.R.J.	Public Health Administration	1953-1955
Bradley, L.O.	Hospital Administration	1947-1953
Brandon, K.F.	Epidemiology and Biometrics	1935-1937
Brink, G.C.	Public Health Administration	1944-1955
Broddy, Miss J.J.	Public Health Administration	1950-1953
Brooks, V.B.	Physiological Hygiene	1949-1951
Brown, M.H.	Hygiene and Preventive Medicine	1933-1940
		1940-1946***
		1946-1955
______	Public Health Administration	1946-1955
Brown, W.G.	Public Health Administration	1949-1955
Burke, F.S.	Hygiene and Preventive Medicine	1928-1930
Cahoon, Miss M.	Public Health Administration	1951-1955
Caldwell, E.F.	Public Health Nutrition	1951-1955
Calvin, Miss B.M.	Epidemiology and Biometrics	1943-1944
______	Office of Director, School of Hygiene	1944-1951
Cameron, D.W.	Epidemiology and Biometrics	1930-1931
Camilleri, Miss A.	Hygiene and Preventive Medicine	1945-1949
Carley, Miss M.	Hygiene and Preventive Medicine	1950-1952
Carpenter, Miss H.M.	Public Health Administration	1947-1948
Cartwright, Miss E.	Public Health Administration	1944-1946
Cavan, Mrs. M.J.	Public Health Nutrition	1950-1952
Caverly, D.S.	Public Health Administration	1950-1951
______	Chemistry in Relation to Hygiene and Sanitation	1951-1955
Chapman, S.H.	Physiological Hygiene	1949-1950
Christian, Miss C.	Hygiene and Preventive Medicine	1953-1955
Clark, Miss P.	Physiological Hygiene	1944-1947
Clarke, C.H.D.	Hygiene and Preventive Medicine	1936-1937
Cohn, S.H.	Physiological Hygiene	1948-1950
Collins, Miss M.E.	Hygiene and Preventive Medicine	1937-1939
Corkill, J.M.	Hygiene and Preventive Medicine	1937-1938
Cornett, Miss M.	Nutrition	1943-1944
Cory, Miss J.	Physiological Hygiene	1944-1946
Cowan, C.R.	Physiological Hygiene	1937-1942
Cowan, Miss G.	Hygiene and Preventive Medicine	1933-1936
Craigie, J.	Office of School of Hygiene	1935-1946
______	Epidemiology and Biometrics	1933-1943
______	Virus Studies [Virus Infections, 1944]	1942-1947
Crawford, Miss R.	Public Health Nutrition	1946-1947
Crawley, J.F.	Virus Infections	1951-1955
Cryderman, Miss E.	Public Health Administration	1949-1953
Cunningham, J.G.	Physiological Hygiene	1928-1955
Currey, D.V.	Public Health Administration	1944-1948
		1951-1955
Czajka, Miss F.L.	Public Health Administration	1953-1955
Daly, Miss M.	Hygiene and Preventive Medicine	1928-1930
Davey, E.L.	Hygiene and Preventive Medicine	1940-1941
______	Epidemiology and Biometrics	1940-1941
Day, Miss J.M.	Public Health Administration	1946-1950

Defries, R.D.	Associate Director	1928-1940
______	Acting Director	1940-1941
______	Director, School of Hygiene	1941-1955
______	Hygiene and Preventive Medicine	1928-1955
______	Epidemiology and Biometrics	1928-1944
______	Public Health Administration	1944-1955
Dempster, G.	Virus Infections	1950-1955
Denkert, Miss E.	Physiological Hygiene	1953-1955
Dewar, J.E.	Parasitology	1952-1953
Deyman, W.	Epidemiology and Biometrics	1939-1941
Dolman, C.E.	Hygiene and Preventive Medicine	1933-1936
Duff, D.C.B.	Hygiene and Preventive Medicine	1928-1930
Edge, G.A.	Public Health Administration	1948-1955
Elder, Miss M.O.	Physiological Hygiene	1948-1949
Elkerton, L.E.	Public Health Administration	1952-1955
Elliott, H.R.	Public Health Administration	1942-1945
Emory, Miss F.H.M.	Department of Public Health Nursing	1928-1933
Esler, Mrs. E.M.	Public Health Nutrition	1948-1950
Evans, Miss N.	Physiological Hygiene	1948-1953
Fahey, J.	Hygiene and Preventive Medicine	1951-1953
Fallis, A.M.	Hygiene and Preventive Medicine	1937-1944
______	Parasitology	1944-1955
Farrell, Miss L.N.	Hygiene and Preventive Medicine	1950-1955
Ferguson, Mrs. H.	Nutrition	1943-1945
Fine, S.	Physiological Hygiene	1948-1950
Fisher, A.M.	Chemistry in Relation to Hygiene	1945-1950
______	Physiological Hygiene	1950-1955
Fisher, J.W.	Virus Studies [Virus Infections, 1944]	1943-1945
FitzGerald, J.G.	Director, School of Hygiene	1928-1940
______	Hygiene and Preventive Medicine	1928-1940
Fleming, Zoe	Parasitology	1949-1950
Flintoff, Miss S.	Public Health Nutrition	1951-1952
Fox, C.H.	Physiological Hygiene	1947-1948
Fraser, Miss C.J.	Hygiene and Preventive Medicine	1928-1932
Fraser, D.T.	Associate Director, School of Hygiene	1942-1955
______	Hygiene and Preventive Medicine	1928-1955
Fraser, Miss F.H.	Hygiene and Preventive Medicine	1928-1955
Freeman, S.J.	Physiological Hygiene	1948-1950
Freeman, R.S.	Parasitology	1952-1955
Fryer, D.H.	Hygiene and Preventive Medicine	1937-1938
Fussell, Mrs. M.I.	Physiological Hygiene	1945-1948
Gallagher, J.B.	Physiological Hygiene	1948-1955
Gamey, T.	Physiological Hygiene	1947-1948
Gavin, Miss E.G.	Physiological Hygiene	1930-1937 1939-1943
______	Nutrition	1941-1943
Geiger, K.	Chemistry in Relation to Hygiene	1949-1955
Gibbons, R.J.	Hygiene and Preventive Medicine	1933-1935
Gibson, Miss M.	Physiological Hygiene	1949-1951

Giles, Miss M.	Public Health Nutrition	1949-1955
Goddard, I.G.	Physiological Hygiene	1940-1941
Goodwin, J.E.	Physiological Hygiene	1947-1955
Gould, C.	Physiological Hygiene	1950-1951
Goulding, A.M.	Hygiene and Preventive Medicine	1944-1955
Graham, A.F.	Virus Infections	1949-1955
Gray, R.	Physiological Hygiene	1950-1951
Grimaldi, J.	Physiological Hygiene	1949-1951
Gurvitch, Miss N.	Physiological Hygiene	1946-1948
Haddon, Mrs. R.E.	Epidemiology and Biometrics	1953-1955
Haist, R.E.	Physiological Hygiene	1940-1946
Hann, R.	Physiological Hygiene	1940-1941
Hare, R.	Hygiene and Preventive Medicine	1937-1947
______	Virus Studies [Virus Infections, 1944]	1942-1947
Hatcher, G.H.M.	Public Health Administration	1947-1955
Hawke, R.J.	Physiological Hygiene	1946-1949
Hawkins, W.	Nutrition	1943-1946
Heimbecker, R.O.	Physiological Hygiene	1948-1949
Hendrick, E.B.	Physiological Hygiene	1947-1948
Hipson, Miss L.	Public Health Nutrition	1951-1953
Hnatko, S.	Hygiene and Preventive Medicine	1951-1952
Holmes, Miss M.E.	Hospital Administration	1949-1951
Holland, Miss M.J.	Chemistry in Relation to Hygiene	1946-1953
Horner, Miss C.M.	Epidemiology and Biometrics	1942-1943
Hornstein, Mrs. N.	Physiological Hygiene	1948-1951
Horwood, J.	Physiological Hygiene	1942-1955
Hosler, Miss D.	Public Health Nutrition	1949-1951
Hubbard, Miss E.F.	Public Health Nutrition	1951-1953
Hunter, J.	Physiological Hygiene	1943-1946
Hutchison, Miss I.	Public Health Nutrition	1950-1951
Jackson, F.W.	Public Health Administration	1953-1955
James, Miss E.	Nutrition	1941-1946
______	Physiological Hygiene	1942-1943
Jaques, L.B.	Physiological Hygiene	1940-1942
Jeffs, Miss D.E.	Nutrition	1943-1944
Jersak, Miss J.	Physiological Hygiene	1953-1955
Jest, G.	Physiological Hygiene	1951-1952
		1953-1955
Joyce, Miss P.K.	Hospital Administration	1948-1949
Katzmayr, F.	Physiological Hygiene	1952-1953
Kerns, K.	Epidemiology and Biometrics	1937-1944
______	Office of Director	1944-1946***
Keyes, Louise E.	Hygiene and Preventive Medicine	1949-1950
Kimm, G.	Chemistry in Relation to Hygiene	1937-1943
Kirkup, Miss F.	Epidemiology and Biometrics	1946-1947
Kitching, J.S.	Hygiene and Preventive Medicine	1935-1938
Kozaruk, J.	Physiological Hygiene	1944-1945
Kuitunen-Ekbaum, Mrs. E.	Epidemiology and Biometrics	1942-1944
______	Parasitology	1944-1955

Laberge, L.	Hygiene and Preventive Medicine	1938-1939
Labzoffsky, N.A.	Epidemiology and Biometrics	1939-1942
Langley, Margaret	Hygiene and Preventive Medicine	1946-1950
Lau, R.	Public Health Nutrition	1949-1950
Lazarus, A.S.	Epidemiology and Biometrics	1939-1940
Leeson, Miss H.J.	Physiological Hygiene	1942-1943
———	Nutrition	1942-1947
Lehman, Leone	Hygiene and Preventive Medicine	1951-1955
Leyerle, D.B.	Physiological Hygiene	1943-1944
Lindner, E. Joan	Hygiene and Preventive Medicine	1950-1951
Lock, Miss J.	Physiological Hygiene	1943-1946
Loheed, Mrs. M.	Hospital Administration	1951-1955
MacDonald, Mrs. E.	Physiological Hygiene	1943-1944
MacDonald, Miss J.	Epidemiology and Biometrics	1941-1943
———	Public Health Administration	1941-1943
MacFarland, H.N.	Physiological Hygiene	1943-1950
MacFarland, Mrs. M.	Public Health Nutrition	1944-1950
MacIntyre, D.M.	Hospital Administration	1951-1955
MacIntyre, Lillias	Hygiene and Preventive Medicine	1951-1956
Mack, G.E.	Physiological Hygiene	1944-1949
MacLean, D.L.	Secretary, School of Hygiene	1946-1955
———	Physiological Hygiene	1930-1939
		1940-1946***
———	Epidemiology and Biometrics	1946-1955
MacLeod, D.R.E.	Epidemiology and Biometrics	1947-1955
MacNabb, A.L.	Epidemiology and Biometrics	1941-1943
———	Public Health Administration	1941-1952
Mackley, Miss A.M.	Physiological Hygiene	1946-1947
Mader, Miss E.M.	Hygiene and Preventive Medicine	1931-1932
Mahon, Miss L.	Physiological Hygiene	1930-1942
Malyon, R.H.	Epidemiology and Biometrics	1942-1943
———	Public Health Administration	1943-1945
Marsh, T.	Chemistry in Relation to Hygiene	1933-1934
Marten, C.	Chemistry in Relation to Hygiene	1937-1938
Mather, J.M.	Epidemiology and Biometrics	1940-1941
McAllister, J.S.	Hygiene and Preventive Medicine	1949-1955
———	Virus Infections	1949-1955
McAvoy, Miss M.J.	Physiological Hygiene	1952-1955
McCausland, Miss S.R.	Epidemiology and Biometrics	1937-1955
McClelland, Miss L.	Hygiene and Preventive Medicine	1940-1941
McCullough, J.W.S.	Epidemiology and Biometrics	1928-1936
McFarland, H.N.	Physiological Hygiene	1941-1944
McGanity, W.J.	Public Health Nutrition	1947-1952
McGhie, B.T.	Public Health Administration	1943-1945
McGill, D.	Physiological Hygiene	1947-1948
McHenry, E.W.	Physiological Hygiene	1928-1943
———	Nutrition	1941-1946
———	Public Health Nutrition	1946-1955
McKay, A.L.	Epidemiology and Biometrics	1933-1941
McKerrow, Miss J.R.	Public Health Nutrition	1946-1947
		1950-1951

McKinnon, N.E.	Hygiene and Preventive Medicine	1931-1932
———	Epidemiology and Biometrics	1928-1940
		1940-1944***
		1944-1955
Meister, D.	Physiological Hygiene	1950-1951
Mickle, Miss G.	Hygiene and Preventive Medicine	1941-1955
Mihalyi, L.	Physiological Hygiene	1952-1953
Miles, Miss A.	Epidemiology and Biometrics	1944-1947
Millar, J.G.	Physiological Hygiene	1944-1946
Mills, Miss E.R.	Physiological Hygiene	1950-1955
Mingay, Miss M.	Physiological Hygiene	1942-1945
Moloney, P.J.	Hygiene and Preventive Medicine	1928-1943
———	Chemistry in Relation to Hygiene	1933-1946
———	Chemistry in Relation to Hygiene and Sanitation	1946-1955
Moore, W.	Epidemiology and Biometrics	1937-1946***
Moorhouse, Miss B.L.	Public Health Administration	1951-1953
Mortimer, Miss N.	Department of Public Health Nursing	1929-1933
Mosley, W.	Public Health Administration	1941-1943
		1943-1946***
		1946-1955
———	Epidemiology and Biometrics	1940-1943
Moss, G.W.O.	Public Health Administration	1952-1955
Muller, Miss D.L.	Epidemiology and Biometrics	1949-1955
Munro, Mrs. O.	Hygiene and Preventive Medicine	1943-1946
		1947-1948
Murray, D.	Physiological Hygiene	1949-1950
Musson, Mrs. J.M.	Public Health Administration	1950-1951
———	Office of Director, School of Hygiene	1951-1955
Naylor, P.E.	Hygiene and Preventive Medicine	1949-1950
Neale, Miss D.	Public Health Nutrition	1946-1950
Neill, Miss F.E.	Hygiene and Preventive Medicine	1941-1943
Nyeky, A.	Parasitology	1953-1955
Ozawa, Miss Grace	Public Health Nutrition	1953-1955
Parker, R.C.	Virus Studies [Virus Infections, 1944]	1942-1955
Parr, Miss E.M.	Hygiene and Preventive Medicine	1938-1940
Partridge, Mrs. Ruth C.	Physiological Hygiene	1928-1953
Patterson, Miss Jean	Physiological Hygiene	1940-1943
Patterson, Miss J.M.	Nutrition	1941-1945
Pequenat, L.A.	Public Health Administration	1953-1955
Perry, Miss Helen	Nutrition	1941-1943
	Physiological Hygiene	1941-1943
Phair, J.T.	Epidemiology and Biometrics	1933-1943
———	Public Health Administration	1941-1955
Phaneuf, Miss I.	Physiological Hygiene	1946-1947
Pichler, Miss K.	Hygiene and Preventive Medicine	1930-1931
Pike, E.	Physiological Hygiene	1941-1942
Pimblett, R.	Physiological Hygiene	1952-1953
Pinder, R.	Physiological Hygiene	1951-1952

Plummer, Miss Helen C.	Hygiene and Preventive Medicine	1928-1955
Podoski, Mary H.	Hygiene and Preventive Medicine	1946-1949
Porter, G.D.	Hygiene and Preventive Medicine	1928-1936
Powers, O.C.	Public Health Administration	1943-1946
Proctor, Miss M.	Public Health Nutrition	1946-1949
Puffer, D.S.	Public Health Administration	1950-1955
Randall, R.L.	Epidemiology and Biometrics	1933-1940
Randall, Mrs. A.	Epidemiology and Biometrics	1947-1949
Rao, Lakshmi	Hygiene and Preventive Medicine	1953-1955
Raven, S.	Epidemiology and Biometrics	1937-1939
Reid, D.B.W.	Epidemiology and Biometrics	1947-1955
Richardson, Mrs. M.R.	Epidemiology and Biometrics	1944-1955
Rhodes, A.J.	Virus Infections	1947-1955
Richuk, Miss A.	Physiological Hygiene	1947-1949
Ridout, Miss Jessie H.	Physiological Hygiene	1928-1940
		1940-1941***
		1941-1942
Riggs, Miss A.E.C.	Physiological Hygiene	1941-1942
______	Nutrition	1941-1942
______	Epidemiology and Biometrics	1941-1942
Robinson, C.E.A.	Public Health Administration	1949-1955
Rogers, G.W.	Physiological Hygiene	1952-1953
Roseblade, K.	Physiological Hygiene	1942-1943
		1943-1946***
Ross, Miss M.A.	Office of Director, School of Hygiene	1943-1945
Ross, Miss Mary A.	Epidemiology and Biometrics	1928-1945
Roy, Miss I.S.	Hygiene and Preventive Medicine	1934-1935
Russell, Miss E.K.	Director, Department of Public Health Nursing	1928-1933
Rutland, Miss M.	Physiological Hygiene	1943-1945
Sanderson, Miss M.	Nutrition	1945-1948
Sanderson, Miss R.E.	Epidemiology and Biometrics	1952-1953
Schrader, G.	Physiological Hygiene	1952-1953
Scott, Mrs. J.	Nutrition	1943-1946
Secker, J.J.	Physiological Hygiene	1949-1950
Selfe, A.	Physiological Hygiene	1950-1951
Sellers, A.H.	Epidemiology and Biometrics	1936-1941
______	Public Health Administration	1948-1955
Semmons, Mrs. E.M.	Nutrition	1943-1945
Shaver, Miss E.M.	Public Health Nutrition	1947-1949
Shaw, G.	Hygiene and Preventive Medicine	1947-1949
Sheppard, Mrs. C.	Public Health Nutrition	1946-1948
Shier, Mrs. L.	Public Health Nutrition	1948-1955
Siebenmann, C.O.	Hygiene and Preventive Medicine	1950-1955
Skelding, L.	Physiological Hygiene	1937-1938
Slovik, J.	Physiological Hygiene	1945-1955
Smith, D.C.	Public Health Administration	1949-1950
Smith, Miss Florence	Public Health Nutrition	1950-1953
Smith, Miss J.	Physiological Hygiene	1940-1943
______	Nutrition	1941-1943
Smith, Miss M.D.	Chemistry in Relation to Hygiene	1933-1938

Smith, R.	Physiological Hygiene	1943-1946
Sneath, P.A.T.	Hygiene and Preventive Medicine	1928-1937
Soga, K.K.	Physiological Hygiene	1953-1955
Solandt, D.Y.	Physiological Hygiene	1940-1955
Somerville, Miss O.E.	Office of Director, School of Hygiene	1928-1935
Sprent, J.F.A.	Parasitology	1948-1952
Staples, W.	Physiological Hygiene	1937-1940
		1941-1946***
Steckley, Mrs. A.	Public Health Nutrition	1949-1950
Steele, Miss A.C.	Physiological Hygiene	1945-1948
Stenhouse, Miss G.E.	Epidemiology and Biometrics	1947-1952
Struthers, R.G.	Public Health Administration	1943-1944
———	Parasitology	1948-1955
Stuart, Miss E.M.	Hospital Administration	1949-1955
Sutherland, Miss M.L.	Epidemiology and Biometrics	1943-1944
Swanson, A.L.	Hospital Administration	1953-1955
Tanton, Miss F.	Nutrition	1944-1945
Taylor, Miss E.M.	Hygiene and Preventive Medicine	1928-1933
———	Chemistry in Relation to Hygiene	1933-1955
Taylor, M.G.	Public Health Administration	1952-1955
Thompson, Miss N.	Physiological Hygiene	1939-1941
Thomson, Miss A.H.	Epidemiology and Biometrics	1942-1943
———	Public Health Administration	1942-1943
Thomson, Miss H.E.	Epidemiology and Biometrics	1943-1944
Toshach, S.	Hygiene and Preventive Medicine	1949-1951
Tosoni, A.L.	Chemistry in Relation to Hygiene and Sanitation	1950-1955
Townsend, Mrs. R.	Physiological Hygiene	1943-1944
Tracey, P.M.	Hygiene and Preventive Medicine	1953-1955
Trimble, W.B.S	Hospital Administration	1948-1949
van Rooyen, C.E.	Virus Infections	1947-1955
Virtue, Miss R.	Nutrition	1945-1946
Walker, V.C.R.	Public Health Administration	1950-1955
Webster, Miss Dorothy	Parasitology	1946-1949
Wellington, Mrs. E.	Physiological Hygiene	1946-1947
Wheler, Miss E.	Epidemiology and Biometrics	1940-1943
———	Public Health Administration	1941-1945
White, Miss Jean	Public Health Nutrition	1953-1955
White, R.E.	Physiological Hygiene	1951-1952
Whittaker, Elizabeth I.	Hygiene and Preventive Medicine	1949-1951
Wilson, R.J.	Hygiene and Preventive Medicine	1938-1942
		1942-1947***
		1947-1955
Wiman, Mrs. K.	Public Health Administration	1943-1944
Wishart, F.O.	Epidemiology and Biometrics	1933-1934
———	Hygiene and Preventive Medicine	1937-1955
Wood, Miss R.	Nutrition	1944-1946
Yasny, Miss D.	Physiological Hygiene	1953-1955
Young, D.M.	Nutrition	1943-1944
Zeman, H.B.L.	Hygiene and Preventive Medicine	1952-1953

Staff of Connaught Laboratories and Connaught Medical Research Laboratories University of Toronto, 1928-1955

Allan H.W.	1950-1955
Allen, K.E.	1933-1955
Anderson, Miss E.A.	1931-1938
Anderson, Miss J.	1930-1931
Angus, J.	1943-1955
Armbrust, Miss K.E.	1946-1952
Bailey, Mrs. G.F.	1951-1953
Ballantyne, E.E.	1944-1946
Best, C.H.	1928-1955
Bett, H.D.	1940-1955
Bolton, Miss A.J.	1928-1950
Boyd, I.W.	1932-1955
Briggs, Miss R.M.	1946-1955
Brown, M.H.	1929-1940
	1940-1946*
	1946-1955
Buchner, Miss B.K.	1950-1955
Cameron, D.W.	1931-1940
Campbell, Miss E.K.	1944-1950
Campbell, J.	1937-1938
Campbell, L.A.	1944-1945
Campbell, Miss R.B.	1952-1955
Carlyle, R.E.	1944-1947
Carter, Miss A.	1929-1930
Carter, G.R.	1944-1946
Caulfield, A.H.W.	1928-1940
Chang, Miss H.	1947-1955
Chapman, Mrs. M.	1944-1946
Chapman, Miss M.G.	1945-1951
Charles, A.F.	1930-1955
Chen, H.K.	1948-1955
Christie, D.C.	1944-1945
Clark, Miss E.M.	1943-1955
Clarke, Miss D.	1945-1946
Corkill, J.M.	1940-1955
Coval, Mrs. H.J.	1952-1953
Coval, M.L.	1950-1955
Cowan, Miss L.I.	1952-1953
Craigie, J.	1932-1947
Crawley, J.F.	1945-1955
Curl, Miss M.E.	1945-1947

*On leave of absence for duration of war

Defries, R.D.	1928-1955
Degen, K.A.B.	1952-1955
Dempster, G.	1950-1955
Dix, D.G.	1946-1949
Dolman, C.E.	1932-1955
Fahey, J.E.L.	1953-1955
Farrell, Miss L.N.	1936-1955
Finegan, Miss H.	1928-1943
Fisher, A.M.	1933-1955
FitzGerald, J.G.	1928-1940
Franklin, A.E.	1952-1955
Fraser, Miss C.J.	1929-1932
Fraser, D.T.	1928-1955
Fraser, Miss F.H.	1928-1955
French, R.P.C.	1936-1955
Geiger, K.H.	1951-1955
Gerald, W.P.	1941-1955
Gibbons, R.J.	1936-1938
Giles, Mrs. J.I.	1952-1955
Gill, Miss J.Y.	1952-1953
Glass, D.G.	1948-1955
Goldsmith, L.	1953-1955
Goodwin, Miss G.F.	1948-1951
Graham, A.F.	1948-1955
Graham, G.D.	1950-1955
Green, W.A.	1948-1949
Greey, P.H.	1949-1950
Gruson, E.S.	1953-1955
Hannah, B.	1928-1953
Harbour, E.M.	1942-1955
Hare, R.	1937-1947
Healy, G.M.	1950-1955
Howard, Miss N.M.	1953-1955
Hunter, A.	1936-1938
Hunter, J.F.	1951-1955
Hutchison, F.L.	1928-1952
Ivan, S.W.	1942-1943
Jackson, Miss L.K.	1947-1951
Jamieson, Miss M.K.	1947-1955
Jeffrey, A.M.	1928-1929
Johnston, Mrs. M.M.	1928-1929
Keefe, W.N.	1944-1945
Kerslake, E.G.	1932-1955
Kitching, J.S.	1936-1938
Klopp, K.W.	1944-1948
Knowles, Mrs. D.S.	1949-1952

Labzoffsky, N.A.	1942-1943
Lang, Miss E.M.	1943-1955
Lawson, K.F.	1952-1955
Lazier, Miss R.	1929-1930
Lesley, S.M.	1951-1955
Lewis, Miss A.H.	1946-1955
Lockwood, Miss E.M.	1943-1944
Lucas, A.R.	1945-1953
Mackenzie, Mrs. D.	1946-1947
MacKinnon, A.J.	1944-1945
MacLean, D.L.	1930-1939
	1939-1946*
	1946-1955
MacLeod, D.R.E.	1947-1955
Macmorine, Miss H.M.G.	1940-1955
Macpherson, N.L.	1944-1951
MacQuarrie, Miss M.J.	1947-1955
Mader, Miss E.W.	1931-1932
Malcolmson, Mrs. M.E.	1943-1944
McClelland, Miss L.	1941-1949
McCutcheon, Mrs. P.G.	1952-1955
McEachern, R.D.	1947-1950
McHenry, E.W.	1931-1955
McIntyre, Miss S.J.	1953-1955
McKay, A.L.M.	1928-1933
McKinnon, N.E.	1928-1940
	1940-1944*
	1944-1955
McKinnon, Miss R.	1930-1931
McVicar, G.A.	1940-1955
Meldrum, Miss R.E.J.	1943-1946
Merry, Miss M.I.	1929-1931
Moloney, P.J.	1928-1955
Moon, Miss M.	1943-1955
Morgan, Miss J.	1940-1943
Morgan, J.F.	1948-1953
Morton, Miss H.J.	1948-1952
Moss, G.W.O.	1953-1955
Murray, L.M.	1928-1929
Orr, M.D.	1929-1955
Overend, D.W.	1937-1939
Parker, R.C.	1943-1955
Phillips, Miss M.B.	1951-1955
Pichler, Miss K.	1944-1946
Plummer, Miss H.C.	1928-1955
Polley, J.R.	1944-1945
Rake, G.W.	1937-1938
Ranta, L.E.	1940-1950
Reid, D.B.W.	1948-1955

Reid, Miss M.R.	1944-1947
Rhodes, A.J.	1947-1955
Richardson, Miss M.J.	1944-1945
Ridout, Miss J.H.	1928-1943
Robertson, Miss L.E.	1951-1952
Romans, R.G.	1940-1955
Russell, Miss E.E.	1943-1945
Scott, D.A.	1928-1955
Semmons, Mrs. E.M.	1946-1947
	1948-1949
Shimada, F.T.	1950-1955
Shirkie, Mrs. L.K.	1943-1944
Siebenmann, Mrs. C.	1931-1932
Siebenmann, C.O.	1931-1955
Silverthorne, L.N.	1932-1946
	1948-1955
Sims, H. des B.	1930-1932
Slim, Miss G.S.	1947-1951
Smith, Miss D.M.	1932-1938
Sneath, P.A.T.	1928-1937
Somerville, Miss O.E.	1928-1946
Spaulding, Miss J.J.	1944-1948
Stevens, H.B.	1944-1945
Taylor, Miss E.M.	1928-1955
Thicke, Miss J.C.	1951-1952
Tosoni, A.L.	1945-1955
van Rooyen, C.E.	1947-1955
Vipond, Miss E.A.	1945-1947
Walker, V.C.R.	1949-1955
Waters, G.G.	1940-1955
Watson, D.W.	1943-1944
Wilson, J.D.	1950-1953
Wilson, R.J.	1947-1955
Wood, W.	1952-1955
Woodward, Miss M.	1940-1943
Wright, F.J.	1952-1953
Wright, Mrs. N.C.	1944-1945
Young, D.M.	1944-1947
	1951-1955

INDEX

Abrasive Grains Association 126
Adams, Fred 13
Advisory Committee on Venereal Diseases for Military District No. 2 (Toronto region) 23
African public health problems 161, 168
Agnew, G. Harvey 141, 142, 143, 146, 147, 148, 149, 150, 155, 157, 158
AIDS 185
Air Pollution Board 130
Albert Lasker Award 1955 to Dr. R.D. Defries 178
Allcutt, A.E. 130
Allin, A.E. 117
American Bacteriologists, Society of, 170
American College of Hospital Administrators 146
American College of Surgeons, hospital services 143, 145, 146
American Conference of Professors of Preventive Medicine 148
American Foundations and health in Canada 29, 30, 95, 107, 109, 110, 126, 161, 162, 170
American Hospital Association, Council on Community Relations and Administrative Practices 145
American Institute of Nutrition 165
American Public Health Association, Committee on Professional Education: School accredited after visits of committee in 1945, 1947, 1949 109, 109, 127
American public health officers, comparisons with Canada 63
Amyot, John A. 8, 9, 10, 13, 18, 21, 22, 24
An Introduction to the Practice of Preventive Medicine 28, 29
Antitoxin Laboratory of Department of Hygiene, Faculty of Medicine, University of Toronto 18
Associated Medical Services 146
Association of University Programs in Hospital Administration 155
Atmospheric Pollution 128, 129
Avison, D.B. 87

Bacteriology 1, 3, 4, 7
Bain, E.M.F. 77
Banting Foundation For Medical Research 91
Banting, Sir Frederick 29, 40
Barber, L. 90
Barrett, H.M. 77, 89, 90, 128, 129
Barron, R.D. 116
Bates, Gordon xi
B. diphtheriae 23
Beaton, George 163
Beaton, John 163
Bell, W.J. 27
Bennett, D.F. 167-168
Bernard, Leon 29
Berry, Albert E. 28, 57, 58, 87, 133-134
Best, Charles 40, 46, 81, 126, 127
Bickell Foundation 170
Binnington, Vera 81
Birch, W.J. 152
Blackflies in Ontario 168
Blue Cross Insurance Plan 137
Boards of Health 2
Boyd, A.R.J. 134
Bradley, L.O. 149, 152, 155

Brandon, K.F. 54, 55
Breast Cancer 124
Brink, G.C. 134
British Fifth Army 22
British model for health boards 2
British Nutrition Society 165
Brown, Milton H. 38, 39, 76, 120-122, 134
Brown, W.G. 134
Bryce, Peter H. 3
Budapest Institute of Hygiene 1874 7
Bulmer, F.M.R. 127
Burke, F.S. 38
B. typhosus 35

Cahoon, M. 13
Cameron, D.W. 47
Canada Approved White Bread 95
Canada, Department of Health 3, 9, 23, 24, 65
Canada, Department of Pensions and National Health 65, 87-90; Division Nutrition Services 73
Canada, Department of National Health and Welfare 102; Health Insurance Studies 104-106
Canada, federal role in public health 64,65
Canada, House of Commons, Select Standing Committee on Industrial and International Relations, submission by FitzGerald (1929) 63,64
Canada, House of Commons, Special Standing Committee on Social Security (1943), submissions by Cunningham on industrial medicine 89, Defries on health insurance 104, 105, Agnew on postwar hospital insurance 146, 147
Canada, National Health Grants Program 105, 106, 108, 117
Canada, National Research Council 56, 126
Canada's postwar health care system 104-105
Canadian Anti-Tuberculosis Association 9
Canadian Corps, Sanitary Section, First Canadian Division 22
Canadian Council of Nutrition 93
Canadian Expeditionary Force 1915 22
Canadian Federation of Biological Societies 165
Canadian Hospital 143
Canadian Hospital Association (successor to Canadian Hospital Council in 1953) 143
Canadian Hospital Council 143, 145, 146, 147, 148, 149, 155
Canadian Journal of Public Health 100-103, 134
Canadian Life Insurance Officers' Association 170
Canadian Medical Association, Department of Hospital Services 142, 143
Canadian Medical Association, Committee on Industrial Medicine 89, 90
Canadian Physiological Society 165
Canadian Public Health Association 9, 10, 55, 57, 64-65, 100-101, 103, 104, 106
Canadian Public Health Charter (1942) 103, 104
Canadian Public Health Journal (successor to *The Public Health Journal*) 10, 65, 66, 67, 68, 100, 103
Canadian Red Cross 21, 27
Canadian Westinghouse (Hamilton) 94
Canniff, William 3
Cassidy, H.M. 111
Cathcart, Bob 150
Caverly, D.S. 133
C. diphtheriae 122

Certificate in Public Health 99
Chan, D.O. 116
Chemotherapeutic studies 71
Chemistry in public health 53
Chen, C.H. 55
Cheung, A.O.T. 116
Chiang, T.H. 116
Child Welfare 10, 25
Chlorination of water 2, 10
Clark, E.M. 96
Cody, Canon H.J. 31, 98-99
Collins, J.J. 90
Colombo Plan 118, 163
Committee for Atmospheric Pollution, Canada 127
Compulsory pasteurization of milk (Toronto) 10
Compulsory vaccination 27
Connaught Laboratories (see also its academic division University of Toronto School of Hygiene):
Agglutination of red blood cells, test for influenza viruses 170;
Antitoxins 1, 2, 18, 21, 37, 52;
American Tissue Culture Association, course in Hygiene Building 173;
Blood serum (dried) for Second World War 73, 74, 81, 131;
Bundaberg incident 49;
Changes in name: Antitoxin Laboratory, Connaught Antitoxin Laboratories, Connaught Laboratories 18, Connaught Medical Research Laboratories 107;
Charles, A.F. 130-131;
Crawley, J.F. 172, 175;
Culture Stations and antitoxin depots 18;
Diphtheria antitoxin 1, 2, 7, 18, 19, 20, 21, 27, 49, 51, 53, 57;
Diphtheria immunization accidents 49;
Diphtheria toxoid 18, 49, 51, 52, 53, 57-59, 80-81;
Fellowships 40, 41, 42, 117;
Fenton, W. 18;
Founders: J.G. FitzGerald 13, 14, 15, 18, R.D. Defries 15, 16, 17;
French influences 46, 48, 52;
Gas gangrene antitoxin 74, 80, 81;
Immunochemistry 52;
Immunology and immunization 1, 23, 49, 41, 55;
Industrial Medical Services for staff 137;
Influenza vaccines 74, 81;
Insulin 30, 37, 42, 119-121, 130-132;
Kerslake, E. 173;
Knox College Building 72, 118;
Laboratories, development in Canada 4, 10, 176;
McClelland, Laurella 81, 83, 175;
"Medium 199" 176;
Morton, Helen J. 176;
Morgan, Joseph F. 176;
National Foundation for Infantile Paralysis Incorporated of New York 126, 177;
Penicillin 72, 74, 132;
Poliomyelitis vaccine (Salk type), development of 175-178;
Protamine Zinc Insulin 131;
R. prowazeki 96;

Salk, Jonas 176-177;
Scarlet Fever Streptococcus toxin and antitoxin 80;
School Children, diphtheria toxoid campaigns 59;
Scott, D.A. 46, 130, 131;
Silverthorne, L.N. 46, 51;
Siminovitch, Louis 172, 173;
Smallpox vaccine, production of 21;
Staff increases: in 1930s 46, Second World War 72, Post 1945 118;
Tetanus antitoxin 21;
Tetanus toxoid 51, 74, 81;
Tissue Culture Association 173;
Tissue culture studies 79;
Tissue culture technology, development of 176;
Toronto drugstores for distribution of diphtheria antitoxin 18;
Typhoid bacteriophages 59, 54-55;
Typhoid-paratyphoid vaccine 2;
Typhus vaccine in Second World War 74, 79, 81, 96;
Vaccines 2;
Vaccinia 54;
Vi-agglutinogen 54, 55;
Virological research in Canada, origins 55
Contagious diseases 1, 2, 3, 59
County Health Units 55
Coverton, W. 7,8
Craigie, James 53-55, 74, 81, 95, 96
Cunningham, J. Grant 28, 40, 56, 57, 87-90, 127
Curative medicine 138, 148
Currey, D.V. 134
Curtin, Ann 81
Cytology 79, 173

Davey, E. 103
Davis, Graham 148-49
Death certificates 103
Deck tennis 46, 47
Defries, Robert Davies 10, 13, 15, 16, 17, 38, 65, 71, 83, 100-106, 109-111, 118, 120, 131, 134-135, 138, 139, 141, 148, 149, 157, 158, 161, 166, 170, 176, 177, 178, (death of) 179, 180, 183, 184, 185
Degrees or Diplomas in Hospital Administration 156-158
Dempster, George 172
Dental Public Health education 98-99
Diet and mental illness 94
Diet surveys 91
Diploma of Public Health 4
Diploma in Public Health 10, 13, 40, 55, 65, 68, 81, 83-86, 99, 100
Diploma in Industrial Hygiene 99, 126, 127
Diploma in Dental Public Health 116, 127
Diploma in Veterinary Public Health 99, 100, 135
Diploma in Hospital Administration 149-157
Diploma tradition in medical education 156-58
District Health Units 10
Dolman, Claude C. 38, 121
Dominion Bureau of Statistics, 38

Dominion Council of Health 24, 25, 40, 51, 103, 133, 134
Doughty, J.H. 116
Dow, Ruth P. 81
Dublin Chair of Hygiene (1867) 7
Duff, D.C.B. 38
Dyke, Eunice 26

East York Health Unit 81, 85-87, 99
East York-Leaside Health Unit 121, 135, 137
Eastern Ontario Health Unit 86
Ecology 127
Edge, G.A. 134
Electron Microscope, first used in Canada 169
Elkerton, L.E. 134
Engineers, instruction of 57
"Entering wedges" of health insurance 145
Entomology 166
Environmental Health 8, 127
Evaluation of Schools of Public Health 108

Falconer, Sir Robert 31
Fallis, A. Murray 97, 98 166-168
Fang, J.J. 116
Farquharson, R.F. 89
Felton, R. 42
Ferguson, Helen 94
Fisher, Albert 130-131
Fisher, J.W. 96
FitzGerald, John Gerald 1, 2, 7, 8, 13, 15, 18, 21, 22, 23, 25, 27, 28, 29, 30, 31, 32, 38, 40, 42, 45, 46, 47, 48, 49, 50, 51, 57, 59, 61, 62, 63, 64, 65, (death of) 71, 179, 182, 183, 184
Fleming, A. Grant 13
Flexner, Simon 21
Food Allowances for relief, recipients in 1930s 91
Food sanitation 2, 28
Francis Trial 177
Fraser, C.J. 38
Fraser, Donald Thomas 24, 38, 49-51, 71, 96, 97, 98, 120, 121, (death of) 122
Fraser, Frieda 38, 49, 79, 80, 122
Fraser, William T. 49
Freeman, R.S. 167

Gallagher, John B. 128
Gaston, Ramon 46, 48
Gastrointestinal diseases 2, 22, 65
Gavin, Ethel G. 40, 81, 82, 90
Geiger, K.H. 132
Germ Theory of Disease 3
Gillespie, Peter 28
Gordon Research Conference on Vitamins 163
Go-Home Bay 49
Gonorrhoea 23, 79
Gooderham, Colonel Sir A.E., Memorial Fellowship 117

Goodwin, J.E. 128
Graham, Angus F. 172, 173, 175
Gregoire, J. 98
Group plans for hospitalization in U.S.A. 145

Haddon, Mrs. R.E. 126
Hagedorn, H.C. 131
Haldenby, E.W. 32
Hannah, J. 146
Hare, R. 38, 74, 81, 169
Harvard School of Public Health 30, 161
Hastings, C.J. 10, 11, 26, 27, 29, 57, 59
Hastings Memorial Fellowship 117
Hastings, J. 117, 138-139
Hatcher, G.H.M. 137, 138
Health care delivery 28, 29, 107
Health care planning, originating in School of Hygiene 29, 31, 103-105, 134-135, 137-138
Health educators 135
Health expenditures in 1929 64
Health insurance 63-69, 89, 103-106, 137-138, 143-147
Health professionals including Medical Officers of Health 2, 3, 27-28, 55-63, 83-86, 103-105
Health Units 83-87, 103-105
Hill, H.H. 13
Histamine, early research by E.W. McHenry 91
Honey, S.L. 99
Horner, Charlotte 81
Horner, W.A. 81
Horwood, J. 128
Hospital Administration as a profession 147-149, 156-158
Hospital for Sick Children, The, Toronto 28, 176
Hospitals in Canada (1929) 64, 143; in 1941 146
Hospital Insurance 145-147, 147-148, 158
Hospital Insurance and Diagnostic Services Act (1957) 158
Hospital management, extension course in 155
Hospitals, post-1945 growth in Canada 147-148
Hospital survey in Canada (1931) 143-145
Hunter A. 28
Hygiene (now FitzGerald) Building (see also University of Toronto School of Hygiene) 31-37, 42-46
Hygiene, School of, see University of Toronto School of Hygiene
Hygiene and Preventive Medicine, Faculty of Medicine, University of Toronto 31-38, 120-122

Illuminating Engineering Society of New York 126, 127
Imperial Cancer Research Fund Laboratories 170
Indigents, need for hospital care 146
Industrial Hygiene 26, 56, 57, 87-90, 126-130, 134
Infant mortality in Canadian cities 24
Influenza epidemic (1918) 24
Inseparable relations between Connaught and School 32, 118-119
International Academy of Aviation and Space Medicine 127
International Course in Tissue Culture, first course held in Toronto (1948) 173
Institute of Public Health, University of Western Ontario 26

Jones, E.W. 149
Jackson, F.W. 111, 134, 137-138

James, E. 90
Johns Hopkins School of Hygiene and Public Health 30

Kellogg Foundation, courses on Hospital Administration 117, 148-149, 156
Koch, R. 3
Koch Institute 4
Kohli, F.A. 99
Kovacs, E. 117
Kuitunen, Ella 98

Labzoffsky, N.A. 55
Lancaster, H.M. 28
Lazarus, A.S. 55
League of Nations, Health Division 49
L'École d'hygiène de L'Université de Montréal 108
Lee, J. 155
Leeson, J. 94
Legge, R.T. 90
L'Institut Pasteur (Paris and Brussels) 7, 15, 46
Lister, J. 3
Local Boards of Health 1, 2, 103-105
London School of Hygiene and Tropical Medicine, hospital administration course 148

Ma, Y.C. 116-117
MacDonald, Miss J. 87
MacEachern, M.T. 145
MacIntosh, W.A. 110
MacIntyre, Donald M. 155
Mackenzie, J.J. 4, 6, 7
MacLean, Donald 39, 40, 46, 76, 116, 126
MacLean's Magazine xi, 37
MacLeod, D.R.E. 125-126
MacLeod, J.J.R. 26
MacMurchy, Helen 143
Mader, Eva 81
"Manual of Sanitary Inspectors" 103
Massey Foundation 118
Mass immunization programmes 57, 59
Mather, J.M. 77
Mathers and Haldenby, Architects 32
Malcolmson, Mrs. M.E. 96
Malnutrition in Canada (1930s) 91
May, Eva Susan 116
McCausland, S. 126
McClure, Wallace 97
McCullough, J.W.S. 10, 13, 18, 21, 25, 26, 27, 38, 55, 64
McGhie, B.T. 83-86
McGanity, W. 162
McHenry, E.W. 40, 90-95, 163-165
McKinnon, N.E. 38, 59, 65, 122-125, 126
McLennan Physics Laboratory 169
McNabb, A. 87

Medical Care Insurance 137-138
Medical Care Administration Studies 137-138, 143
Medical Certification of Deaths 103
Medical Health Officers (see Medical Officers of Health) 3
Medical Inspection of Immigrants 3
Medical Inspection of School Children 10
Medical Model of Health Care 137-138
Medical Survey of 1920s 143
Medical Officers of Health in Ontario 3, 8, 83-86, 100, 103
Medical Services in factories in Second World War 87-90
Mental Hygiene 134
Methods of Tissue Culture 79, 96
Microbiology, origins in School of Hygiene 1, 4, 51
Microscopes, first used in Ontario 4
Microscopes, electron 169
Military Service of Amyot and FitzGerald 21, 22, 23
Milk, pasteurized 10, 57, 65, 91
Moloney, P.J. 38, 52-53, 59, 131-133
Moloney Test 53
Moore, W. 103-105
Mosley, W. 86, 87, 121
Moss, G.W.O. 116, 134
Mortality statistics for diphtheria and typhoid fever 2
Mulock, Sir William 37
Munich Institute of Hygiene 7
Municipal physicians in Manitoba and Saskatchewan 64

Nasmith, George 10, 12
National Cancer Institute, Washington D.C. 173
Naval medical problems in Second World War 81
Nazi persecution of scientists 71
Newman, Sir George 31
Niagara-on-the-Lake Military Camp 22
Noble, Doris L. 117, 163
Non-medical health workers and administrators 148
Northwestern University 152
Nursing Profession in Public Health 26, 62
Nutrition Foundation Incorporated 95
Nutrition Society of Canada 165
Nutrition surveys 91, 94, 162
Nutritional abnormalities in pregnancy 162

Occupational diseases in Second World War 88-90
Onchocerciasis (river blindness) 168
Olfactometer 128
Oldright, W. 8
Ontario Agricultural College 117
Ontario Blue Cross Plan 146
Ontario Cancer Institute 173
Ontario Department of Health 25-26, 55, 56-57, 83-86, 87-90, 126, 135
Ontario Department of Public Welfare 91, 94
Ontario Division of Industrial Hygiene 127

Ontario Education Association 93
Ontario, Free Distribution of antitoxins and vaccines 18, 21
Ontario Health Survey Committee 149
Ontario Hospital Association 146
Ontario Inter-Departmental Nutrition Committee 165
Ontario Medical Association's family diet in 1930s 91
Ontario's Mr. Water 57, 133-134
Ontario, mortality reductions 59, 122-124
Ontario Provincial Board of Health 3, 4, 6, 7, 8-9, 10, 18, 25, 28, 55, 56, 57
Ontario Provincial Diagnostic Laboratory 4, 7, 8, 9, 97
Ontario Public Health Act 85
Ontario Public Health Nursing Education 26-27
Ontario Public Health School Book 49
Ontario Provincial Laboratory 4, 6, 7, 8, 9, 18
Ontario Research Foundation 97, 166, 167, 168
Ontario Vaccine Farm 21
Ontario Veterinary College 99, 135, 173
Ontario Water Resources Commission 133-134
Ontario Workmen's Compensation Board 89
Owens, Alma 94

Pan American Sanitary Bureau 108
Parasitology 96-98, 166-168
Parker, J.M. 117, 121
Parker, R. 79, 95, 96, 176
Partridge, Ruth C. 40, 79, 81
Pasteur, L. 3, 18, 49
Pasteurization of milk 9, 10, 57, 65
Patterson, Jean 90, 94
Peacock, G.W. 150
Pequenat, L.A. 134
Perry, Helen 90, 94
Phair, J.T. "Persuasive lobbyist for national and provincial health policies" 55, 65, 83-86, 87, 134
Physicians' Services Incorporated 146
Physiology 4
Piercey, W.D. 156
Plant physicians, courses for 89-90
Plummer, H.C. 38, 79, 81, 122
Poliomyelitis vaccine 175-178
Pollution, atmospheric in Toronto 128, 129, 130
Porter, G.D. 9, 38, 65
Poverty and Public Health, early concerns 3, 4, 9, 10, 13, 15, 18, 21, 23
Preventive Medicine, teaching of, criticism of 7, 8, 121, 138
Primrose, A. 59
Public Health advances 7
Public Health, some aspects of history 2, 4, 23-24
Public Health Education, courses 7, 8, 59-63, 85, 86
Public Health Engineering 57
Public Health expenditures in Canada (1938) 103
Public Health in war, influence of First World War 21-24; Second World War 71, 74, 76
Public Health, interdisciplinary approach 161, 168, 184
Public Health lobby 64-65

Public Health Model of Health Care 103-105, 161, 184
Public Health Nurses 26, 27, 38, 81, 85
Public Health Nutrition 93
Public Health problems in 1920s 27-28; 1930s 65
Public Health, philosophy of ix, 1, 18, 46, 47, 179
Public Health Profession in Canada ix, x, 61-63, 103, 111, 179
Public Health reform in Ontario, in Toronto 2, 3, 83, 86
Public Health sciences 4
Public Health services, federal and provincial (1938-1939) 83, 86, 103
Public Health system in Ontario 2, 83, 86, 103-105
Puffer, D.S. 134

Quebec and Ontario Industrial Medicine Association 89
Quebec physicians trained in School of Hygiene 98
Quebec District Health Units 98

Rabies 7, 18
Ranta, L.C. 117
Randall, R.L. 100, 103
Rationing during Second World War 93, 94
Ratnasingham, P.K. 116
Refugee scientists 71
Reid, D.B.W. 125
Reny, A. 98
Rhodes, A.J. 107, 156, 157, 176, 177
Riboflavin 94
Richards, J. 77
Richardson, M.R. 126
Ridout, J. 40, 79, 81, 82
Robinson, C.E.A. 134, 135
Rockefeller Foundation, International Health Board 28, 29, 30, 31, 40, 45, 48, 51, 53, 68, 86-87, 110, 121, 126, 135, 137, 138, 148-149, 156; Division of Natural Sciences 95, 161
Rockefeller Institute of Medical Research 21
Rockefeller Schools of Public Health 21, 30, 31, 68, 109, 119, 148
Roseblade K. 77
Ross, Mary 38, 59, 79, 103-106
Roth, F.B. 141, 152
Rothman, B.G. 150
Rowell, N. 23, 24
Royal Canadian Air Force School of Aviation (Toronto) 89, 90
Royal Canadian Army Medical Corps 137
Royal Canadian Navy 126
Royal Canadian Institute (Toronto) 3
Russell, F.F., of Rockefeller Foundation 42, 45
Russell, Kathleen 27

Saint Michael's College (Toronto) 52
Salmonella typhi 54, 55
Sanitary engineering 1, 9, 57
Sanitary inspectors 85, 103
Sanitary sciences 1, 4, 7, 8
Saskatchewan Deputy Minister of Health 141

Saskatchewan Health Services Planning Commission 138
Schnitzer, R.F. 71
School of Hygiene, see University of Toronto School of Hygiene
Sellers, A.H. 77-79, 117, 134
Serology 55
Sewage and Water Treatment 2, 9, 53, 57, 133
Sheard, C. 8
Siminovitch, L. 173
Simmons, Evelyn 95
Simulium of Central Africa 168
Sinclair-Loutit, K.W.C. 116
Slovik, J. 128
Smallpox: in Toronto 27
Smallpox vaccination 21, 22, 27
Smith, C.E. 61, 62
Smith, H.H., Rockefeller Foundation 161
Smith, J. 90
Smith, President Sidney (of University of Toronto in 1940s and 1950s) 111, 155, 158
Sneath, P.A.T. 38, 46, 51, 77, 96, 97
Social Medicine 121, 138
Social reforms and health in Canada 10, 23, 24, 25, 103, 104, 105, 134, 138-139, 179, 184
Solandt, D.Y. 77, 78, 90, 126-131
Speakman, H.B. 167
Sprent, J.F.A. 166
Squibb & Sons (New Jersey) 79
Standard Milk Ordinance 103
Stanford University School of Medicine 61-62
Stanley Park Experimental Sewage Station (Toronto) 9
Staples, W. 77
State medicine 143, 145
Struthers, R.G. 77
Stuart, Eugenie 152-155
Sun Life Assurance Company 143
Sutherland, R.B. 127
Swan, A. Marguerite 81
Swanson, A.J. 147
Swanson, A.L. 155
Syphilis 23, 79

Taylor, Edith 38, 79, 80, 81, 133
Taylor, M.G. 134
Templin, Margaret 81
Textbook of Virology for Students and Practitioners of Medicine 175
The Development of Public Health in Canada 184
The Federal and Provincial Health Services in Canada 184
The First Forty Years: The Connaught Medical Research Laboratory University of Toronto 1914 to 1955
The Public Health Journal, see *Canadian Journal of Public Health*
Todd, Rachel R. 81
Toronto, centre for public health 10, 29; pollution studies in 1930s 129, 130; diet of family in 1930s 91
Toronto Academy of Medicine, Section on Preventive Medicine and Hygiene 145
Toronto area public health system in 1920s 3, 10

Toronto diphtheria toxoid campaign (1920s and 1930s) 57, 59
Toronto Department of Public Health 3, 8, 10, 18, 26, 28
Toronto drugstores and distribution of diphtheria antitoxin 18
Toronto General Hospital School of Nursing, visits of students to patients' homes 121
Toronto Group in public health 3, 4, 5, 6, 7, 8
Toronto Hospital for Sick Children, see Hospital for Sick Children, The, Toronto
Toronto Riverdale Isolation Hospital 68
Torontonensis 142
Toshach, Sheila 122
Tosoni, A. 132
Township of East York 86-87
Trichinosis, work on by Ella Kuitunen 168
Trimble, W.B. 149
Trinity University (Toronto), Medical School 7, 8
Truman, H. President 178
Tuberculosis, travelling clinics in Ontario during 1920s 55
Typhoid Fever, in Ontario 1, 2, 3, 4, 8, 9

Unemployment in 1930s 143, 145
"Union Hospitals" 145
United States of America Typhus Commission Medal, Dr. James Craigie 96
United States Medal of Freedom, Dr. James Craigie 96
University of Edinburgh 170, 172
University of Freiburg, Germany 15
University of St. Andrew's, Dundee, Scotland 53
University of Toronto, Department of Social Sciences 26
University of Toronto Faculty of Medicine: Department of Hygiene and Sanitary Sciences 8, 9; Department of Hygiene and Preventive Medicine 28; re-establishment of, in 1887 4
University of Toronto School of Hygiene (see also its parent body, Connaught Laboratories):
Founders: FitzGerald 13, 14, 15, Defries 15, 16, 17, Fraser 49, 50, 51;
Founding 30, 31, 32;
Administration 46, 48, 110, 111;
Budget 109, 110;
Council 99, 100;
Department of Hygiene and Preventive Medicine 38, 120, 121, 122;
Department of Epidemiology and Biometrics 38, 122, 123, 124, 125, 126;
Department of Physiological Hygiene 90, 126, 127, 128, 129, 130;
Department of Chemistry in Relation to Hygiene 131;
Department of Chemistry in Relation to Hygiene and Sanitation 131, 132, 133;
Department of Public Health Administration 87, 134, 138, 193;
Department of Public Health Nursing 38;
Department of Public Health Nutrition 161, 162, 163, 165;
Department of Hospital Administration 142, 149, 150, 155, 156, 158;
Department of Microbiology 95, 122, 173;
Department of Parasitology 166, 167, 168;
Sub-department of Chemistry in Relation to Hygiene 53;
Sub-department of Parasitology 96, 97, 98;
Sub-department of Public Health Administration 87;
Sub-department of Public Health Nutrition 90, 91, 93, 94, 95;
Sub-department of Virus Infections 95, 107, 169, 170, 172, 173, 175;
Sub-department of Virus Studies 95, 96;
Heads of Departments and Sub-departments 38, 40, 108, 109, 149, 155, 156, 166, 167, 170, 172, 173;

Diploma in Public Health 10, 13, 55, 65, 68, 81, 86;
Diploma in Industrial Hygiene 87-90, 127;
Diploma in Dental Public Health 98, 99;
Diploma in Veterinary Public Health 99, 135;
Diploma in Hospital Administration 148, 149, 156, 157, 158;
Certificate in Public Health 99, 163;
Degrees: School of Graduate Studies, 117, 163, 167, 168 and see Appendix B;
Master of Applied Science in Engineering 132, 133;
Master of Arts see Appendix B;
Master of Science in Agriculture 117, see also Appendix B;
Doctor of Philosophy see Appendix B;
Faculty see Appendix C;
Students 40, 41, 68, 111, 116, 117, 118, 149, 152, 163, 167, 168;
Students from outside Canada 117-118;
Second World War, response to 71, 73, 74, 76, 77, 79, 80, 81, 105, 106;
Virology, early teaching of 169
University of Toronto School of Hygiene Building (now FitzGerald Building); architecture and construction 32, 33, 34, 35, 36, 37; extensions; changes in 1940s 71-72, 118, 119, 120
University of Toronto School of Nursing 120
Urquhart, F. 166

Van Riper, H.E. 177
van Rooyen, C.E. 170, 171, 172, 173, 175
Vaughan, P. 127
Venereal Diseases 23, 79
Veterinary public health 99, 135
Vitamin deficiencies 93
Vitamin B 94, 95
Vitamin C 93, 94
Vincent, G. President, Rockefeller Foundation 29
Virology 169-178
Virus Diseases of Man 173

Walker, Agnes 81
Walker, E.M. 13, 96, 97
Water pollution in Ontario 2, 3, 8, 9, 10, 54, 133
Water treatment 2, 8, 9, 133, 134
Water works systems in Canada (1950s) 133, 134
Wartime blood donations 74
Wartime Day Care Centres and Nurseries 94
Wartime Industrial Hygiene 87-90
Wartime Prices and Trade Board in 1940s 93; Nutrition Advisory Committee in Food Administration 93
Wartime public health problems 2, 21, 22, 74, 76
Wartime rationing 93
Wartime research in First World War 21; Second World War 71, 72, 73, 74, 126
Webb, Jean 81
Well-Baby Clinics 28, 29
Wheler, E. 87
Wilson, D.B., last Rockefeller Foundation Representative in Canada 110
Wilson, R. 38, 77, 122
Winslow, C-E.A. 108, 111, 116, 127

Wishart, F.O. 38, 40, 54, 122, 137
Woodhouse, Catherine 81
Woodward, G. 169
Women in School of Hygiene 79, 80, 81
Workers in Second World War, protection of 87-90
World Health Organization 108, 117, 127
Wright, R.R. 3, 4, 5

Young, H.E 42

Zoology 4

NOTE ON AUTHORS

Paul A. Bator was born in Toronto in 1948. Bator graduated in 1971 from St. Michael's College, University of Toronto. He completed a Ph.D. thesis in 1979 at the University of Toronto on public health reform in Toronto from 1900 to 1930 that led to his work on the history of the School of Hygiene and the Connaught Laboratories. In August, 1987, he attended a conference on the history of the education of public health professionals in Canada, the United Kingdom and the United States, sponsored by the Rockefeller Foundation and held at the Foundation's Villa Serbelloni in Bellagio, Italy. Bator has published a number of articles on the history of public health and medicine in Canada. He is an historical consultant with the Ontario Heritage Foundation.

Dr. Andrew J. Rhodes is an internationally respected medical microbiologist with a distinguished career as a Lecturer in the University of Edinburgh, the London School of Hygiene and Tropical Medicine (University of London), as well as a Research Associate at the Connaught Medical Research Laboratories, a Professor of Virus Infections in the University of Toronto School of Hygiene, the Director of The Research Institute of The Hospital for Sick Children in Toronto, the Director of the University of Toronto School of Hygiene from 1956 to 1970 and the first head of its Department of Microbiology, the Medical Director of the Public Health Laboratories of the Ontario Ministry of Health and until recently, the Chairman of the Rabies Advisory Committee, Ontario Ministry of Natural Resources. Professor Emeritus of Microbiology, University of Toronto, Rhodes is the author of 200 articles on his scientific research and public health. His two books on viruses with Dr. C.E. van Rooyen appeared in seven editions and also in Spanish and Japanese.